Foundations
of
Aerodynamics

2nd **edition**

Foundations

of

Aerodynamics

A. M. KUETHE

J. D. SCHETZER

Department of
Aeronautical Engineering

UNIVERSITY OF MICHIGAN

NEW YORK · JOHN WILEY & SONS, INC. · LONDON

SECOND EDITION

Third Printing, January, 1963

Preface

TO THE SECOND EDITION

In keeping with the objectives of the first edition, *Foundations* has been revised to include some of the important topics on which recent technological advances are based. Some sections of the first edition have been deleted to keep the text within reasonable bounds and others have been rewritten to incorporate the experience of nine years of classroom use.

The chapter on energy relations has been rewritten, and the treatment of one-dimensional compressible flows has been expanded to include sections on heat addition. The material on wings in compressible flow is now presented from the point of view of lifting surface theory. A major revision of the material on viscous fluids greatly expands the discussion of compressibility in both laminar and turbulent flow. The coverage of isotropic turbulence has been reduced to that considered adequate for an understanding of the concept of turbulent shearing stress and its role in establishing turbulent shear flow. Real gas effects at high altitudes and temperatures are introduced in an appendix.

In addition to these major changes, suggestions of other users have been incorporated throughout the book. New problems and graphical material have been added, and all charts and tables have been grouped together in the back of the book for convenience in problem solving. Finally, the material on aerodynamic characteristics of wings that formerly appeared in Chapter 18 and additional comparisons between theory and experiment have been included in an appendix.

The objectives of the second edition coincide with that of the first, "to present in a form suitable for classroom use, the foundations on which aerodynamics rests." In general, specific technical applications are not treated except as illustrations of the underlying principles.

We wish to thank the many users of the first edition who have given us the benefit of their advice, and, in particular, H. Buning, of the University of Michigan, for his helpful criticism.

A. M. KUETHE

J. D. SCHETZER

Ann Arbor, Michigan
September 1959

Preface

The object of this book is to present, in a form suitable for classroom use, the foundations on which aerodynamics rests. An effort has been made to treat the successive steps in the consideration of problems in viscous compressible fluids, to explain the concepts involved, and to show the extent to which the various approximation methods are valid. Our aim throughout has been to give an understanding of the basic concepts rather than a complete coverage of methods and data.

The field of aerodynamics expanded so rapidly during the 1940's that the individual who has kept abreast of all phases of it is rare indeed. However, whether a person specialized in problems in perfect, viscous, or compressible fluids, whether he is an experimentalist, a theoretician, or a practicing engineer, he must have a perspective of the entire field. Our purpose has been to provide this perspective in textbook form.

Inevitably, the attempt to treat perfect, viscous, and compressible fluids in a single volume involves many compromises. In the final result given here the mathematician will note compromises with rigor, and the practicing engineer will find a scarcity of numerical data; both will feel that certain important subjects have been omitted. We have, for instance, not attempted to discuss the theory of thick airfoils, oscillating-wing theory, the flow around bodies of revolution, jet and wake phenomena, and interference effects. We feel that to give all these subjects the space they demand is inconsistent with the primary object of providing, in one volume, the foundations of the science of aerodynamics.

The notes on which this book is based have been used at the University of Michigan in the following manner: Chapters 1 through 6 and selected portions of the other chapters have been presented in undergraduate courses, and the remainder has formed the basis of a one-semester course on the senior-graduate level. The book may also be used for a first-year (two-semester) graduate course for students whose undergraduate training is in engineering, mathematics, or physics.

We have assumed throughout that the reader has no previous knowledge of aerodynamics. Undergraduate physics and mathematics through advanced calculus are the prerequisites that we have kept in mind; the material on perfect fluids can be studied concurrently with advanced calculus. Many of the equations are expressed in vector notation, but vector operations, other than the scalar product, are not employed.

The material presented incorporates the suggestions of many people, especially Professor M. V. Morkovin, of the University of Michigan, and Professor G. Graetzer, of the Air Forces Institute of Technology. Professor H. W. Liepmann, of the California Institute of Technology, has kindly provided us with some illustrations of his experimental investigations, and we have drawn especially heavily from the work of the engineers and scientists of the National Advisory Committee for Aeronautics. Messrs. C. E. Wittliff, J. W. Hindes, R. R. Lewis, Jr., and S. I. Cheng assisted in the preparation of the manuscript and drawings. Mrs. Helen M. Anderson and her secretarial staff typed the copy. We gratefully acknowledge the contributions of all these people.

A. M. KUETHE
J. D. SCHETZER

Ann Arbor, Michigan
March 1950

Contents

The Fluid Medium

CHAPTER 1

1.1 INTRODUCTION

The science of aerodynamics concerns itself with the determination of the characteristics of the flow past bodies of various shapes. Once the flow pattern has been established, the aerodynamic forces and moments acting on the body can be calculated.

The aim of this book is to build up from first principles a background of concepts which may be utilized in the application of aerodynamics to problems in aeronautics and other fields of engineering. The necessity for a clear understanding of these concepts lies mainly in the fact that, because of mathematical complexities and in many instances hypothetical physical premises, we are constantly dealing with approximations to the actual problems we are attempting to solve. Therefore, many of the more difficult problems involve in their solution an intuitive approach. This approach must be disciplined by a comprehension of those physical laws which have been shown by experiment to be valid.

Before proceeding with the analysis of flow problems, it is necessary to have an understanding of the fluid medium with which we are dealing. Fluids are of two types, liquid and gaseous. We are concerned with a gaseous fluid, air, but many of the concepts to be studied apply equally well to the flow of liquids.

1.2 PROPERTIES OF GASES AT REST

A gas consists of a large number of molecules each of which has a random motion. The *ideal* gas that we premise is composed of molecules which are small compared to the mean distance between them, and so the potential energy arising from their mutual attraction may be neglected. Collisions between molecules or between molecules and the containing vessel are assumed to be perfectly elastic. The average distance a molecule travels before colliding with another is termed the *mean free path* and is given the symbol l. The mass of a molecule and its mean random velocity are designated m and c, respectively. The important properties of a gas at rest are listed below.

1. DENSITY. The total mass of the molecules in a unit volume is defined as the *density* of the gas. Mass is defined as weight divided by the acceleration of gravity, and in foot-pound-second units it is measured in slugs. The mass of 32.2 lb of matter is 1 slug. Density is measured in slugs per cubic foot.

2. PRESSURE. When molecules strike a surface they rebound, and, by Newton's law, the surface experiences a force equal and opposite to the time rate of change of momentum of the rebounding molecules. *Pressure* is defined as the force per unit area exerted on a surface immersed in the fluid. Because the molecular bombardment of the surface is elastic, we have the first important result: *fluid pressure acts normal to a surface*.

It is instructive to interpret the pressure in terms of the kinetic energy of the molecular motion. Consider a cube of unit length, shown in Fig. 1. The picture is simplified by assuming that one-third of the molecules are traveling in each of the three coordinate directions. Then, since half of these are moving in each direction, one-sixth of the molecules within a small layer of thickness Δx will strike the surface in time $\Delta t = \Delta x/c$. The collisions are assumed to be elastic so the momentum of the molecules is reversed, and the force exerted on the wall by each collision is $2mc$. Then, if N is the number of molecules per unit volume, the pressure p is given by $(N\Delta x/6)(2mc)/\Delta t$. After we substitute $\Delta t = \Delta x/c$, this becomes $(\frac{1}{3})(Nmc^2)$, and, since $Nm = \rho$, this may be written $(\frac{2}{3})(\frac{1}{2}\rho c^2)$. The second important result is: *the pressure is proportional to the kinetic energy of the random motion per unit volume*.

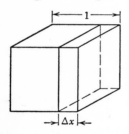

FIG. 1. Model for interpretation of pressure.

3. TEMPERATURE. According to the kinetic theory of gases, the absolute temperature is proportional to the mean kinetic energy of the molecules. It can be interpreted, in terms of the *equation of state* for an ideal gas, as

$$p = \rho R T \qquad \rho = \frac{m}{V} \qquad Pv = mRT$$

where p and ρ are the pressure and density, respectively, R is the gas constant, and T is the absolute temperature. For systems in which the mass per unit volume remains constant, any operation, such as the addition of heat, that increases the kinetic energy of the random motion will increase the temperature and pressure proportional amounts.

4. ELASTICITY. When a pressure is applied to a gas, its volume per unit mass changes. *Elasticity* is defined as the change in pressure per unit change in specific volume.

$$E = \frac{-dp}{d\dfrac{1}{\rho} \bigg/ \dfrac{1}{\rho}} = \rho \frac{dp}{d\rho}$$

It will be shown later that $dp/d\rho$ is the square of the velocity of sound through the medium. Therefore, the density and velocity of sound define the elasticity.

1.3   STANDARD ATMOSPHERE

In order to establish uniformity in the analysis of data, standard atmospheric conditions have been adopted and are in general use. Commonly referred to as sea level conditions, they are

$$p = 2116 \text{ lb/ft}^2$$

$$\rho = 0.002378 \text{ slug/ft}^3$$

$$T = 460 + 59° \text{ F} = 519° \text{ Rankine}$$

Under these standard conditions, the speed of sound a is 1116 ft/sec.

The temperature, density, and pressure in the atmosphere vary with altitude; the variation is shown in Table 1 at the end of the book.

1.4   GASES IN MOTION—VISCOSITY

If a gas is in motion with a velocity v, then each molecule has in addition to its random speed c an ordered velocity v. The concept of viscosity has meaning only for gases that have an ordered velocity.

The viscosity of a fluid is manifested by its tendency to adhere to a surface. If one cylinder is rotating inside another coaxial cylinder and the intervening space is filled with air, a torque is exerted which will tend to rotate the outer cylinder. The air in the immediate vicinity of the outer cylinder will be stationary while that near the inner cylinder will be moving with a velocity equal to that of the surface. Figure 2 illustrates the experiment.

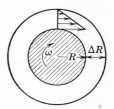

FIG. 2.   Determination of coefficient of viscosity.

As with the other properties of a gas, the random motion of the molecules provides a physical picture of the phenomenon. This random motion tends to destroy any discontinuities in velocity: molecules moving from the vicinity of the inner wall carry with them an average speed in the direction of rotation of ωR; those originating at the outer wall carry zero average velocity. The resulting *mixing process* finally establishes a velocity distribution like that shown in Fig. 2. If R is large, any segment of the coaxial cylinder will approximate parallel planes in relative motion, as shown in Fig. 3. The lower plane will

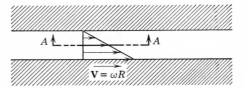

Fig. 3.   Shearing stress in a fluid.

have a speed $V = \omega R$ and, through the action of the intervening fluid, will tend to drag the upper plane to the right. For ΔR small, experiment shows that the force per unit area exerted on the upper plane is proportional to the relative speed V and inversely proportional to the distance between the planes $s = \Delta R$.

$$\tau = \mu \frac{V}{s}$$

The constant of proportionality μ is called the *coefficient of viscosity*. The above formula may be generalized by considering the shearing stress exerted between two adjacent layers of fluid, say the layers immediately above and immediately below the section AA in Fig. 3. For this example, the relative speed of the layers is an infinitesimal dV, and the distance between layers is also an infinitesimal ds. Then we may write

$$\tau = \mu \frac{dV}{ds} \tag{1}$$

It is understood that the derivative in Eq. 1 is always in a direction perpendicular to the plane on which the shearing stress is being computed. When air is flowing with a velocity u over a solid surface, the mixing by the random molecular motion results in the formation of the boundary layer shown in Fig. 4. Each infinitesimal section of the boundary layer can be visualized as two planes in relative motion, and so the shearing stress at any point is given by Eq. 1. At the surface the shearing stress is given by

$$\tau_0 = \mu \left(\frac{du}{dy}\right)_{y=0}$$

The velocity gradient du/dy is large at the surface and becomes substantially zero at $y = \delta$, where δ is defined as the thickness of the boundary layer.

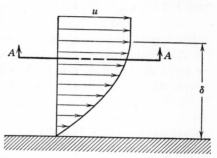

A more detailed discussion of the shearing stress and boundary layers will be reserved for later chapters. However, it should be pointed out here that the above concept of viscosity depends upon the statement made earlier that the air in the immediate vicinity of the solid surface has

Fig. 4.   Boundary layer.

zero velocity relative to the surface. This is known as the condition of *no slip at the surface* and is stated mathematically as the boundary condition: $u = 0$ at $y = 0$. This condition is satisfied for all fluids including air as long as the *mean free path* of the molecules between collisions is small compared with the dimensions of the solid surface. For air under standard conditions, the mean free path of the molecules is approximately 3.5 times 10^{-6} in. Since the mean free path will depend upon the number of molecules per unit volume, that is, upon the density, only for extremely small bodies or for extremely low densities (high altitudes) would the condition of no slip have to be abandoned. Further, the condition of no slip cannot be imposed if the viscosity of the fluid is neglected, as it is for many of the analyses in this book. In this case, it is obvious that all shearing stresses are zero.

1.5 DISSIPATION OF ENERGY

The effect of viscosity in causing the frictional stress, τ, as illustrated in Figs. 2, 3, and 4, is also manifested by a heating of the fluid and the solid surfaces. This physical phenomenon is *dissipation*. A *dissipative process* in general involves a transfer of energy from the directed to the random form in such a way that the process cannot be reversed completely.* In other words, the dissipative force (friction) causes dissipa-

* If *all* of the energy could be transferred back to the directed form the process would be *reversible;* this process is called *conservative* or *nondissipative*. Dissipative processes are treated from the thermodynamic standpoint in Chapter 8.

tion of the energy residing in the directed velocity distributions shown in the figures into random energy, or heat.

We can write the mathematical expression for dissipation immediately from the physical law: the heat generated per unit time in a dissipative process is equal to the rate at which the dissipative forces perform work on the system. Then, the shearing stress, τ, performs work per second at the rate

$$q' = \tau u \tag{2}$$

The boundary layer shown schematically in Fig. 4 is, according to Eq. 2, a dissipation region. We show in later chapters, however, that for gases the resulting heating is not significant unless the speeds are comparable with the speed of sound. We can show also that the *shock waves* that may occur in a supersonic flow involve large frictional stresses and are therefore dissipation regions. In some of the applications treated in succeeding chapters we shall be concerned with *avoiding* dissipation regions such as boundary layers and shock waves; in others we shall develop means for *calculating the rate of dissipation* in these regions.

1.6 INTERPRETATION OF THE COEFFICIENT OF VISCOSITY AND THERMAL CONDUCTIVITY

The coefficient of viscosity μ may be interpreted by considering the source of the shearing stress τ associated with it. The shearing stress exerted by the fluid beneath AA on the fluid above AA in Fig. 4 is a retarding effect. The shear stress is equal to the time rate of loss of ordered momentum of the fluid above AA through unit area of AA.

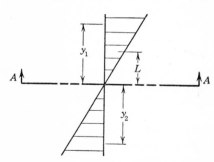

FIG. 5.   Kinetic interpretation of coefficient of viscosity.

To calculate the shearing stress, we consider the transport of ordered momentum through AA by the random motion of the molecules. If we attach the axis of reference to AA, the flow configuration of Fig. 4 will appear as shown in Fig. 5. A molecule originating at y_1 and moving downward through AA will carry with it a positive momentum $m(du/dy)y_1$. Similarly, a molecule moving upward through AA and originating at y_2 will carry with it a negative momentum $m(du/dy)y_2$. Both these excursions represent a loss of ordered momentum from the fluid above AA, and it is the sum of such losses that occur in 1 sec through unit area of AA that equals the shear stress τ.

As in the pressure calculation of Section 1.2, the random molecular motion is assumed to be split equally among the three coordinate directions. Then, if there are N molecules per unit volume, if their average speed is c, and if one-third of them are assumed to have a motion perpendicular to AA, $(\frac{1}{3})Nc$ molecules will pass through AA each second. Each of these molecules will carry with it a momentum corresponding to the position y at which it originates. The sum of these momenta is the shear stress. There is an effective height at which all the molecules could originate with the same resulting shear stress. If we call this height L, the shear stress becomes

$$\tau = \left(\frac{1}{3}Nc\right) m \frac{du}{dy} L$$

The product Nm is the density ρ; therefore,

$$\tau = \frac{1}{3}\rho c L \frac{du}{dy} \tag{3}$$

A comparison of Eqs. 1 and 3 indicates that $\quad (\#1)\ \ T = \mathcal{M}\frac{dV}{ds}$

$$\mu = \tfrac{1}{3}\rho c L$$

The effective height L is related to the mean free path l, and more accurate calculations show that

$$\mu = 0.49\rho c l \tag{4}$$

As the density of a gas goes down, the mean path increases in such a manner that the product ρl tends to remain constant. Then μ is proportional to c, which in turn is proportional to the square root of the absolute temperature. Thus, the coefficient of viscosity changes only with the temperature and is therefore independent of the pressure. The degree to which air conforms to these deductions is discussed in Chapter 14.

The random molecular motion may transport properties of the gas other than the ordered momentum. For example, if a gradient exists in the temperature, the temperature will tend to become equalized by the random process. The transport of high-temperature fluid to regions of lower temperature must be interpreted as heat conduction. In general, let Q be a property of the gas. Then, by an argument similar to that leading to Eq. 3, we can write

$$\frac{d(Q/A)}{dt} = \frac{1}{3}\rho c L \frac{d(Q/M)}{ds}$$

where $d(Q/A)/dt$ is the property transported through unit area each second and Q/M is the property per unit mass. From the above formula, it is clear that all properties of the fluid which are subject to transport by the random molecular motion have a time rate of transport that is related to the viscosity by the equation

$$\frac{d(Q/A)}{dt} = \mu \frac{d(Q/M)}{ds} \tag{5}$$

For the case of heat conduction, let Q/M be the heat content of the gas per unit mass which may be written in terms of the specific heat C_p and temperature as *

$$\frac{Q}{M} = c_p T \tag{6}$$

From Fourier's law of heat conduction through a continuum we have

$$\frac{d(Q/A)}{dt} = k \frac{dT}{ds} \tag{7}$$

where dT/ds is the temperature gradient and k is the thermal conductivity. k is the proportionality constant that relates heat transfer to temperature gradient in the same manner that μ relates shearing stress to velocity gradient. Equation 7 is comparable to Eq. 1, and Figs. 4 and 5 illustrate Fourier's law if the velocity distributions are considered to be temperature distributions.

A comparison of Eqs. 5 and 7 leads to the result

$$\mu \frac{d(Q/M)}{ds} = k \frac{dT}{ds}$$

After using the value for Q/M from Eq. 6 and considering c_p to be constant, the following relation is obtained among c_p, μ, and k:

$$\mu c_p = k \tag{8}$$

The measured value of the viscosity coefficient at standard temperature (59° F) is 3.72 times 10^{-7} slug/ft sec.

* The specific heats of a gas are defined in Chapter 8.

Another parameter of importance in determining the flow characteristics is the kinematic viscosity $\nu = \mu/\rho$. Because the viscous forces
are proportional to μ and the inertia forces are proportional to ρ, the
kinematic viscosity may be interpreted as a measure of the relative
importance of viscous and inertia forces. That is, for two flows in
which the velocity patterns are identical, the viscosity plays a relatively
greater role in the fluid that has the greater kinematic viscosity. Under
standard conditions the kinematic viscosity of air has a value of
0.0001567 ft^2/sec.

1.7   FORCE ON A BODY MOVING THROUGH A FLUID

The force on a body arising from the motion of the body through a
fluid depends upon the properties of the body, the properties of the
fluid, and the relative velocity between body and fluid. The size,
shape, and orientation of the body are of consequence in determining
the force arising from the relative motion. The fluid properties of importance are the density, viscosity, and elasticity, the last being determined by the density ρ and velocity of sound a.

For bodies of given shape, we may describe the size by specifying a
characteristic dimension l. Then, for a body of given shape and
orientation moving through a fluid with velocity V, the force experienced may be written in the following functional form:

$$F = f(\rho, V, l, \mu, a)$$

or, alternatively,

$$g(F, \rho, V, l, \mu, a) = 0 \tag{9}$$

Equation 9 states a relation among physical quantities, and therefore
its form is partially dictated by the dimensions of the parameters
involved. The method of *dimensional analysis* * shows that Eq. 9
can always be written in the equivalent form

$$f_1 \left\{ \frac{F}{\rho V^2 l^2}, \frac{\rho V l}{\mu}, \frac{V}{a} \right\} = 0$$

where each of the three combinations of parameters is a dimensionless
quantity. The above equation may be solved for the first dimensionless combination, and then we have the fundamental relation

$$\frac{F}{\rho V^2 l^2} = g_1 \left\{ \frac{\rho V l}{\mu}, \frac{V}{a} \right\} \tag{10}$$

* The method of dimensional analysis and its application to the present problem
may be found in Appendix A.

To interpret Eq. 10, consider a body of a given shape and orientation in motion in a fluid such that the quantities $F/(\rho V^2 l^2)$, $\rho V l/\mu$, and V/a have certain definite values. Then, if a geometrically similar body with the same orientation is moved through the same or another fluid such that $\rho V l/\mu$ and V/a have the same values as for the first body, then $F/(\rho V^2 l^2)$ will also have the same value.

Assume for the moment that μ and a in Eq. 9 have no influence on the force F. Then an application of dimensional analysis will lead to the result

$$f_1 \left\{ \frac{F}{\rho V^2 l^2} \right\} = 0$$

the solution of which is

$$F = C_F \rho V^2 l^2 \tag{11}$$

where C_F is a dimensionless constant. Equation 11 states that, for a body of given orientation and shape which is in motion through a fluid, the force experienced is proportional to the *kinetic energy* per unit volume of the relative motion of the fluid $(\rho/2)V^2$ and a characteristic area l^2. For example, if the force on an airplane of given shape, orientation, and size is known at a given flight speed and altitude, the force on another airplane of geometrically similar shape and the same orientation and flying at a different speed and altitude can be predicted from Eq. 11. This result was given by Newton, and the dimensionless constant C_F is sometimes referred to as the Newtonian coefficient. C_F is a dimensionless quantity that characterizes the force and in the following chapters will be called the *force coefficient*. The force coefficient is of great importance in experimental aerodynamics, for it makes possible the prediction of forces on full-scale airplanes at various altitudes and flight speeds from data obtained on models tested in wind tunnels.

Newton's result, Eq. 11, is an approximation that is accurate only under specialized conditions to be described later. The viscosity and elasticity of the fluid are important in general, and Eq. 10 shows that the force coefficient is not a constant for a body of given shape and orientation. It is a function of the combinations $\rho V l/\mu$ and V/a, which bear the names *Reynolds number* and *Mach number*, respectively, after the men who investigated the effects of these parameters in flow problems.

Dimensional analysis has shown that the force coefficient for a body of given orientation and shape is a function of the Reynolds number and the Mach number. The accuracy of this result depends entirely on the correctness with which the parameters governing the force are initially chosen. If important properties of the flow are omitted from the initial choice of parameters, the method of dimensional analysis will not expose this fact. For example, properties that were neglected and that influence the force on the body are surface roughness, turbulence of the stream, the presence of other bodies in the vicinity, etc. In applying data from model tests to the full-scale airplane, these facts must be considered.

Finally, if the geometries of the two flows are similar (geometric similarity), and in addition the Mach numbers are equal and the Reynolds numbers are equal, the flows are said to be *dynamically similar*. Dynamically similar flows have *equal* force coefficients. The Mach and Reynolds numbers are called *similarity parameters*.

1.8 THE APPROXIMATE FORMULATION OF FLOW PROBLEMS

Strictly speaking, a gas is a compressible, viscous, inhomogeneous substance, and the physical principles underlying its behavior are not completely enough understood to permit us to formulate, exactly, *any* flow problem. Even if this were possible, the resulting equations would, in all probability, be too difficult to solve. Therefore all methods used in this book are approximations, and the answers they yield must be tested by experiment.

In order to make the problems of aerodynamics tractable, we consider three different fluids, each of which provides a good approximation for airflow problems of particular types. The fluids are:

1. PERFECT FLUID. This fluid is homogeneous (not composed of discrete particles), inelastic, and inviscid. The assumption of a perfect fluid gives good agreement with experiment for flows outside of the boundary layer and wake of well-streamlined bodies moving with velocities of less than 200 mph at altitudes under about 100,000 ft. There is no scale effect on problems treated by perfect-fluid theory, and the force coefficient is given by Eq. 11.

2. COMPRESSIBLE, INVISCID FLUID. This fluid differs from the perfect fluid in that the elasticity, characterized by the velocity of sound, is taken into account. It provides a good approximation for problems involving the flow outside the boundary layer and wake of bodies for all speeds at altitudes below about 100,000 ft.

3. VISCOUS, COMPRESSIBLE FLUID. This fluid differs from that described under (2) in that the viscosity is taken into account. Although it is not feasible to treat the entire flow around a body, that within the boundary layer and wake is amenable to accurate analysis, provided the flow is *laminar*; *turbulent* flow has so far yielded only to semi-empirical analyses. The agreement of the analyses with experiment is good for all speeds at altitudes below about 100,000 ft.

At altitudes above about 200,000 ft the mean free path of the molecules will in general not be small compared with a significant dimension of the body. Then, as the altitude increases further, the characterization of air as a fluid becomes more and more approximate. Finally, at altitudes above approximately 500,000 ft the flow (if it can be termed a flow) consists simply of the collision of the body with those molecules directly in its path.

1.9 PLAN FOR THE FOLLOWING CHAPTERS

The objective as stated in Section 1.1 may, in view of the intervening discussion, be rephrased as follows: to provide a background of concepts for finding approximate solutions of problems in the flow of a compressible, viscous, inhomogeneous gas. The approximations that may be made depend upon the particular aspect of the flow being investigated. It has, for instance, been abundantly demonstrated experimentally that the *lift* and *moment* acting on a streamlined body such as an airfoil at a low angle of attack and at a speed under a few hundred miles per hour are very slightly affected by compressibility and viscosity. Therefore, the first six chapters of this book are devoted to a study of the flow of a perfect fluid and to the application of perfect-fluid theory to the prediction of the lifting characteristics of wings.

The following five chapters deal with the compressible inviscid fluid and its application to the flow through channels and about wings. Both the subsonic and supersonic flow problems are formulated and the basic differences between the two regimes are discussed in physical terms. In some cases exact solutions of the equations are given; in others, useful approximations that neglect the nonlinear terms are introduced.

The effects of viscosity on the flow of incompressible and compressible fluids are taken up in Chapters 12 through 16. Here we are concerned with the flow in boundary layers and in tubes. The main objectives are to give an understanding of the approximations that have been made and to analyze the problems of viscous drag and flow separation.

Tables, four appendices, and problems follow the sixteen chapters. In Appendix A a brief treatment of dimensional analysis is given. The equations of motion and energy for a viscous compressible fluid are given in Appendix B and the reduction to the boundary layer equations is carried out. Appendix C groups together various aspects of wing theory and compares the theoretically predicted behavior with experiment. Finally, Appendix D describes the behavior of real fluids in flow regimes that are beyond the usual limits encountered in aircraft flight.

Kinematics of a Fluid Field

CHAPTER 2

2.1 FIELDS

The term *field* denotes a region throughout which a quantity is defined as a function of location within the region and time. If the quantity is independent of time, the field is *steady* or *stationary*. Unless stated otherwise, all fields discussed in the following sections are steady.

The empirical laws upon which fluid mechanics is based apply to fluid elements of fixed identity. For example, in a region of space through which fluid is flowing the conservation of mass principle states that the mass of a *fluid element* is neither created nor destroyed. That is, the indestructibility of matter is a *particle property* as distinct from a *field property*. Similarly, other conservation principles which are discussed in detail later involve particle properties and not field properties.

The field concept is introduced for mathematical convenience. The fluid characteristics at a fixed point in the field will be described, though it must be recognized that different fluid elements occupy a given field point from instant to instant. In the following paragraphs, several mathematical concepts associated with fields are discussed without reference to the physics of fluid flow. At points in the discussion where physical principles are introduced, a conversion from particle properties to field properties is necessary.

2.2 SCALAR FIELD, DIRECTIONAL DERIVATIVE, GRADIENT

The scalar field is a region throughout which a scalar quantity such as temperature or pressure is described. The value of the scalar at any point is defined by expressing it as a function of the position of that

13

point referred to an arbitrarily located origin. In cartesian coordinates the scalar field can be represented as

$$\text{scalar} = f(x,\, y,\, z)$$

where x, y, and z are the distances to three orthogonal axes through the origin.

The types of scalars dealt with in the aerodynamics of perfect fluids are continuous single-valued functions of position. If the value of the scalar is known at some point A, it may be found at any other point B by forming the Taylor expansion about A. Calling the scalar Q, its value at point B is

$$Q_B = Q_A + \left\{\frac{\partial Q}{\partial x}\right\}_A (x_B - x_A) + \left\{\frac{\partial Q}{\partial y}\right\}_A (y_B - y_A) + \left\{\frac{\partial Q}{\partial z}\right\}_A (z_B - z_A)$$
$$+ \left\{\frac{\partial^2 Q}{\partial x^2}\right\}_A \frac{(x_B - x_A)^2}{2!} + \cdots$$

Letting B approach A, we may write in the limit

$$dQ = \frac{\partial Q}{\partial x}\,dx + \frac{\partial Q}{\partial y}\,dy + \frac{\partial Q}{\partial z}\,dz$$

where dx, dy, and dz are the cartesian components of $\boldsymbol{B} - \boldsymbol{A}$ in the limit as B approaches A.

The three partial derivatives represent rates of change of the scalar in the directions of the reference axes. The directional property of the derivatives suggests the concept of the *directional derivative*, which is simply the rate of change of the quantity in a specified direction.

Assume that it is required to find the rate of change of the scalar Q along a specified path s. If the increments are taken along s, then x, y, and z will be functions of the position along the path.

$$x = x(s)$$
$$y = y(s)$$
$$z = z(s)$$

Since Q is a function of x, y, and z, and since these variables, in turn, are dependent upon s, the derivative of Q with respect to s is

$$\frac{dQ}{ds} = \frac{\partial Q}{\partial x}\frac{dx}{ds} + \frac{\partial Q}{\partial y}\frac{dy}{ds} + \frac{\partial Q}{\partial z}\frac{dz}{ds}$$

For geometrical simplicity, the problem is reduced to two dimensions.

Referring to Fig. 1,

$$\frac{dx}{ds} = \cos \alpha \qquad \frac{dy}{ds} = \sin \alpha$$

$$\frac{dQ}{ds} = \frac{\partial Q}{\partial x} \cos \alpha + \frac{\partial Q}{\partial y} \sin \alpha \qquad (1)$$

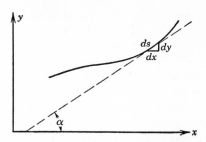

FIG. 1.   Directional derivative.

Two paths are of special importance. One is the path along which the scalar is constant; the other is the path along which the rate of change of the scalar is the maximum. The former is called an isoline; the latter, a gradient line. The slope of a gradient line at any point is the tangent of the value of α which makes Eq. 1 maximum, and the slope of an isoline is the tangent of the value of α which makes Eq. 1 vanish.

By setting the left-hand side of Eq. 1 equal to zero, the slope of an isoline is obtained.

$$\tan \alpha = -\frac{\partial Q/\partial x}{\partial Q/\partial y} \qquad (2)$$

To find the slope of a gradient line, dQ/ds is differentiated with respect to α and set equal to zero.

$$\frac{d}{d\alpha}\left\{\frac{dQ}{ds}\right\} = -\frac{\partial Q}{\partial x} \sin \alpha + \frac{\partial Q}{\partial y} \cos \alpha = 0$$

$$\tan \alpha = +\frac{\partial Q/\partial y}{\partial Q/\partial x} \qquad (3)$$

Because the slopes of isolines and the gradient lines are negative reciprocals, *gradient lines and isolines are everywhere orthogonal.*

Illustrative Example

The equations of the two lines are found by integration. For example, assume that the scalar is defined by the expression

$$Q = x^3 y$$

Then $\partial Q/\partial y = x^3$, and $\partial Q/\partial x = 3x^2 y$. The slope of the gradient line is

$$\frac{dy}{dx} = \tan \alpha = +\frac{\partial Q/\partial y}{\partial Q/\partial x}$$

$$\frac{dy}{dx} = \frac{x^3}{3x^2 y} = \frac{x}{3y}$$

Integration yields the equation of the gradient line

$$x^2 - 3y^2 = \text{constant}$$

For the isoline,

$$\tan \alpha = -\frac{\partial Q/\partial x}{\partial Q/\partial y}$$

$$\frac{dy}{dx} = -\frac{3y}{x}$$

and the equation of the isoline becomes

$$x^3 y = \text{constant}$$

The last equation could have been obtained directly from the definition of an isoline by setting the scalar equal to a constant.

The gradient of a scalar is a vector whose direction is given by the slope of the gradient line at the point in question and whose absolute value equals the magnitude of the directional derivative along the gradient line at the same point.

It has been shown that dQ/ds is the maximum when

$$\alpha = \tan^{-1}\frac{\partial Q/\partial y}{\partial Q/\partial x}$$

Putting this value in Eq. 1,

$$\left\{\frac{dQ}{ds}\right\}_{\text{max.}} = \sqrt{\left(\frac{\partial Q}{\partial x}\right)^2 + \left(\frac{\partial Q}{\partial y}\right)^2}$$

In three dimensions, the absolute value of the gradient at any point is given by the expression

$$|\operatorname{grad} Q| = \sqrt{\left(\frac{\partial Q}{\partial x}\right)^2 + \left(\frac{\partial Q}{\partial y}\right)^2 + \left(\frac{\partial Q}{\partial z}\right)^2} \tag{4}$$

2.3 VECTOR FIELD—METHOD OF DESCRIPTION

The vector field is a region throughout which a vector quantity, such as velocity or force, is defined. Because a vector quantity has both magnitude and direction, its mathematical description involves, for the three-dimensional case, three equations. Consider the velocity vector $\mathbf{V}$ whose x-, y-, and z-components are denoted by u, v, and w, respectively. The vector is defined at each point in the field, both in magnitude and direction, if each of its components is given as a function of the field coordinates.

$$u = u(x, y, z)$$
$$v = v(x, y, z)$$
$$w = w(x, y, z)$$

The velocity components above are field properties and do not apply to any one particle. For example, at x_1, y_1, z_1 in the field, u has the value u_1. This means that at a given instant in time, the particle occupying position x_1, y_1, z_1 in the field will have a value of u equal to u_1. At a later instant, the particle will have moved to a different position in the field and its u component will correspond to that of the field position it occupies at the later instant.

A streamline is defined as a path whose tangent at any point is in the direction of the velocity at that point. A velocity field may alternatively be described in terms of streamlines and the absolute value of the vector. Letting the absolute value of $\mathbf{V}$ be denoted by $|\mathbf{V}|$, and representing a streamline by two intersecting surfaces, we may write the alternative description as

$$|\mathbf{V}| = f(x, y, z)$$
$$f_1(x, y, z) = 0$$
$$f_2(x, y, z) = 0$$

In two dimensions, two equations suffice to describe the field by either representation

Illustrative Example

Frequently, in the following material, something will be known about the streamlines and absolute value of the velocity. For mathematical operations, however, the components are needed as functions of the field coordinates, and a conversion from the second method of representation to the first is necessary. In treating the two-dimensional case, the conversion is readily performed by remembering that the tangent to a streamline is v/u and the absolute value of the vector is $\sqrt{u^2 + v^2}$. These values provide two equations in two unknowns:

$$\frac{dy}{dx} = \frac{v}{u}$$
$$|\mathbf{V}| = \sqrt{u^2 + v^2}$$

For example, assume that it is known that the streamlines are circular and the absolute value of the velocity is constant along a circular path. Then the equation of the streamlines is

$$x^2 + y^2 = \text{constant}$$

and the absolute value of the velocity is

$$|\mathbf{V}| = f(x^2 + y^2)$$

From the first equation above,

$$\frac{dy}{dx} = -\frac{x}{y} = \frac{v}{u}$$

and from the second,

$$\sqrt{u^2 + v^2} = f(x^2 + y^2)$$

$$u\sqrt{1 + \left(\frac{v}{u}\right)^2} = f(x^2 + y^2)$$

Substituting $-x/y$ for v/u and solving for u,

$$u = -\frac{yf(x^2 + y^2)}{\sqrt{x^2 + y^2}} = -\frac{yf(r)}{r}$$

Similarly,

$$v = +\frac{xf(x^2 + y^2)}{\sqrt{x^2 + y^2}} = +\frac{xf(r)}{r}$$

The symbol r in the above equations and in the material that follows represents the absolute value of the radius vector in polar coordinates. The signs on u and v must be opposite in order to satisfy the condition $v/u = dy/dx$. The sense of **V** determines the component that bears the negative sign.

Each component of the vector is a continuous single-valued function of the field coordinates. The values of the components at any point B can be expressed in terms of their values at a neighboring point A and nine first-order derivatives. Again letting dx, dy, dz represent the components of **B–A** for the limit as $B \rightarrow A$, we can write the following three equations:

$$u_B = u_A + \left\{\frac{\partial u}{\partial x}\right\}_A dx + \left\{\frac{\partial u}{\partial y}\right\}_A dy + \left\{\frac{\partial u}{\partial z}\right\}_A dz$$

$$v_B = v_A + \left\{\frac{\partial v}{\partial x}\right\}_A dx + \left\{\frac{\partial v}{\partial y}\right\}_A dy + \left\{\frac{\partial v}{\partial z}\right\}_A dz$$

$$w_B = w_A + \left\{\frac{\partial w}{\partial x}\right\}_A dx + \left\{\frac{\partial w}{\partial y}\right\}_A dy + \left\{\frac{\partial w}{\partial z}\right\}_A dz$$

The equations above are derived from the Taylor expansion of each component about the point A. The field is characterized by nine derivatives that determine its properties:

$$\begin{vmatrix} \dfrac{\partial u}{\partial x} & \dfrac{\partial u}{\partial y} & \dfrac{\partial u}{\partial z} \\[2mm] \dfrac{\partial v}{\partial x} & \dfrac{\partial v}{\partial y} & \dfrac{\partial v}{\partial z} \\[2mm] \dfrac{\partial w}{\partial x} & \dfrac{\partial w}{\partial y} & \dfrac{\partial w}{\partial z} \end{vmatrix}$$

It will be shown in the following sections that the nine derivatives are not independent; that is, the physics of the problem places definite relations among them.

2.4 DIVERGENCE OF A VECTOR, THEOREM OF GAUSS

The three derivatives in the diagonal extending from the upper left- to the lower right-hand corners of the matrix have a property in common. Each represents the rate of change of a component of the velocity in the direction of that component. The sum of these extension derivatives is called the divergence of the velocity and is written

$$\operatorname{div} \mathbf{V} = \frac{\partial u}{\partial x} + \frac{\partial v}{\partial y} + \frac{\partial w}{\partial z}$$

The divergence of a vector can be interpreted physically as the efflux per unit volume from a point. To see this, consider the vector $\rho \mathbf{V}$, where ρ is a scalar quantity representing the mass per unit volume or density of the fluid. $\mathbf{V}$ as before is the velocity. Both ρ and $\mathbf{V}$ are field properties.

Let $\hat{R}$ be a fixed region in the field called a control volume and $\hat{S}$ an imaginary control surface enclosing the control volume. At any instant of time, a fluid particle in the control volume has a particle velocity equal to the field velocity at the point it occupies at that instant. Fluid particles occupying the control surface have particle velocities corresponding to the field velocities on the control surface.

In Fig. 2, a control volume $\hat{R}$ has been drawn with the scalar quantities ρu, ρv, ρw indicated at its center. ρu can be interpreted as the

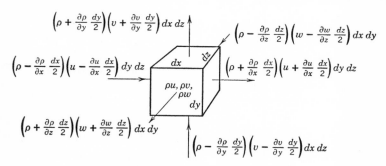

FIG. 2. Interpretation of divergence.

mass flow per second through unit area perpendicular to u. To find the mass flux through the control surface enclosing $\hat{R}$, field values of ρ, u, v, w have been indicated on the six faces of the control surface.

Only those components that contribute to a flux through the surface have been indicated on the figure. Values of the scalars on the faces have been derived from their values at the center of the control volume by the argument of Section 2.2. For example, the value of the scalar density at a point in the fluid which is removed from the center of the control volume by a distance $dx/2$ differs from the value of the density at the center of the control volume by an increment $(\partial\rho/\partial x)(dx/2)$. It will be remembered from the discussion in Section 2.2 that this is an exact statement only when dx is vanishingly small. Consequently, for a control volume of infinitesimal proportions the value of the density on the right hand face $dy\,dz$ is $\rho + (\partial\rho/\partial x)(dx/2)$. The proof of this statement from considerations on a cube of finite dimensions is left to the reader.

The efflux per unit volume from a point is by definition

$$\lim_{\hat{R}\to 0} \frac{\text{mass outflow/sec—mass inflow/sec}}{\hat{R}} \tag{5}$$

With the aid of Fig. 2, Eq. 5 becomes

$$\frac{\partial\rho u}{\partial x} + \frac{\partial\rho v}{\partial y} + \frac{\partial\rho w}{\partial z}$$

which is precisely the definition of div $\rho\mathbf{V}$. A positive value of div $\rho\mathbf{V}$ at a point in the field means more fluid is leaving the point per unit volume per second than is entering the point. The divergence of a vector is a scalar quantity.

A theorem connecting the surface and volume integrals may be written

$$\iiint_{\hat{R}} \text{div } \mathbf{A}\, d\hat{R} = \iint_{\hat{S}} A_n\, d\hat{S} \tag{6}$$

where $\mathbf{A}$ is any vector, and A_n is the component of the vector normal to the surface $\hat{S}$ which encloses the region $\hat{R}$.

If $\rho\mathbf{V}$ is the vector $\mathbf{A}$, the truth of the theorem can be seen from the following consideration. Divide the region into small cubes, and sum the values of div $\rho\mathbf{V}$ at the center of each cube. The flux through common faces of adjacent cubes cancel because the inflow through one face equals the outflow through the other. Only the faces on the surface enclosing the region will contribute to the summation. It can be concluded that in the limit, as the cubes approach zero volume, the integral of div $\rho\mathbf{V}$ throughout the region is equal to the normal flux through the surface enclosing the region. Applied to any vector $\mathbf{A}$, this is precisely the statement of Eq. 6.

This theorem, usually attributed to Gauss, is called the *divergence theorem*.

For convenience in working with cartesian coordinates, *cubic* regions have been used in the above arguments. The truth of the conclusions is in no way affected by the shape of the regions.

2.5 CONSERVATION OF MASS AND THE EQUATION OF CONTINUITY

One of the empirical laws that forms the basis of the science of aerodynamics states that, for problems in aerodynamics, mass can be neither created nor destroyed. This conservation principle applies to elements of fixed identity, and in order to express the principle in terms of field properties resort is made to the following physical reasoning.

Consider a control volume $\hat{R}$ fixed in the field, as shown in Fig. 3. If more mass flows out of $\hat{R}$ each second than flows into $\hat{R}$, the mass within $\hat{R}$ must be decreasing. Specifically, the net efflux of mass through $\hat{S}$ is equal to the time rate of decrease of mass within $\hat{R}$. Through any incremental area $d\hat{S}$ of the control surface the mass flux is $\rho V_n \, d\hat{S}$

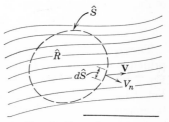

FIG. 3. Control volume.

where V_n is the component of the velocity normal to $d\hat{S}$ and is counted positive when directed outward. Then the net efflux through the control surface is

$$\iint_{\hat{S}} \rho V_n \, d\hat{S}$$

where ρ and V_n are field properties. $\rho \, d\hat{R}$ represents an increment of mass at a fixed field point within $\hat{R}$. The total mass within $\hat{R}$ is

$$\iiint_{\hat{R}} \rho \, d\hat{R}$$

where ρ is a field property.

The conservation of mass principle stated in terms of field properties is

$$\iint_{\hat{S}} \rho V_n \, d\hat{S} = -\frac{\partial}{\partial t} \iiint_{\hat{R}} \rho \, d\hat{R} \tag{7}$$

As a simple application of the above principle consider the steady flow of a fluid through the tube shown in Fig. 4. The control volume is contained within the dotted line. There is no flux through the sides of the tube, and it is assumed that ρ_1 and V_1 are average values across the area A_1, and ρ_2 and V_2 are average values across A_2. Because the

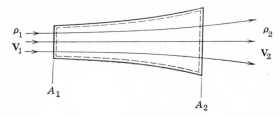

Fig. 4.   Simple application of conservation of mass principle.

flow is steady, the right hand side of Eq. 7 is zero and the conservation of mass principle becomes

$$\rho_2 V_2 A_2 - \rho_1 V_1 A_1 = 0$$

The equation of continuity is a statement of the conservation of mass principle in terms of field properties at a point. It may be derived from Eq. 7 by an application of the divergence theorem as given by Eq. 6. Let A in Eq. 6 be the vector $\rho\mathbf{V}$. Then the left-hand side of Eq. 7 may be converted to a triple integral and after rearrangement becomes

$$\iiint_{\hat{R}} \left(\text{div } \rho\mathbf{V} + \frac{\partial\rho}{\partial t} \right) d\hat{R} = 0 \qquad (8)$$

The order of differentiation and integration has been interchanged. This is permissible because the limits of the space integration are independent of time.

Equation 8 must hold for all control volumes no matter how small and therefore the integrand must be identically zero. The equation of continuity becomes

$$\text{div } \rho\mathbf{V} = -\frac{\partial\rho}{\partial t} \qquad (9)$$

The field properties ρ and $\mathbf{V}$ in a physically possible flow must satisfy the equation of continuity or the conservation of mass principle will be violated. When the flow is steady, the field properties are not functions of time, and *continuity* reduces to

$$\text{div } \rho\mathbf{V} = 0 \qquad (10)$$

If the fluid is incompressible, ρ is a constant and may be divided out of the equation. *Continuity* becomes

$$\text{div } \mathbf{V} = 0 \qquad (11)$$

A velocity pattern represents a physically possible situation only if *continuity* is satisfied.

For example, say the two-dimensional flow of an incompressible fluid is described as having streamlines radiating from the origin of coordinates with the absolute value of the velocity varying inversely with the nth power of the distance from the origin.

$$y = mx$$

$$|\mathbf{V}| = \frac{k}{r^n}$$

where $r^2 = x^2 + y^2$ is the radius vector. After solving for u and v and performing the required differentiation, the sum of the derivatives is found, in general, to be different from zero.

$$\frac{\partial u}{\partial x} + \frac{\partial v}{\partial y} = k \left\{ \frac{2}{r^{n+1}} - \frac{n+1}{r^{n+1}} \right\} = (1 - n) \frac{k}{r^{n+1}}$$

Only for the special case $n = 1$ does the flow pattern described by the equations correspond to a physically possible situation. Hence, a two-dimensional flow radiating from a point with the velocity inversely proportional to the radius vector satisfies the equation of continuity everywhere except at $r = 0$; it is, therefore, a physically possible flow except at $r = 0$. This flow is called a *source* if the velocity is directed away from the point and a *sink* if directed toward the point.

At the source itself, $r = 0$, another method must be employed to determine whether *continuity* is satisfied. An application of Eq. 6 reveals immediately that div $\mathbf{V}$ is not zero at $r = 0$. To show this, Eq. 6 can be written

$$\iiint_{\hat{R}} \text{div } \mathbf{V} \, d\hat{R} = \iint_{\hat{S}} V_n \, d\hat{S}$$

Let $\hat{R}$ be a region enclosing the source. Because div $\mathbf{V}$ is known to vanish at every point other than the point $r = 0$, it is clear that the triple integral on the left-hand side of the equation is equal to the value of the integrand at $r = 0$.

$$(\text{div } \mathbf{V} \, d\hat{R})_{r=0} = \iint_{\hat{S}} V_n \, d\hat{S}$$

But the double integral on the right is equal to the volume of fluid passing out of the region. Therefore, at $r = 0$, div $\mathbf{V}$ times an infinitesimal $d\hat{R}$ is equal to a finite quantity. It can be concluded that div $\mathbf{V}$ at the source is infinite.

Thus, source flow corresponds to a physically possible situation everywhere except at the source itself.

2.6 STREAM FUNCTION IN TWO-DIMENSIONAL INCOMPRESSIBLE FLOW

As a consequence of the conservation of mass, it is possible to define uniquely a function of the field coordinates from which the velocity in both magnitude and direction is derivable for two-dimensional incompressible flow.* In Fig. 5, let ab and cd represent streamlines in a two-dimensional incompressible flow. A streamline is a path whose direction at every point coincides with that of the velocity, and therefore

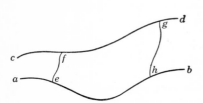

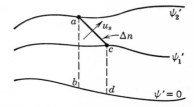

FIG. 5. Derivation of stream function.

FIG. 6. Velocity components from stream function.

no fluid can cross cd or ab. Because incompressible flow has been assumed, the density of the fluid within the boundary $efgh$ does not vary with time, and, therefore the same mass of fluid must cross ef that crosses hg or any other path connecting the streamlines. If the streamline ab is arbitrarily chosen as a base, every other streamline in the field can be identified by assigning to it a number equal to the *mass* of fluid passing, per second, between the base streamline and the streamline in question. Through the use of this characteristic, a parameter, ψ', may be defined at each point in the field. ψ' represents the mass of fluid passing between a given point and the base streamline each second. Isolines of this parameter represent streamlines. The isoline $\psi' = 0$ represents the base streamline.

The component of the velocity u_s in any direction s is readily found from the following consideration. Let Δn be an incremental length in the field perpendicular to the direction s. Let ψ_1' and ψ_2' be the values of ψ' at the endpoints of Δn. See Fig. 6. The fluid crossing the line ab each second must be equal to the fluid crossing the lines cd and ac each

---

* Such a function can be found in three dimensions for flows with axial symmetry; for example, the flow about a body of revolution. A stream function for a compressible flow is derived in Section 7.2.

second. Using the definition of ψ', we can write the following equation:

$$\psi_2' = \psi_1' + \rho u_s \, \Delta n$$

$$u_s = \frac{1}{\rho} \frac{\psi_2' - \psi_1'}{\Delta n}$$

or taking the limit

$$u_s = \frac{1}{\rho} \frac{d\psi'}{dn} \tag{12}$$

For an incompressible flow, ρ may be taken inside the differentiation sign

$$u_s = \frac{d(\psi'/\rho)}{dn} \tag{13}$$

The ratio ψ'/ρ is called the stream function and is given the symbol ψ. As defined here, the value of the stream function equals the *volume* of fluid per unit distance normal to the plane of motion per second passing between the base streamline, $\psi = 0$, and the point in question.

The velocity component in any direction is found by differentiating the stream function at right angles to that direction. The usual convention of differentiating at right angles to the left is adopted. Then, in cartesian coordinates, the velocity components are

$$u = \frac{\partial \psi}{\partial y}$$

$$v = -\frac{\partial \psi}{\partial x} \tag{14}$$

In polar coordinates, if increasing values of θ and r are measured counterclockwise and outward from the pole, respectively, the components are

$$u_r = \frac{1}{r} \frac{\partial \psi}{\partial \theta}$$

$$u_\theta = -\frac{\partial \psi}{\partial r} \tag{15}$$

2.7   THE SHEARING DERIVATIVES—ROTATION AND STRAIN

The six remaining derivatives in the matrix at the end of Section 2.3 (those off the diagonal from upper left to lower right) are similar in that the rate of change in each case is normal to the direction of the velocity component.

The derivative $\partial u / \partial y$ indicates that layers of fluid parallel to the xz-plane have different velocities in the x-direction; that is, there is a relative motion between fluid layers. In a real fluid, this relative motion causes a shearing stress (Chapter 1), thus suggesting the name *shearing derivative* for $\partial u / \partial y$. Each of the other five derivatives has an analogous characteristic.

It will be noticed that the derivatives $\partial u / \partial y$ and $\partial v / \partial x$ are associated with the xy-coordinate plane. See Fig. 7. Similarly, the pairs $(\partial w / \partial x,$ $\partial u / \partial z)$ and $(\partial v / \partial z, \partial w / \partial y)$ are associated with the xz- and yz-coordinate planes, respectively. The physical meaning of the derivatives can be seen by considering the coplanar pairs separately. The following demonstration utilizes the pair $(\partial u / \partial y, \partial v / \partial x)$, but it holds equally well for the pairs $(\partial w / \partial x, \partial u / \partial z)$ and $(\partial v / \partial z, \partial w / \partial y)$.

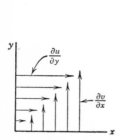

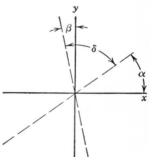

FIG. 7. Shearing derivatives.   FIG. 8. Strain and rotation of a fluid element.

At a given instant consider two *needles* of fluid particles intersecting orthogonally at a point in the field. Attach the coordinate system to the point of intersection of the needles, and after an interval of time observe the positions of the two needles. In general, each will have rotated as shown by the dotted lines on Fig. 8. Counterclockwise rotation is taken as positive. The immediate neighborhood of a point is being considered, and, consequently, the needles in their final position have been shown on Fig. 8 as straight lines.

The strain (γ) and angular velocity (ω) at the point of intersection are defined by the following equations:

$$\gamma = -\frac{d\delta}{dt} = -\frac{d}{dt}(90° - \alpha + \beta) = -\frac{d}{dt}(\beta - \alpha)$$

$$\omega = \frac{d}{dt}\left(\frac{\alpha + \beta}{2}\right) = \frac{1}{2}\frac{d}{dt}(\beta + \alpha)$$

(16)

The derivative $d\beta/dt$ is equal to $-\partial u/\partial y$. This may be seen from Fig. 9. The solid vertical line represents the needle at time t_1, and the dotted line represents the needle at time t_2. In the time interval $(t_2 - t_1)$ a fluid particle situated at a distance y from the intersection will have traveled a distance $(\partial u/\partial y) \cdot y(t_2 - t_1)$, and the angle β is

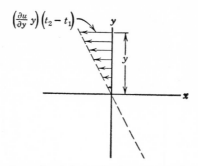

$$\left(\frac{\partial u}{\partial y}\, y\right)\left(t_2 - t_1\right)$$

Fig. 9. Rate of angular deformation in terms of shearing derivative.

given by $-\tan^{-1}[(\partial u/\partial y) \cdot (t_2 - t_1)]$. The negative sign is needed because the positive sense for angular displacement is taken counterclockwise. The derivative becomes

$$\frac{d\beta}{dt} = \lim_{(t_2 - t_1) \to 0} \frac{\beta_2 - \beta_1}{t_2 - t_1} = \lim_{(t_2 - t_1) \to 0} \frac{-\tan^{-1}[(\partial u/\partial y) \cdot (t_2 - t_1)]}{t_2 - t_1} = -\frac{\partial u}{\partial y}$$

In a similar manner it can be shown that $(d\alpha/dt) = +(\partial v/\partial x)$. If these relations are used in Eqs. 16, strain and angular velocity in the xy-plane become

$$\gamma_z = \left(\frac{\partial v}{\partial x} + \frac{\partial u}{\partial y}\right)$$

$$\omega_z = \frac{1}{2}\left(\frac{\partial v}{\partial x} - \frac{\partial u}{\partial y}\right)$$

(17)

A clear picture of strain and angular velocity can be formed by considering two special cases. Let $\partial v/\partial x$ and $\partial u/\partial y$ have equal positive values. From Eq. 17, the angular velocity vanishes and the element as pictured in Fig. 10 is said to be undergoing pure strain. As a second example, let $\partial u/\partial y$ and $\partial v/\partial x$ have equal magnitudes but opposite signs. For this case Eq. 17 indicates zero strain, and the element as pictured in Fig. 11 is said to have a pure angular velocity.

It is instructive to consider the expression for angular velocity as defined by Eqs. 16 in terms of the natural coordinates of the system.

Let s be a coordinate in the direction of the tangent to a streamline, and let n be a coordinate normal to s and lying in a plane determined

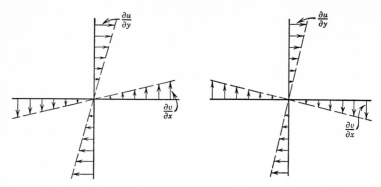

Fig. 10.   Pure strain.   Fig. 11.   Pure rotation.

by the tangent and the center of curvature of the streamline at the point in question. See Fig. 12.

In the interval $(t_2 - t_1)$, the tangent needle rotates by the amount the streamline rotates, that is, the angular velocity V/R times $(t_2 - t_1)$. The amount the vertical needle rotates depends upon the difference in velocity between its upper and lower ends $(dV/dn)\,\Delta n$. The difference in linear displacement of the upper and lower ends is $(dV/dn)\,\Delta n(t_2 - t_1)$. This expression divided by Δn gives the angular displacement. The mean angular displacement in the interval $(t_2 - t_1)$ is $\frac{1}{2}(V/R + dV/dn)(t_2 - t_1)$, and the angular velocity is given by

$$\omega = \frac{1}{2}\left(\frac{V}{R} + \frac{dV}{dn}\right) \qquad (18)$$

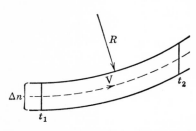

Fig. 12.   Angular velocity in terms of natural coordinates.

where R and n have the same direction. Outward along a radius and counterclockwise are considered positive.

The above analysis indicates the restrictions zero angular velocity places upon the flow pattern. These restrictions greatly simplify the formulation of flow problems.

2.8   CIRCULATION, CURL OF A VECTOR

The *scalar product* of two vectors is defined as the product of the absolute value of the vectors and the cosine of the angle included between them. The scalar product of the vectors **A** and **B** in Fig. 13 is $|\mathbf{A}||\mathbf{B}|\cos\alpha$. The scalar product is equivalent to the product of $|\mathbf{A}|$ and the component of **B** in the direction of **A**, or, alternatively, it is equivalent to the product of $|\mathbf{B}|$ and the component of **A** in the direction of **B**. The scalar product of two vectors is a scalar and is usually denoted by placing a *dot* between the vectors. Thus

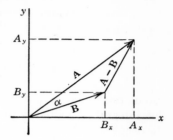

FIG. 13.   Scalar product.

$$|\mathbf{A}||\mathbf{B}|\cos\alpha = \mathbf{A}\cdot\mathbf{B}$$

The cartesian form of the scalar product may be written from simple geometrical considerations. In Fig. 13 let A_x, A_y, B_x, and B_y represent the components of the vectors **A** and **B**. The absolute value of the vector **A–B** may be written

$$|\mathbf{A-B}| = \sqrt{(A_x - B_x)^2 + (A_y - B_y)^2}$$

$$= \sqrt{|\mathbf{A}|^2 + |\mathbf{B}|^2 - 2(A_xB_x + A_yB_y)}$$

The absolute value of the vector **A–B** may also be written, from the triangle law,

$$|\mathbf{A-B}| = \sqrt{|\mathbf{A}|^2 + |\mathbf{B}|^2 - 2|\mathbf{A}||\mathbf{B}|\cos\alpha}$$

A comparison of these two expressions will show that

$$|\mathbf{A}||\mathbf{B}|\cos\alpha = A_xB_x + A_yB_y$$

In three dimensions, the cartesian form of the scalar product is similar:

$$\mathbf{A}\cdot\mathbf{B} = A_xB_x + A_yB_y + A_zB_z$$

Consider the *line integral* along a path in a vector field of the component of the vector in the direction of the path. If dx, dy, and dz are components of the incremental path length $d\mathbf{s}$, the line integral between two points in the field, m and n, may be written

$$\oint_m^n \mathbf{A}\cdot d\mathbf{s} = \oint_m^n (A_x\,dx + A_y\,dy + A_z\,dz)$$

where A_x, A_y, and A_z, the components of **A**, are each functions of x, y, and z. If the equation of the path is known, the line integral may be reduced to a definite integral and evaluated by the usual methods.

If the vector **A** is a force, the line integral of **A**·*ds* represents work or energy. The line integral around a *closed* path of the velocity component in the direction of the path has special significance in airfoil theory and is given the name *circulation*. Circulation, from the preceding discussion, is evaluated by the formula

$$\oint \mathbf{V} \cdot ds = \oint (u\,dx + v\,dy + w\,dz) \tag{19}$$

Circulation is given the symbol Γ and is counted positive when the line integral is evaluated in the *clockwise* sense. This deviation from the usual convention for positive sense is for convenience in the application of the concept of circulation to airfoil theory, which is discussed in Chapter 4.

It is convenient at this point to employ the concept of circulation to define another important kinematical property of vector fields, namely, the *curl* of a vector. The curl of a *vector* is a *vector* whose component in any direction n is defined as

$$\operatorname{curl}_n \mathbf{A} = \lim_{\Delta \hat{S} \to 0} \frac{\oint \mathbf{A} \cdot ds}{\Delta \hat{S}} \tag{20}$$

$\Delta \hat{S}$ is the area enclosed by the path about which the line integral is taken. The direction n coincides with the normal to the surface as $\Delta \hat{S}$ approaches zero. The reader is referred to textbooks on vector analysis for the usual definition of the curl of a vector.

The x-component of the curl involves the line integral about a path that in the limit encloses an area $\Delta \hat{S}$ in the yz-plane. Similarly, the y- and z-components of the curl are associated with areas in the zx- and xy-planes, respectively. The resultant value of the curl in both magnitude and direction is formed from its components in the same manner as any other vector is formed from its components. The sense is given by the right-hand rule.

Consider the z-component of the curl **V** at a point in a velocity field. In cartesian coordinates, it is convenient to evaluate the line integral of Eq. 20 around a rectangular path. The shape of the path, however, can have no effect on the value of the curl. Let the path have sides of length Δx and Δy, as shown in Fig. 14.

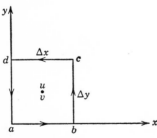

FIG. 14.   Evaluation of curl.

Using Eq. 20, the value of the z-component of curl $\mathbf{V}$ is given by

$$\text{curl}_z\ \mathbf{V} = \lim_{\Delta_x\ \Delta_y \to 0} \frac{\oint_a^b \mathbf{V}\cdot d\mathbf{s} + \oint_b^c \mathbf{V}\cdot d\mathbf{s} + \oint_c^d \mathbf{V}\cdot d\mathbf{s} + \oint_d^a \mathbf{V}\cdot d\mathbf{s}}{\Delta x\ \Delta y} \tag{21}$$

According to Eq. 19, $\oint_a^b \mathbf{V}\cdot d\mathbf{s}$ is simply the x-component of the velocity along the path ab times Δx. The y-component of the velocity makes no contribution because the y-component of $d\mathbf{s}$ along the path ab is zero. If the velocity components at the center of the rectangle are given by u and v, then the x-component of velocity along the path ab is $u - (\partial u/\partial y)\cdot(\Delta y/2)$, and the first integral becomes

$$\oint_a^b \mathbf{V}\cdot d\mathbf{s} = \left\{ u - \frac{\partial u}{\partial y}\cdot\frac{\Delta y}{2} \right\} \Delta x$$

In evaluating the integral, it is assumed that $\{u - (\partial u/\partial y)\cdot(\Delta y/2)\}$ is an average value over the length ab. This assumption does not introduce an approximation because the length ab will eventually be shrunk to zero.

Similarly, for the other integrals,

$$\oint_b^c \mathbf{V}\cdot d\mathbf{s} = \left(v + \frac{\partial v}{\partial x}\cdot\frac{\Delta x}{2} \right) \Delta y$$

$$\oint_c^d \mathbf{V}\cdot d\mathbf{s} = -\left(u + \frac{\partial u}{\partial y}\cdot\frac{\Delta y}{2} \right) \Delta x$$

$$\oint_d^a \mathbf{V}\cdot d\mathbf{s} = -\left(v - \frac{\partial v}{\partial x}\cdot\frac{\Delta x}{2} \right) \Delta y$$

Substituting these values in Eq. 21 and proceeding in the same manner with the x- and y-components,

$$\text{curl}_z\ \mathbf{V} = \frac{\partial v}{\partial x} - \frac{\partial u}{\partial y}$$

$$\text{curl}_x\ \mathbf{V} = \frac{\partial w}{\partial y} - \frac{\partial v}{\partial z} \tag{22}$$

$$\text{curl}_y\ \mathbf{V} = \frac{\partial u}{\partial z} - \frac{\partial w}{\partial x}$$

2.9 IRROTATIONAL FLOW

From the demonstration of Section **2.7**, the angular velocity of a fluid element in the xy-plane is given by Eq. **17**:

$$\omega_z = \frac{1}{2}\left(\frac{\partial v}{\partial x} - \frac{\partial u}{\partial y}\right)$$

Comparing this with Eq. 22 clearly shows $\text{curl}_z\ \mathbf{V}$ to be equal to twice the mean angular velocity of the fluid element in the xy-plane.

In a similar manner $\text{curl}_y\ \mathbf{V}$ is related to the angular velocity in xz-plane and $\text{curl}_x\ \mathbf{V}$ is related to the angular velocity in yz-plane.

Finally, it can be said that curl $\mathbf{V}$ at a point in a field is equal to twice the mean rotational velocity of the fluid element at that point. The directions of the angular velocity and curl are the same.

Illustrative Example

Usually, the plane of rotation of a fluid element is oriented in an arbitrary manner with respect to the coordinate planes, and the angular velocity has, therefore, three components. For the following example, assume that the x- and y-components of the angular velocity are zero and that the fluid is rotating as a solid body. If the center of rotation is chosen as the origin of coordinates, then the absolute value of the velocity and the equation of the streamlines, respectively, may be written

$$|\mathbf{V}| = \omega r$$

$$x^2 + y^2 = \text{constant}$$

ω is the angular velocity of the rigid-body rotation and should, therefore, equal $\frac{1}{2}$ $\text{curl}_z\ \mathbf{V}$. The truth of this statement is easily demonstrated. Solving for the velocity components from the equations,

$$u = -\omega y$$

$$v = +\omega x$$

$$\text{curl}_z\ \mathbf{V} = \frac{\partial v}{\partial x} - \frac{\partial u}{\partial y} = 2\omega_z$$

In general, the curl of a vector has a definite value at each point in the field. The curl vanishes only if the shearing derivatives are zero— as, for instance, in the case of a uniformly moving fluid, or if for each coplanar pair the shearing derivatives have equal magnitudes and are of the same sign. The last condition, which is apparently highly restrictive, is actually fulfilled by a large class of fluid fields treated in aerodynamics. Flows for which the curl vanishes are called *irrotational*.

Of special interest is a two-dimensional irrotational flow in which the streamlines are circular and the velocity is constant along a streamline. These conditions are expressed

$$\left.\begin{array}{c} \dfrac{\partial v}{\partial x} - \dfrac{\partial u}{\partial y} = 0 \\[2mm] x^2 + y^2 = \text{constant} \\[2mm] |\mathbf{V}| = f(r) \end{array}\right\} \tag{23}$$

Solving for u and v from Eq. 23 (see illustrative example, p. 17),

$$u = -\frac{yf(r)}{r}$$

$$v = +\frac{xf(r)}{r}$$

Applying the condition curl $\mathbf{V} = 0$ and solving for $f(r)$,

$$f(r) = \frac{k}{r} = |\mathbf{V}|$$

where k is a constant. This flow, which represents a fluid field with circular streamlines and with the absolute value of the velocity varying inversely with the distance from the center of the streamlines, is termed *vortex flow* and is, in general, irrotational.

The term *in general* is given meaning by investigating curl $\mathbf{V}$ throughout the field.

$$u = -\frac{ky}{r^2}$$

$$v = +\frac{kx}{r^2}$$

$$\frac{\partial v}{\partial x} = +\frac{k}{r^2}\left(-\frac{2x^2}{r^2} + 1\right)$$

$$\frac{\partial u}{\partial y} = -\frac{k}{r^2}\left(-\frac{2y^2}{r^2} + 1\right)$$

For all values of r different from zero, the derivatives are finite and their difference is zero. When $r = 0$, the derivatives do not exist and nothing can be said about the value of the curl.

The field, therefore, is irrotational at every point except at the origin where the value of the curl is still undetermined. It can be evaluated by a theorem developed in the next section.

2.10 THEOREM OF STOKES

A theorem connecting the surface integral and the line integral is implied in the definition of curl given by Eq. 20:

$$\operatorname{curl}_n \mathbf{V} = \lim_{\Delta\hat{S}\to 0} \frac{\oint \mathbf{V}\cdot d\mathbf{s}}{\Delta\hat{S}}$$

In the above formula, it is understood that n is in the direction of the normal to $\Delta\hat{S}$. If any arbitrarily warped surface in space is considered, the value of the component of the curl normal to the surface at any point is readily determined. Let the surface be divided into k segments

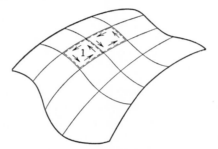

Fig. 15.   Stokes' theorem.

as shown in Fig. 15. Applying the above definition of curl to the segment 1, the following approximate expression can be written:

$$(\operatorname{curl}_n \mathbf{V}\,\Delta\hat{S})_1 \simeq \left(\oint \mathbf{V}\cdot d\mathbf{s}\right)_1$$

For k segments,

$$\sum_{i=1}^{k} (\operatorname{curl}_n \mathbf{V}\,\Delta\hat{S})_i \simeq \sum_{i=1}^{k} \left(\oint \mathbf{V}\cdot d\mathbf{s}\right)_i \qquad (24)$$

In summing the line integrals on the right-hand side of the equation, it will be observed that the integrals over paths that are common to any two segments can make no contribution to the summation. Therefore, the sum of the line integrals about the segments $\Delta\hat{S}_i$ is just equal to the line integral about the entire surface $\hat{S}$. Equation 24 comes closer to the truth as $\Delta\hat{S}$ approaches zero, and it is exact in the limit. Under these conditions the summation becomes a surface integral and Eq. 24 may be written

$$\iint_S \operatorname{curl}_n \mathbf{V}\,d\hat{S} = \oint \mathbf{V}\cdot d\mathbf{s} = -\Gamma \qquad (25)$$

The relation between the double integral and the line integral in Eq. 25 bears the name of Stokes. The negative sign on Γ arises because circulation is counted positive clockwise and the positive sense for curl is counterclockwise.

It is evident from Eq. 25 that the circulation around a closed path in an irrotational field is zero. It is further evident that, if every point in a field is irrotational except one, the circulation about every path enclosing the point will be the same and numerically equal to the value of curl_n $\mathbf{V}$ $d\hat{S}$ at that point.

Curl_n $\mathbf{V}$ $d\hat{S}$ at the point $r = 0$ in the vortex flow of Section 2.9 may be evaluated by applying Stokes' theorem. For vortex flow, the streamlines are circles, and the velocity is inversely proportional to the distance from the center.

$$x^2 + y^2 = c^2$$

$$|\mathbf{V}| = \frac{k}{r}$$

The flow is irrotational everywhere except at $r = 0$, where the value of the curl is undetermined. Then the circulation around every path enclosing the point $r = 0$ will be the same and equal to the value of curl_n $\mathbf{V}$ $d\hat{S}$ at $r = 0$.

If a streamline is chosen as the path of integration, the product $\mathbf{V} \cdot d\mathbf{s}$ is simply $(k/r)(r\, d\theta)$, and the circulation Γ becomes

$$\Gamma = -\oint \mathbf{V} \cdot d\mathbf{s} = -\int_0^{2\pi} \frac{k}{r} (r\, d\theta) = -2\pi k$$

Thus, at $r = 0$, $\mathrm{curl}\ \mathbf{V}\ d\hat{S} = -2\pi k$. Because $d\hat{S}$ is infinitesimal, $(\mathrm{curl}\ \mathbf{V})_{r=0} = \infty$.

If k is replaced with its equivalent $-\Gamma/2\pi$, the equations that describe vortex flow become

$$x^2 + y^2 = c^2$$

$$|\mathbf{V}| = \frac{\Gamma}{2\pi} \frac{1}{r}$$

(26)

The sense of the velocity is clockwise when Γ is a positive number.

Vortex flow is irrotational everywhere except at the center of the vortex itself, where the angular velocity is infinite. It can be verified that vortex flow satisfies the equation of continuity everywhere and therefore represents a physically possible flow.

This important flow is discussed at greater length in Section 2.12.

2.11 VELOCITY POTENTIAL

From Stokes' theorem, it is apparent that the line integral of $\mathbf{V} \cdot d\mathbf{s}$ around a closed path in an irrotational field is zero.   Then, if A and B of Fig. 16 represent two points on a closed path in an irrotational field, the line integral from A to B along either branch must be the same. Since an infinite number of closed paths may be drawn

through A and B around each one of which the line integral is zero, it must be concluded that the line integral along any path connecting A and B is independent of the path; that is,

FIG. 16. Line integral in an irrotational field.

$$\oint_A^B \mathbf{V} \cdot d\mathbf{s} = \oint_A^B (u\, dx + v\, dy + w\, dz) = f(A, B)$$

A line integral can be independent of the path of integration only if the integrand is an exact differential. Therefore, $\mathbf{V} \cdot d\mathbf{s}$ must be an exact differential of some function of the field coordinates. This function is given the symbol $\phi(x,\, y,\, z)$ and called the velocity potential. Writing the total differential in the form

$$d\phi = \frac{\partial \phi}{\partial x}\, dx + \frac{\partial \phi}{\partial y}\, dy + \frac{\partial \phi}{\partial z}\, dz$$

and remembering that, by definition,

$$d\phi = u\, dx + v\, dy + w\, dz$$

it is apparent that

$$u = \frac{\partial \phi}{\partial x}, \quad v = \frac{\partial \phi}{\partial y}, \quad w = \frac{\partial \phi}{\partial z}$$

Then

$$|\mathbf{V}| = \sqrt{u^2 + v^2 + w^2} = \sqrt{\left(\frac{\partial \phi}{\partial x}\right)^2 + \left(\frac{\partial \phi}{\partial y}\right)^2 + \left(\frac{\partial \phi}{\partial z}\right)^2}$$

and

$$\mathbf{V} = \operatorname{grad} \phi$$

The velocity potential arises as a consequence of the irrotationality of the flow just as the stream function arises as a consequence of the conservation of mass. Both functions serve the purpose of permitting a complete description of the flow by means of a single function of the field coordinates. Every two-dimensional incompressible flow possesses a stream function. Every irrotational flow possesses a velocity potential. The line integral of the velocity component in the direction of the path between any two points in an irrotational field is equal to the difference in potential between these points.

$$\oint_A^B \mathbf{V} \cdot d\mathbf{s} = \phi_B - \phi_A$$

If point A is a position of zero potential, the line integral from A to any other point in the field is the value of the potential at that point.

Summarizing, if a field is irrotational, that is, if

$$\text{curl}_x \mathbf{V} = \frac{\partial w}{\partial y} - \frac{\partial v}{\partial z} = 0$$

$$\text{curl}_y \mathbf{V} = \frac{\partial u}{\partial z} - \frac{\partial w}{\partial x} = 0$$

$$\text{curl}_z \mathbf{V} = \frac{\partial v}{\partial x} - \frac{\partial u}{\partial y} = 0$$

then a scalar potential ϕ exists such that

$$\mathbf{V} = \text{grad } \phi \qquad (27)$$

In coordinates, the derivative of ϕ in any direction s is equal to the component of velocity in that direction.

$$\frac{\partial \phi}{\partial s} = V_s \qquad (28)$$

The force of gravity exerted on unit mass is inversely proportional to the square of the distance between the unit mass and the earth's center. The reader may verify that the gravitational acceleration field is irrotational and therefore a scalar quantity U may be found such that

$$g_x = \frac{\partial U}{\partial x}, \quad g_y = \frac{\partial U}{\partial y}, \quad g_z = \frac{\partial U}{\partial z}$$

where g_x, g_y, and g_z are the three components of the gravitational acceleration. If the axes are so chosen that the positive z-axis points vertically downward, then g_x and g_y are zero, and

$$g_z = \frac{\partial U}{\partial z}$$

$$U = gz + \text{constant}$$

The constant of integration can be made to vanish if the potential at the level from which z is measured is taken as zero.

2.12 POINT VORTEX, VORTEX FILAMENT, LAW OF BIOT AND SAVART

The vortex flow described by Eq. 26 is of great importance in aerodynamics. The equations describe a flow pattern in a nonviscous, incompressible fluid and therefore it cannot be expected that an example of this pattern is to be found in nature. The waterspout and tornado approximate vortex flows in the region in which viscosity plays a minor role, that is, outside the central core.

In a vortex flow the fluid travels in concentric circles, and, except for a central core, the motion is irrotational throughout. It has been shown that for such a field the speed must be inversely proportional to the first power of the distance from the center.

The mathematical description of vortex flow gives a picture of a region in which the linear velocity of a fluid particle increases steadily as the center is approached. At the limit, the path over which the fluid element travels becomes infinitesimal while the speed of the element becomes infinite. *The center point is referred to as a point vortex whose strength is defined as the circulation about that point.* It is customary to speak of the point vortex as *inducing* a flow in the surrounding region. However, it should be remembered that the point vortex and the flow in the surrounding region simply coexist. One is not actually the cause of the other.

The two-dimensional velocity field described by Eqs. 26 is a vortex flow in the xy-plane with the point vortex at the origin of coordinates. Two-dimensional flow means the pattern is identical in all planes parallel to the xy-plane from $-\infty$ to $+\infty$. This point vortex, then, must be duplicated in every parallel plane, the configuration of the points forming a straight line perpendicular to the xy-plane and extending from $-\infty$ to $+\infty$. In three dimensions, such a line is called a vortex filament and may be defined as a line coinciding with the axis of rotation of successive fluid elements.

It is convenient to speak of the velocity *induced* in the region surrounding a vortex filament by an element ds of the filament. Figure 17 shows the filament lying in the xz-plane. The increment of velocity induced at p by element ds of the filament is given by *

$$dV = \frac{\Gamma}{4\pi}\frac{\cos\beta\,ds}{r^2} \tag{29}$$

* A proof of this law may be found in textbooks on hydrodynamics or vector analysis. For example, see J. G. Coffin, *Vector Analysis*, p. 165, John Wiley and Sons, New York, 1911; or L. Prandtl–O. G. Tietjens, *Fundamentals of Hydro and Aeromechanics*, p. 206, McGraw-Hill, New York, 1934.

where Γ is the strength of the vortex filament, r is the distance between the increment of filament and the point p, and β is the angle between the length r and the normal to the filament. The direction of the velocity increment is perpendicular to a plane determined by the length ds and the point p.

Equation 29 is due to Biot and Savart and is completely analogous to the law that gives the strength of a magnetic field induced in a region surrounding a wire that is carrying a current. The velocity at p induced by the entire filament is obtained by integration.

$$V = \int_{-\infty}^{+\infty} \frac{\Gamma}{4\pi} \frac{\cos\beta\, ds}{r^2} \qquad (30)$$

$$r = h \sec \beta \qquad (31)$$

$$s = h \tan \beta$$

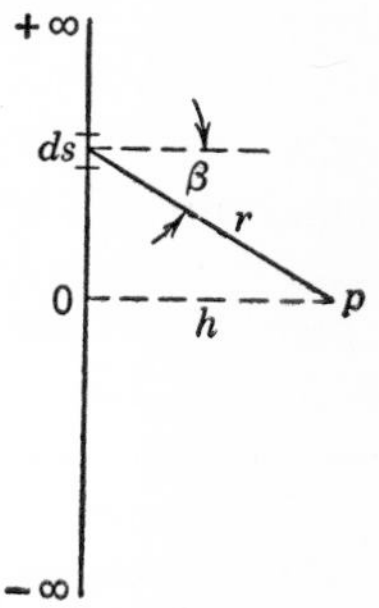

FIG. 17. Velocity induced by a vortex filament.

The h in Eqs. 31 is the perpendicular distance between the filament and the point p. If Eqs. 31 are substituted in Eq. 30 and if the integration with respect to β between the limits $\pm\pi/2$ is performed,

$$V = \frac{\Gamma}{2\pi h} \qquad (32)$$

This is precisely the velocity induced at p, arising from a point vortex at the origin, a necessary agreement for consistency between the two- and three-dimensional cases.

The concept of the vortex filament is extended by lifting the restriction that it must be a straight line perpendicular to the plane of the two-dimensional point vortex. The picture now is one of a line curving arbitrarily in space in such a manner that it coincides with the axis of rotation of successive fluid particles. The law of Biot and Savart as given by Eq. 29 is applicable to the curved filament.

2.13 VORTEX SHEETS

A further extension of the vortex concept from a line to a surface will be found useful in the treatment of problems involving the flow about thin bodies. The cross section of a vortex filament is a point of concentrated vorticity at which the value of the curl is infinite. As shown in Fig. 18, the vortex surface or sheet can be thought of as an infinite number of vortex filaments, placed side by side, each of which has an infinitesimal strength. The integral of curl V over an area containing unit width of the sheet then has a finite value, which is called the strength of the sheet. By Stokes' theorem, then, the strength of the sheet, γ, at any point is given by

$$\gamma = \lim_{l \to 0} \frac{1}{l} \oint \mathbf{V} \cdot d\mathbf{s}$$

where l is the width of the enclosed sheet. If the circulation is clockwise, γ is a positive number.

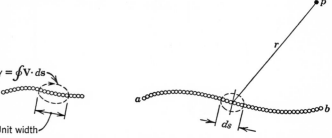

FIG. 18.   Vortex sheet.

FIG. 19.   Velocity induced by a vortex sheet.

If the elements of the sheet are straight, doubly infinite vortex filaments, then the velocity induced in the surrounding field at any point p by an increment of sheet ds is

$$dV = \frac{\gamma \, ds}{2\pi} \frac{1}{r}$$

See Fig. 19.

It is apparent that the velocity field induced by a vortex sheet will satisfy *continuity* at all points in the field because each element individually induces a field that satisfies *continuity* at all points. *Irrotationality* is satisfied at all points in the field by the same argument. The argument fails at the sheet itself where the value of the curl $\mathbf{V}$ is infinite.

It can easily be seen that the velocity is finite at all points in the field, excluding the points of the sheet, by realizing that the velocity at point p induced by any finite increment of the sheet is finite and therefore the velocity at p induced by the entire sheet is finite. For points on the sheet, the demonstration is more involved, but it can be shown that the velocity induced at any point on the sheet by the entire sheet is finite, except for the points a and b, that is, at the edges of the sheet. At these points, the velocity is infinite.

No discontinuities in the velocity occur anywhere in the field except at the sheet itself, where the velocity component parallel to the sheet jumps by an amount equal to the strength of the sheet when the sheet is crossed. The velocity jump may be seen by considering the circulation around a unit width of sheet. The value of the circulation is equal to the integral of the curl **V** over the enclosed area, which by definition is the strength of the sheet. Then

$$(u_1 - u_2) + (v_1 - v_2)\, \Delta n = \iint_{\hat{S}} \text{curl } \mathbf{V} \, d\hat{S} = \gamma$$

The geometry is shown in Fig. 20.

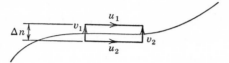

FIG. 20.   Velocity discontinuity at a vortex sheet.

The integral of curl **V** is not changed when Δn is made vanishingly small. It follows, therefore, that

$$\gamma = u_1 - u_2 \tag{33}$$

2.14 HELMHOLTZ' VORTEX THEOREMS

It is readily shown, by the following device, that the strength of a vortex filament is constant along its length. Enclose a segment of the vortex filament with a *sheath* from which a slit has been removed, as pictured in Fig. 21. Since the curl of the velocity at every point on the curved surface enclosed by the perimeter of the split sheath is zero, it follows, from Stokes' theorem, that the line integral of the velocity along the perimeter is also zero. In traversing the perimeter, the contributions to the total circulation of the line integrals from b to c and d to a will be of equal magnitude and opposite sign, providing the slit is very narrow. In order for the total circulation to be zero, therefore, the line integrals around the sheath from a to b and from c to d must be of equal magnitude and opposite sign. This means that the vorticity enclosed by the top and bottom perimeters of the cylinder must be identical, which demonstrates the truth of Helmholtz' first theorem:

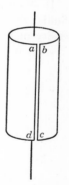

FIG. 21.   Split sheath.

The strength of a vortex filament is constant along its length.

Carrying the demonstration a step further, presume the split sheath so placed that the filament ends midway between the top and bottom edges. The line integrals around the sheath from a to b and from c to d can no longer be of equal magnitude, and the condition that the circulation around the perimeter be zero is therefore violated. Hence, the vortex filament cannot end in space; this conclusion is embodied in Helmholtz' second theorem:

A vortex filament cannot end in a fluid; it must extend to the boundaries of the fluid or form a closed path.

A third theorem of Helmholtz which may be proved theoretically by considerations of the *continuity* and *equilibrium* of a nonviscous incompressible fluid is stated as follows:

In the absence of rotational external forces, a fluid that is initially irrotational remains irrotational.

From the theorem of Stokes, a corollary may be written immediately:

In the absence of rotational external forces, if the circulation around a path enclosing a definite group of particles is initially zero, it will remain zero.

The way in which an external rotational force may be applied to a fluid is discussed in detail at the beginning of Chapter 6.

It should be noted that the vortex theorems apply only to perfect fluids; they also apply to viscous-fluid flows in regions where the viscosity may be neglected.

Dynamics of a Fluid Field

CHAPTER 3

3.1 ACCELERATION

In the last chapter the motions in a fluid field have been discussed without regard to the forces producing them. In the present chapter, Newton's law of motion is applied to a fluid element of *fixed identity*.

$$\mathbf{F} = M \times \text{particle acceleration}$$

$\mathbf{F}$ is the resultant force on a particle of mass M. The first task is to express the *particle acceleration* in terms of time rates of change of *field velocities*.

The steady velocity field has been defined as a region throughout which a velocity is described as a function of the field coordinates alone. If the velocity field represents the flow of a fluid, the picture is one of fluid particles traveling from point to point within the field. At any instant, each particle has the velocity corresponding to its location within the field at that instant. Because the individual particle is changing its position from instant to instant, and therefore its velocity, the particle is accelerating. The time rate of change of velocity of the particle because of its motion through the field is called *convective* acceleration.

The x-component of the convective acceleration is, by definition,

$$\lim_{t_2 \to t_1} \frac{u_2 - u_1}{t_2 - t_1} \tag{1}$$

where u_1 and u_2 are the x-components of the particle velocity at times t_1 and t_2. u_1 and u_2 also represent field velocities at the positions the particle occupies at times t_1 and t_2. In Section 2.2 it is shown that the

43

field velocity u_2 can be written

$$u_2 = u_1 + \left\{\frac{\partial u}{\partial x}\right\}_1 \Delta x + \left\{\frac{\partial u}{\partial y}\right\}_1 \Delta y + \left\{\frac{\partial u}{\partial z}\right\}_1 \Delta z + \left\{\frac{\partial^2 u}{\partial x^2}\right\}_1 \frac{\Delta x^2}{2!} + \cdots \quad (2)$$

Substituting Eq. 2 in Eq. 1, the convective acceleration becomes

$$\frac{\partial u}{\partial x}\frac{dx}{dt} + \frac{\partial u}{\partial y}\frac{dy}{dt} + \frac{\partial u}{\partial z}\frac{dz}{dt}$$

where dx/dt, dy/dt, and dz/dt are u, v, and w, respectively. The symbol du/dt represents the x-component of the *convective* acceleration. Therefore, du/dt is finally written

$$\frac{du}{dt} = u\frac{\partial u}{\partial x} + v\frac{\partial u}{\partial y} + w\frac{\partial u}{\partial z} \quad (3)$$

The y- and z-components are found in a similar manner.

$$\frac{dv}{dt} = u\frac{\partial v}{\partial x} + v\frac{\partial v}{\partial y} + w\frac{\partial v}{\partial z}$$

$$\frac{dw}{dt} = u\frac{\partial w}{\partial x} + v\frac{\partial w}{\partial y} + w\frac{\partial w}{\partial z}$$

$$(3)$$

In general, the velocity at any point in a velocity field is a function of time as well as the coordinates of the field; that is, the velocity at a fixed point (sometimes called a local point) is a function of time. The time rate of change of velocity at a local point is termed *local acceleration* and is given the symbol $\partial \mathbf{V}/\partial t$. By definition, the local acceleration in a steady field is zero. If the field is unsteady, the velocity of a particle is changing because (1) its coordinates are changing and (2) the velocity at a local point is changing. The *substantial* or total acceleration of the particle is equal to the sum of the convective and local accelerations. The script letter $\mathfrak{D}$ is used to indicate substantial time rate of change. The three components of the substantial acceleration are written

$$\left.\begin{aligned}
\frac{\mathfrak{D}u}{\mathfrak{D}t} &= \frac{\partial u}{\partial t} + u\frac{\partial u}{\partial x} + v\frac{\partial u}{\partial y} + w\frac{\partial u}{\partial z}\\[2mm]
\frac{\mathfrak{D}v}{\mathfrak{D}t} &= \frac{\partial v}{\partial t} + u\frac{\partial v}{\partial x} + v\frac{\partial v}{\partial y} + w\frac{\partial v}{\partial z}\\[2mm]
\frac{\mathfrak{D}w}{\mathfrak{D}t} &= \frac{\partial w}{\partial t} + u\frac{\partial w}{\partial x} + v\frac{\partial w}{\partial y} + w\frac{\partial w}{\partial z}
\end{aligned}\right\} \quad (4)$$

The terms convective and local time rates of change are not confined to velocity. They apply in an identical manner to other properties of the fluid field, such as density or temperature. For example, the substantial time rate of change of density of a fluid element in an unsteady field is

$$\frac{\mathfrak{D}\rho}{\mathfrak{D}t} = \frac{\partial \rho}{\partial t} + u \frac{\partial \rho}{\partial x} + v \frac{\partial \rho}{\partial y} + w \frac{\partial \rho}{\partial z} \tag{5}$$

Equations 4 and 5 represent time rates of change of particle properties in terms of field properties.

3.2 EULER'S EQUATION

Newton's law applied to a fluid element of fixed mass $\rho \, \Delta x \, \Delta y \, \Delta z$ is

$$\mathbf{F} = \rho \, \Delta x \, \Delta y \, \Delta z \frac{\mathfrak{D}\mathbf{V}}{\mathfrak{D}t} \tag{6}$$

where the differentiation is a substantial time rate of change of velocity and $\mathbf{F}$ is the sum of the forces acting on the element. These forces arise from shearing stresses, static pressure stresses, and the weight of the element. For the present, it is assumed the fluid is nonviscous; that is, shearing stresses are absent.

The force on the fluid element arising from the static pressure variation in the fluid is obtained from a consideration of Fig. 1. If the

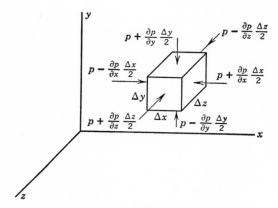

FIG. 1.   Dynamic equilibrium of a fluid element.

pressure at the center of the element is p, the pressures acting on the six faces will be those indicated on the figure. The resultant force in the direction of each of the three axes is:

in the x-direction:

$$\left(p - \frac{\partial p}{\partial x}\frac{\Delta x}{2}\right)\Delta y\ \Delta z - \left(p + \frac{\partial p}{\partial x}\frac{\Delta x}{2}\right)\Delta y\ \Delta z = -\frac{\partial p}{\partial x}\Delta x\ \Delta y\ \Delta z$$

in the y-direction:

$$\left(p - \frac{\partial p}{\partial y}\frac{\Delta y}{2}\right)\Delta x\ \Delta z - \left(p + \frac{\partial p}{\partial y}\frac{\Delta y}{2}\right)\Delta x\ \Delta z = -\frac{\partial p}{\partial y}\Delta x\ \Delta y\ \Delta z$$

in the z-direction:

$$\left(p - \frac{\partial p}{\partial z}\frac{\Delta z}{2}\right)\Delta x\ \Delta y - \left(p + \frac{\partial p}{\partial z}\frac{\Delta z}{2}\right)\Delta x\ \Delta y = -\frac{\partial p}{\partial z}\Delta x\ \Delta y\ \Delta z$$

The resultant pressure force on the fluid element is seen to be the negative of the pressure gradient multiplied by the incremental volume.

$$\text{resultant} = (-\operatorname{grad} p)\ \Delta x\ \Delta y\ \Delta z$$

Let **g** represent the acceleration due to gravity. The weight of the fluid element is $(\rho\ \Delta x\ \Delta y\ \Delta z)\mathbf{g}$. The total external force becomes

$$(\rho\mathbf{g} - \operatorname{grad} p)\ \Delta x\ \Delta y\ \Delta z \tag{7}$$

After substituting Eq. 7 for the left-hand side of Eq. 6, the equation of dynamic equilibrium becomes

$$\rho\mathbf{g} - \operatorname{grad} p = \rho\ \frac{\mathcal{D}\mathbf{V}}{\mathcal{D}t} \tag{8}$$

This equation, known as Euler's equation of motion, has been named after the Swiss mathematician who is responsible for its formulation. It is applicable to compressible or incompressible flows. In cartesian form, with the substantial derivative expanded, the equations are

$$g_x - \frac{1}{\rho}\frac{\partial p}{\partial x} = \frac{\partial u}{\partial t} + u\frac{\partial u}{\partial x} + v\frac{\partial u}{\partial y} + w\frac{\partial u}{\partial z}$$

$$g_y - \frac{1}{\rho}\frac{\partial p}{\partial y} = \frac{\partial v}{\partial t} + u\frac{\partial v}{\partial x} + v\frac{\partial v}{\partial y} + w\frac{\partial v}{\partial z} \tag{9}$$

$$g_z - \frac{1}{\rho}\frac{\partial p}{\partial z} = \frac{\partial w}{\partial t} + u\frac{\partial w}{\partial x} + v\frac{\partial w}{\partial y} + w\frac{\partial w}{\partial z}$$

The development of Euler's equation has assumed the fluid to be nonviscous. For cases in which shearing stresses cannot be neglected, another term must be added to the force $\mathbf{F}$ of Eq. 6.   This subject is treated in Chapter 12 and Appendix B.

3.3   THE MOMENTUM THEOREM OF FLUID MECHANICS

Euler's equation, developed in the last section, is a statement of the conditions that must be fulfilled at each point in the field if the fluid is to be in dynamic equilibrium.   Frequently, in aerodynamics the details of a flow field are too complicated to deal with and a gross relation involving a group of field points is desired.   The momentum theorem of fluid mechanics provides this relation.   It is derived from the conservation of momentum principle which may be stated: *The time rate of change of momentum of a group of particles of fixed identity is equal to the net force acting on the particles.*

The conservation of momentum principle is stated in terms of particle properties.   Its use in field theory requires a conversion to field properties, which may be made by considering the control surface $\hat{S}$ in Fig. 2.   At time t control surface $\hat{S}$ which is fixed in the fluid contains a definite set of fluid particles.   At time t_1 these particles will have moved to the region enclosed by the dotted curve $\hat{S}_1$.

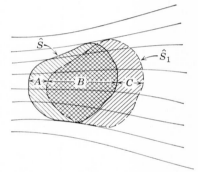

Let A, B, and C be the momentum of the fluid in regions A, B, and C respectively.   Then at time t, the particles have momentum $A + B_t$

FIG. 2.   Conversion to field properties.

and at time t_1, momentum $B_{t_1} + C$.   The momentum change during the interval $t_1 - t$ is

$$(B_{t_1} - B_t) + (C - A) \tag{10}$$

C is the momentum of the fluid that has passed out of $\hat{S}$ during the interval and A is the momentum of the fluid that has entered $\hat{S}$ during the interval.

The time rate of change of momentum is given by the limit of expression 10 as $t_1 \rightarrow t$

$$\lim_{t_1 \to t} \left(\frac{B_{t_1} - B_t}{t_1 - t} + \frac{C - A}{t_1 - t} \right) \tag{11}$$

In the limit, as $t_1 \rightarrow t$, $\hat{S}_1$ coincides with $\hat{S}$, and the first term in expression 11 becomes the time rate of change of momentum of the fluid in region $\hat{R}$ enclosed by $\hat{S}$. This is written as the integral

$$\frac{\partial}{\partial t} \iiint_{\hat{R}} \mathbf{V}\rho \, d\hat{R}$$

The second term in expression 11 is the momentum flux through $\hat{S}$, outward being counted positive. In integral form, the second term is written

$$\iint_{\hat{S}} \mathbf{V}\rho V_n \, d\hat{S}$$

if $\mathbf{F}$ is the force on the fluid particles within $\hat{S}$, the momentum theorem becomes:

$$\mathbf{F} = \frac{\partial}{\partial t} \iiint_{\hat{R}} \mathbf{V}\rho \, d\hat{R} + \iint_{\hat{S}} \mathbf{V}\rho V_n \, d\hat{S} \tag{12}$$

All quantities appearing in Eq. 12 are field properties. A rearrangement of Eq. 12 to the form

$$\frac{\partial}{\partial t} \iiint_{\hat{R}} \mathbf{V}\rho \, d\hat{R} = \mathbf{F} - \iint_{\hat{S}} \mathbf{V}\rho V_n \, d\hat{S} \tag{13}$$

leads to the following convenient statement of the momentum theorem as applied to a fixed control volume.

The time rate of increase of momentum within a fixed control volume $\hat{R}$ is equal to the rate at which momentum is flowing into $\hat{R}$ plus the net force acting on the fluid within $\hat{R}$.

Neglecting gravity and other body forces that may exist, the force $\mathbf{F}$ on the fluid within $\hat{R}$ arises from pressure stresses and shearing stresses. At every point within $\hat{R}$ the stresses are equal and opposite. Therefore, the force $\mathbf{F}$ is equal to the integral of the stresses over the control surface $\hat{S}$ enclosing $\hat{R}$. A general development of $\mathbf{F}$ in terms of the fluid stresses may be found in Appendix B, Section 5.

The three cartesian components of the vector Eq. 13 are written

$$\left. \begin{aligned} \frac{\partial}{\partial t} \iiint_{\hat{R}} u\rho \, d\hat{R} &= F_x - \iint_{\hat{S}} u\rho V_n \, d\hat{S} \\[2mm] \frac{\partial}{\partial t} \iiint_{\hat{R}} v\rho \, d\hat{R} &= F_y - \iint_{\hat{S}} v\rho V_n \, d\hat{S} \\[2mm] \frac{\partial}{\partial t} \iiint_{\hat{R}} w\rho \, d\hat{R} &= F_z - \iint_{\hat{S}} w\rho V_n \, d\hat{S} \end{aligned} \right\} \tag{14}$$

Because of the great importance of the momentum theorem, two simple examples of the application of Eqs. 14 for steady flow are given below. More sophisticated applications appear in Sections 4.9 and 13.6.

Illustrative Example 1

A fluid enters a curved pipe at station 1 and leaves at station 2 as shown in Fig. 3. V_1, ρ_1, and p_1 are average values of the velocity, pressure and density

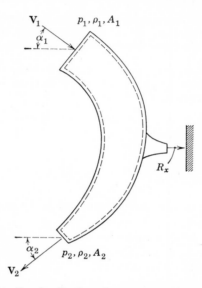

FIG. 3. Application of momentum theorem.

at the entrance. Similarly, V_2, ρ_2, p_2 are average values at the exit. The entrance angle is α_1 and the exit angle is α_2. For steady flow, find the force component R_x on the foundation.

Choose a control surface coinciding with the walls and perpendicular to the entrance and exit velocities as shown by the dotted line in Fig. 3. The force in the x-direction on the fluid in the control volume is exerted at the walls and at the exit and entrance areas A_1 and A_2, respectively. At the walls the force is $-R_x$, and at the entrance and exit the force arises from the pressures p_1 and p_2. The total force is

$$F_x = -R_x + p_1 A_1 \cos \alpha_1 + p_2 A_2 \cos \alpha_2$$

The flux of x momentum through the control surface is:

$$\iint_S u\rho V_n \, d\hat{S} = (V_2\rho_2 A_2)(-V_2 \cos \alpha) - (V_1\rho_1 A_1)(V_1 \cos \alpha)$$

Because the flow is steady, the triple integral in Eqs. 14 is zero and the first of Eqs. 14 becomes

$$-R_x + p_1 A_1 \cos \alpha_1 + p_2 A_2 \cos \alpha_2$$
$$= (V_2 \rho_2 A_2)(-V_2 \cos \alpha_2) - (V_1 \rho_1 A_1)(V_1 \cos \alpha_1)$$

from which the force component R_x on the foundation is

$$R_x = (p_1 + \rho_1 V_1{}^2) A_1 \cos \alpha_1 + (p_2 + \rho_2 V_2{}^2) A_2 \cos \alpha_2$$

Illustrative Example 2

A practical means of determining the drag of a body from velocity measurements in its wake is used as a second illustration of the momentum theorem. Though the method involves a number of approximations, good results can be obtained.

Because of viscosity effects, a wake of retarded flow exists behind the cylinder of Fig. 4. In the wake region, the velocity is less than the upstream value, as illustrated by the profile at the right.

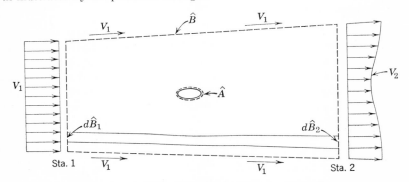

FIG. 4.   Drag of a body from wake measurements.

The control volume is taken as the region enclosed by the two control surfaces $\hat{A}$ and $\hat{B}$ in Fig. 4. Control surface $\hat{A}$ is the contour of the cylinder, and therefore there is no momentum flux through it. Control surface $\hat{B}$ is chosen sufficiently far from the cylinder so that the pressure has effectively returned to the upstream value p_1 over its entire length. Theoretically, control surface $\hat{B}$ must be infinitely removed but in practice a few cylinder chords are adequate. The lateral sides of surface $\hat{B}$ are chosen along streamlines and therefore momentum flows through $\hat{B}$ only at stations 1 and 2.

The net momentum flux in the drag direction through the entire control surface is approximately

$$\iint_{\text{Sta. 2}} V_2 (\rho V_2 \, d\hat{B}_2) - \iint_{\text{Sta. 1}} V_1 (\rho V_1 \, d\hat{B}_1)$$

The fact that V_2 is not quite in the drag direction has been neglected. The integral of the constant pressure force over surface $\hat{B}$ is zero. Over surface $\hat{A}$ the integral of the drag component of the pressure force is $-D'$ where D' is the drag per unit span of the cylinder. Then the momentum theorem for this case may be written

$$-D' = \iint_{\text{Sta. 2}} V_2(\rho V_2 \, d\hat{B}_2) - \iint_{\text{Sta. 1}} V_1(\rho V_1 \, d\hat{B}_1)$$

Finally, the idea of a streamtube, shown crosshatched in Fig. 4, is introduced to connect $d\hat{B}_1$ and $d\hat{B}_2$. From the conservation of mass principle

$$\rho V_2 \, d\hat{B}_2 = \rho V_1 \, d\hat{B}_1$$

Using this in the equation above leads to the following expression for the drag:

$$D' = \rho \iint_{\text{wake}} V_2(V_1 - V_2) \, d\hat{B}_2$$

Velocity measurements in the wake region ($V_2 < V_1$) will provide the cylinder drag. It should be remembered that the surface over which measurements are made must be sufficiently removed from the cylinder for the pressure to have returned to the value p_1.

3.4 BERNOULLI'S EQUATION

For steady incompressible flow Euler's equation, which represents an equilibrium of forces, can be integrated so that an algebraic relation between pressure and velocity is obtained. The integration is possible because viscous forces are absent and the fluid is assumed incompressible. The integrated form of Euler's equation represents the conservation of mechanical energies of the fluid. It was first given by Daniel Bernoulli and bears his name.*

Each term in Eq. 8 represents a force per unit volume. The scalar product of each term in Eq. 8 with an incremental distance $d\mathbf{s}$ represents an incremental energy per unit volume. Equation 15 below is an incremental energy relation obtained from Eq. 8 in this manner.

$$\{\rho\mathbf{g} - \text{grad } p\} \cdot d\mathbf{s} = \left\{ \rho \frac{\mathcal{D}\mathbf{V}}{\mathcal{D}t} \right\} \cdot d\mathbf{s} \tag{15}$$

After expanding according to the usual rule for scalar products and rearranging terms, Eq. 15 becomes:

$$\left(\frac{\mathcal{D}u}{\mathcal{D}t} + \frac{1}{\rho} \frac{\partial p}{\partial x} - g_x \right) dx + \left(\frac{\mathcal{D}v}{\mathcal{D}t} + \frac{1}{\rho} \frac{\partial p}{\partial y} - g_y \right) dy$$

$$+ \left(\frac{\mathcal{D}w}{\mathcal{D}t} + \frac{1}{\rho} \frac{\partial p}{\partial z} - g_z \right) dz = 0 \tag{16}$$

---

* Bernoulli's equation in the form developed here is a direct consequence of the equilibrium of forces or conservation of momentum principle. In contrast, Bernoulli's equation for compressible flow involves an independent physical principle, the conservation of total energy. This subject is treated in detail in Chapter 8.

The left-hand side of the above is an exact differential provided ds is an increment of streamline and the flow is steady. If the path is a streamline, the following relations exist among the components of the path increment dx, dy, and dz and the velocity components u, v, and w:

$$\frac{v}{u} = \frac{dy}{dx}, \quad \frac{w}{u} = \frac{dz}{dx}, \quad \frac{w}{v} = \frac{dz}{dy} \tag{17}$$

Expanding the first group of terms of the integrand of Eq. 16,

$$\left\{ \frac{\partial u}{\partial t} + u\frac{\partial u}{\partial x} + v\frac{\partial u}{\partial y} + w\frac{\partial u}{\partial z} + \frac{1}{\rho}\frac{\partial p}{\partial x} - g_x \right\} dx \tag{18}$$

After dropping the unsteady term and making the substitutions from Eq. 17, Eq. 18 becomes

$$u\frac{\partial u}{\partial x} dx + u\frac{\partial u}{\partial y} dy + u\frac{\partial u}{\partial z} dz + \frac{1}{\rho}\frac{\partial p}{\partial x} dx - g_x\, dx$$
$$= u\, du + \left(\frac{1}{\rho}\frac{\partial p}{\partial x} - g_x \right) dx \tag{19}$$

Similarly, the second and third terms of the integrand reduce to

$$v\, dv + \left(\frac{1}{\rho}\frac{\partial p}{\partial y} - g_y \right) dy$$
$$w\, dw + \left(\frac{1}{\rho}\frac{\partial p}{\partial z} - g_z \right) dz \tag{19}$$

If the relations shown in Eqs. 19 are used, Eq. 16 becomes

$$(u\, du + v\, dv + w\, dw) + \frac{1}{\rho}\left(\frac{\partial p}{\partial x} dx + \frac{\partial p}{\partial y} dy + \frac{\partial p}{\partial z} dz \right)$$
$$- (g_x\, dx + g_y\, dy + g_z\, dz) = 0 \tag{20}$$

As explained in Section 2.11, the gravitational acceleration is derivable from a potential U. The third term of Eq. 20 is, therefore, dU. If we write the first and second terms as differentials, also, Eq. 20 becomes

$$d\left(\frac{u^2 + v^2 + w^2}{2} + \frac{p}{\rho} - U \right) = 0$$
$$\frac{V^2}{2} + \frac{p}{\rho} - U = \text{constant} \tag{21}$$

Equation 21 indicates that the sum of the energies per unit mass of fluid is constant along a streamline. After multiplying through by ρ, each term becomes an energy per unit volume.

$$\rho\frac{V^2}{2} + p - \rho U = \text{constant} \tag{22}$$

The first term is a kinetic energy arising from the ordered motion of the fluid. The second term is a pressure energy attributable to the random motion of the gas molecules. The third term is the potential energy per unit volume that the fluid has by virtue of its height above a reference level. If the coordinate axes are so oriented that gravity acts in the z-direction, the gravitational acceleration potential is simply gz and the third term can be written ρgz.

If the height of the streamline above the reference level does not vary greatly, the variation in the term ρgz is small and may be neglected. For these circumstances Eq. 22 may be written

$$\rho\frac{V^2}{2} + p = \text{constant} + \rho gz = H \tag{23}$$

Care must be taken in choosing between Eqs. 22 and 23 in any particular application. If the variation in the height of the streamline above the reference level is great and the dynamic pressures involved are small, the variation in the term ρgz may not be small enough to be neglected. This circumstance could arise in the motion of a large airship. In such problems, it would not be accurate to calculate the kinetic energy by taking the difference between H and p with H treated as a constant. Equation 22 must be used. For the usual problems involving the flow about airfoils, Eq. 23 may be employed.

Energy per unit volume has the same dimensions as pressure. For this reason, the terms $\frac{1}{2}\rho V^2$ and H are called *dynamic pressure* and *total pressure*, respectively. p is, of course, the static pressure of the fluid.

Equation 23 states, therefore, that the sum of the dynamic and static pressures is constant along a streamline in steady incompressible flow as long as large changes in height are not involved.

The derivation through Eq. 20 does not depend upon the assumption of incompressibility. Beyond this point, however, if ρ is variable, the evaluation of $\int (dp/\rho)$ requires consideration of the relationship between p and ρ. This subject is treated in Chapter 8.

3.5 BERNOULLI'S EQUATION FOR IRROTATIONAL FLOW

Equation 23 of the last section states that the sum of the static and dynamic pressures is constant along a streamline. It gives no information how the sum H varies from streamline to streamline. To get an

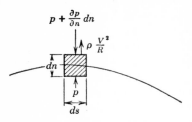

expression for the variation of H normal to the streamlines, it is necessary to consider the equilibrium of the fluid in a direction normal to the streamlines. If the streamlines are curved, there will be an inertia force per unit mass V^2/R, tending to resist the change in direction of the velocity, which must be balanced by an equal and opposite resultant pressure. The force balance normal to a streamline is shown in Fig. 5. As usual, outward along a radius is considered positive. The equilibrium equation is

FIG. 5. Equilibrium of a fluid element perpendicular to a streamline.

$$\rho \frac{V^2}{R} \, ds \, dn \, dz - \frac{\partial p}{\partial n} \, dn \, ds \, dz = 0 \qquad (24)$$

where dz is the dimension perpendicular to the plane of the paper. From Bernoulli's equation,

$$\frac{\partial p}{\partial n} = \frac{\partial H}{\partial n} - \rho V \frac{\partial V}{\partial n} \qquad (25)$$

Substituting Eq. 25 in Eq. 24, and solving for $(\partial H/\partial n)$,

$$\frac{\partial H}{\partial n} = \left[+ \frac{V}{R} + \frac{\partial V}{\partial n} \right] \rho V$$

According to Eq. 18 of Chapter 2, $(V/R) + (\partial V/\partial n)$ is twice the mean rotation, or the curl of the velocity. We have, therefore,

$$\frac{\partial H}{\partial n} = (\text{curl } \mathbf{V}) \rho V \qquad (26)$$

It can be concluded that the value of H along all streamlines is the same if the flow is irrotational.

The same conclusion can be drawn by working in cartesian coordinates and using the relations that are imposed by the condition of irrotationality.

$$\frac{\partial v}{\partial x} = \frac{\partial u}{\partial y}$$

$$\frac{\partial u}{\partial z} = \frac{\partial w}{\partial x}$$

$$\frac{\partial w}{\partial y} = \frac{\partial v}{\partial z} \tag{27}$$

With these relations, it is possible to integrate Euler's equation along any path whatever. In other words, the restriction that the path increment ds must be in the direction of a streamline is no longer necessary. If the relations given by Eq. 27 are substituted into $\mathfrak{D}u/\mathfrak{D}t$, then the first group of terms of the integrand of Eq. 16 becomes

$$\left\{ u\frac{\partial u}{\partial x} + v\frac{\partial v}{\partial x} + w\frac{\partial w}{\partial x} + \frac{1}{\rho}\frac{\partial p}{\partial x} - g_x \right\} dx$$

Similarly, the second and third terms become

$$\left\{ u\frac{\partial u}{\partial y} + v\frac{\partial v}{\partial y} + w\frac{\partial w}{\partial y} + \frac{1}{\rho}\frac{\partial p}{\partial y} - g_y \right\} dy$$

$$\left\{ u\frac{\partial u}{\partial z} + v\frac{\partial v}{\partial z} + w\frac{\partial w}{\partial z} + \frac{1}{\rho}\frac{\partial p}{\partial z} - g_z \right\} dz$$

The sum of the three terms is seen to be identical to the integrand of Eq. 20, and the Bernoulli equation in the forms given in Eqs. 21, 22, and 23 follow immediately.

If the flow is *steady, incompressible,* and *irrotational,* the constant in the energy relation

$$\frac{V^2}{2} + \frac{p}{\rho} - U = \text{constant}$$

does not vary from streamline to streamline. These conditions are not so restrictive as they seem. For example, consider the unaccelerated flight of a wing. If the frame of reference is attached to the wing, an observer stationary with respect to the frame of reference will see the usual streamline picture of a moving fluid about a stationary wing. Except for a restricted area behind the wing, the pattern will be unchanging with time—the flow is steady over most of the field. The streamlines at a great distance ahead of the body will be parallel, and the speed of flow along each streamline will be equal to the speed of the wing. The fluid will appear to the observer to be issuing from a region of constant velocity and, therefore, zero rotation. According to the theorem of Helmholtz, if a fluid is initially irrotational, it remains irrotational. It may be concluded, then, that, in the region where viscosity effects may be neglected, the rotation is zero. In Chapter 12 it is shown that viscosity effects in problems arising in aerodynamics are of importance only in a narrow region next to the body and in the wake. Over most of the field, the flow can be considered irrotational.

The condition of incompressibility is amply satisfied for flow velocities less than a few hundred miles per hour.

The Flow about a Body

CHAPTER 4

4.1 INTRODUCTION

It has been shown in Chapter 2 that only the velocity fields that satisfy the equation of continuity represent physically possible situations. Furthermore, in the absence of viscosity, fields representing the motion of a body that has accelerated from rest to a steady velocity in a stationary fluid must be irrotational.

These kinematical restrictions on the nine derivatives that characterize the field permit a steady incompressible flow pattern to be described by Laplace's equation. For if the flow is irrotational, a velocity potential ϕ exists, and the equation of continuity in terms of the velocity potential becomes

$$\frac{\partial^2 \phi}{\partial x^2} + \frac{\partial^2 \phi}{\partial y^2} + \frac{\partial^2 \phi}{\partial z^2} = 0 \tag{1}$$

Since every physically possible flow pattern must satisfy the equation of continuity, a stream function ψ exists for the two-dimensional incompressible field. Expressing the condition of irrotationality in terms of the stream function,

$$\frac{\partial^2 \psi}{\partial x^2} + \frac{\partial^2 \psi}{\partial y^2} = 0 \tag{2}$$

Any scalar quantity that satisfies Eq. 1 or 2 represents the velocity potential or stream function, respectively, of a steady, irrotational, incompressible flow. The particular solution that represents the flow about a given body is the one that satisfies the boundary conditions of the flow at the body and at infinity.

57

Unless stated otherwise, the discussion of the present chapter applies to two dimensional or plane bodies. A two-dimensional body represented in the x-y-plane may be viewed as a right cylinder of arbitrary cross section and infinite extent in the z-direction. For a flow representing the rectilinear motion of a body in the direction of the negative x-axis, the values of the derivatives of ϕ and ψ at the boundary at infinity are

$$\frac{\partial \phi}{\partial x} = V_\infty \qquad \frac{\partial \psi}{\partial y} = V_\infty$$

$$\frac{\partial \phi}{\partial y} = 0 \qquad \frac{\partial \psi}{\partial x} = 0$$

where V_∞ is the velocity of the body. The coordinate axes are attached to the body. At the body, the velocity must be tangential to the surface; that is, a streamline must conform to the contour of the body. If s is the direction of the tangent to the surface and n is the direction normal to the surface, the boundary condition at the body becomes

$$\frac{\partial \phi}{\partial n} = 0 \qquad \frac{\partial \psi}{\partial s} = 0$$

It can be proved that one and only one irrotational flow without circulation can be found that will satisfy a given set of boundary conditions.* Then, if we can find a scalar function ψ that satisfies Laplace's equation and the boundary condition at infinity, this scalar will represent the stream function for the flow about a given body, provided that one curve of the family, $\psi =$ constant, coincides with the contour of the body.

For flows with circulation, uniqueness is established if the boundary conditions at infinity and at the body are satisfied *and, in addition, if the value of the circulation is specified.*

Thus the kinematical problem of finding the flow pattern of an incompressible nonviscous fluid about a body is reduced to the purely mathematical one of finding a particular solution of Laplace's equation.

The velocity potential and stream function of the source, vortex, and uniform stream studied in Chapter 2 satisfy Laplace's equation. Because Laplace's equation is linear, any linear combination of these three

* For example, see L. M. Milne Thomson, *Theoretical Hydrodynamics*, p. 89, Macmillan, New York, 1938. A simple word argument has been given by M. Munk, "Fluid Mechanics," Pt. 2, *Aerodynamic Theory*, edited by W. F. Durand, California Institute of Technology, Pasadena, 1943.

solutions is also a solution. It is this fact that makes the kinematics of perfect fluid theory problems particularly amenable to theoretical treatment. The object of this chapter is to synthesize flow patterns by combining the source, vortex, and uniform stream in ways that will yield solutions of Laplace's equation which are of particular interest.

The source may be thought of as a point from which fluid issues at a constant rate along radial paths. In Section 2.5, it was shown that source flow satisfies continuity at all points of the field except at the source itself. The source, then, must lie outside the boundaries of the flow considered. For example, if a source is used to build up the flow pattern about a body, then the source itself must lie inside the body, that is, outside the physical field.

The vortex must be treated in a similar manner. In Section 2.10, it was shown that vortex flow is irrotational at every point except at the center of the vortex. If a vortex is used to build up the flow pattern about a body, the vortex itself must lie within the body.

It is pointed out that, in two dimensions, the most practical method of finding flow patterns that satisfy given boundary conditions employs the theory of complex variables. In fact, the flow about a body of any prescribed shape may be found by conformal mapping of the flow about a circle.* The application of complex variables to two-dimensional airfoil theory may be found in other books.†

4.2 SUPERPOSITION OF FLOWS

Any irrotational physically possible flow has a stream function and velocity potential that satisfy Laplace's equation. Conversely, any solution of Laplace's equation represents the stream function or velocity potential of an irrotational physically possible flow. Because Laplace's equation is linear, the sum of any number of solutions is also a solution; that is, the sum of irrotational physically possible flows is also irrotational and physically possible. This is the justification for synthesizing complicated flow patterns by adding together the elementary source, vortex, and uniform stream flows.

That the stream function of the resultant flow is the sum of the stream functions of the component flows can be demonstrated in the following manner: Let ψ represent the stream function of the resultant flow and ψ_1 and ψ_2 the stream functions of the component flows. Then

* T. Theodorsen and I. E. Garrick, *General Potential Theory of Arbitrary Wing Sections*, NACA TR 452, 1933.

† For example, see L. M. Milne Thomson, *Theoretical Aerodynamics*, D. Van Nostrand, New York, 1947; or W. F. Durand, *Aerodynamic Theory*, Vol. 2, California Institute of Technology, Pasadena, 1943.

a point-by-point addition of the two fields leads to the following expressions for the velocity:

$$V = V_1 + V_2$$

$$u = u_1 + u_2 \tag{3}$$

$$v = v_1 + v_2$$

To show that $\psi = \psi_1 + \psi_2$ write the last two equations of Eq. 3 in terms of the stream functions

$$\frac{\partial \psi}{\partial y} = \frac{\partial \psi_1}{\partial y} + \frac{\partial \psi_2}{\partial y} = \frac{\partial}{\partial y}(\psi_1 + \psi_2)$$

$$-\frac{\partial \psi}{\partial x} = -\frac{\partial \psi_1}{\partial x} - \frac{\partial \psi_2}{\partial x} = -\frac{\partial}{\partial x}(\psi_1 + \psi_2)$$

Therefore, keeping in mind the argument of Section 2.2, the directional derivatives of ψ and $\psi_1 + \psi_2$ have the same value in an arbitrary direction s.

$$\frac{\partial \psi}{\partial s} = \frac{\partial}{\partial s}(\psi_1 + \psi_2)$$

and

$$\psi = \psi_1 + \psi_2 + \text{constant}$$

The constant can be made to vanish if the zero streamline of the resultant flow is chosen along the path for which the sum of the stream functions of the component flows vanishes.

A similar demonstration will show that the velocity potential of the sum of two flows equals the sum of the potentials of the component flows, provided that the zero equipotential line is chosen properly.

4.3 SOURCE FLOW

As was explained in Section 4.1, the source is a point from which fluid issues in equal amounts along radial paths. From considerations of continuity in a steady flow, it is apparent that the total fluid crossing any circle whose center is at the source must be equal to the quantity of fluid per second streaming from the source. Letting ρm represent this quantity, and remembering that the velocity is radial, we can write the following relation:

$$\rho(2\pi r)u_r = \rho m$$

From the above equation, u_r is seen to be equal to $m/2\pi r$. The tangential component u_θ is zero. The stream function is found by direct integration of the velocity components.

$$u_r = \frac{m}{2\pi r} = \frac{1}{r}\frac{d\psi}{d\theta}$$

$$\psi = \frac{m}{2\pi}\theta + \text{constant} \tag{4}$$

The constant can be made to vanish if the line from which θ is measured is chosen as the zero streamline. m is defined as the source strength. It has been verified that curl $\mathbf{V}$ for source flow vanishes, and therefore a velocity potential exists. From Eq. 28 of Chapter 2,

$$u_r = \frac{\partial\phi}{\partial r}$$

$$u_\theta = \frac{1}{r}\frac{\partial\phi}{\partial\theta} \tag{5}$$

The values of u_r and u_θ for source flow are substituted in Eq. 5:

$$\frac{\partial\phi}{\partial r} = u_r = \frac{m}{2\pi r}$$

$$\frac{1}{r}\frac{\partial\phi}{\partial\theta} = u_\theta = 0$$

An integration of the above equations yields the velocity potential. Since ϕ does not depend on θ,

$$\phi = \frac{m}{2\pi}\log\frac{r}{R_1} \tag{6}$$

where $-(m/2\pi)\log R_1$ is the constant of integration.

The three-dimensional source is defined in the same manner as the two-dimensional source. The velocity is everywhere radial, and to satisfy continuity the mass flux through all spheres centered at the source must be the same. Therefore, for a three-dimensional source of strength m placed at the origin

$$\rho(4\pi r^2)u_r = \rho m$$

The reader can convince himself that the velocity potential for a three-dimensional source is

$$\phi = -\frac{m}{4\pi}\frac{1}{r} \tag{6a}$$

4.4 FLOW PATTERN OF A SOURCE AND SINK OF EQUAL STRENGTH—DOUBLET

As a first step in the synthesis of the flow pattern for a doublet, the case of a source of strength m at $(-x_0, 0)$ and a sink of strength $-m$ at $(x_0, 0)$ is considered. See Fig. 1.

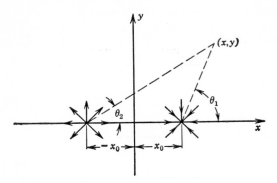

Fig. 1.   Source-sink pair.

The angles θ_1 and θ_2 are measured from the positive x-axis, and the x-axis is also chosen as the zero streamline of each flow. The constant term in the stream function of either flow, as given by Eq. 4, will, therefore, be zero. The stream function of the combined flow may be written

$$\psi = -\frac{m}{2\pi}(\theta_1 - \theta_2)$$

From Fig. 1, θ_1 and θ_2 can be seen to be given by Eqs. 7 following and, after making use of the trigonometric identity Eq. 8, their difference is given by Eq. 9.

$$\theta_1 = \tan^{-1}\frac{y}{x - x_0}$$

$$\theta_2 = \tan^{-1}\frac{y}{x + x_0} \tag{7}$$

$$\tan^{-1}\alpha - \tan^{-1}\beta = \tan^{-1}\left(\frac{\alpha - \beta}{1 + \alpha\beta}\right) \tag{8}$$

$$\theta_1 - \theta_2 = \tan^{-1}\frac{y/(x - x_0) - y/(x + x_0)}{1 + [y^2/(x - x_0)(x + x_0)]} \tag{9}$$

After multiplying Eq. 9 by $-m/2\pi$ and simplifying, the stream function of the combined flow takes the form

$$\psi = -\frac{m}{2\pi} \tan^{-1} \frac{2x_0 y}{x^2 + y^2 - x_0^2} \tag{10}$$

The flow pattern represented by this stream function has a simple geometrical form. The equation of a streamline is given by $\psi =$ constant. It is put in a recognizable form in the following manner:

$$-\tan \frac{2\pi\psi}{m} = \frac{2x_0 y}{x^2 + y^2 - x_0^2}$$

$$x^2 + y^2 + 2x_0 y \cot \frac{2\pi\psi}{m} = x_0^2$$

Completing the square in the bracketed term,

$$x^2 + \left(y + x_0 \cot \frac{2\pi\psi}{m}\right)^2 = x_0^2 + x_0^2 \cot^2\left(\frac{2\pi\psi}{m}\right)$$

The equation is seen to represent a series of circles with centers on the y-axis. When $y = 0$, $x = \pm x_0$ for all values of ψ. The flow pattern is shown in Fig. 2.

Of special interest is the flow pattern that results when a source and sink of equal strength are allowed to approach each other while the product of their strength and distance apart is held constant. The resulting flow when the distance between source and sink is zero is called a doublet, whose strength μ is given by the expression

$$\mu = 2x_0 m$$

The stream function of the doublet is given by the limit of Eq. 10 as x_0 approaches zero.

$$\psi = \lim_{x_0 \to 0} -\frac{\mu}{4\pi x_0} \tan^{-1} \frac{2x_0 y}{x^2 + y^2 - x_0^2}$$

As x_0 approaches zero, $2x_0 y/(x^2 + y^2 - x_0^2)$ becomes small, and we can write

$$-\frac{\mu}{4\pi x_0} \tan^{-1} \frac{2x_0 y}{x^2 + y^2 - x_0^2} = -\frac{\mu}{4\pi x_0} \frac{2x_0 y}{x^2 + y^2 - x_0^2}$$

In the limit, the stream function becomes

$$\psi = -\frac{\mu}{2\pi} \frac{y}{x^2 + y^2} \tag{11}$$

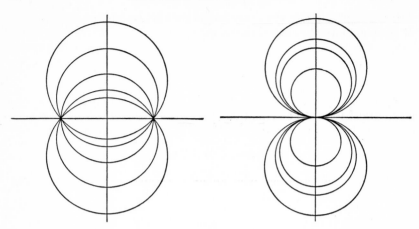

FIG. 2. Streamlines of a source-sink pair.   FIG. 3. Streamlines of a doublet.

The streamlines, which are given by Eq. 11 when ψ is set equal to a constant, have a simple geometrical form. This is readily seen if Eq. 11 is rearranged in the following manner:

$$x^2 + y^2 + \frac{\mu y}{2\pi\psi} = 0$$

$$x^2 + \left(y + \frac{\mu}{4\pi\psi}\right)^2 = \left(\frac{\mu}{4\pi\psi}\right)^2$$

This flow is illustrated in Fig. 3. The streamlines are a series of circles that pass through the origin. The centers lie on the y-axis.

4.5 FLOW ABOUT A CYLINDER IN A UNIFORM STREAM

The stream function for the uniform flow of a fluid with velocity V_∞ in the direction of the positive x-axis is given by the expression

$$\psi = +V_\infty y$$

If the uniform flow is added to the doublet, the flow about a circular cylinder in a uniform stream is obtained. The stream function of the combined flow is

$$\psi = V_\infty y - \frac{\mu}{2\pi}\frac{y}{r^2}$$

or, upon letting $\mu/2\pi V_\infty = a^2$,

$$\psi = V_\infty y \left(1 - \frac{a^2}{r^2}\right) \tag{12}$$

The zero streamline is the x-axis and a circle of radius $r = a$. See Fig. 4. This flow is irrotational and satisfies *continuity* at every point outside of the circle $r = a$. Therefore, it may be taken as the true stream

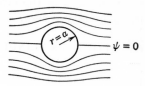

FIG. 4. Circular cylinder in a uniform stream.

function for the uniform flow about a circular cylinder when the velocity at infinity is in the direction of the positive x-axis.

4.6 VORTEX FLOW—CIRCULATORY FLOW ABOUT A CYLINDER

In Chapter 2, vortex flow was found to be the only irrotational flow with circular streamlines. The velocity potential can be found by integrating the velocity components directly. The velocity components are given by Eqs. 26 of Chapter 2.

$$u_r = \frac{\partial \phi}{\partial r} = 0$$

$$u_\theta = \frac{1}{r} \frac{\partial \phi}{\partial \theta} = -\frac{\Gamma}{2\pi} \frac{1}{r}$$

$$\phi = -\frac{\Gamma}{2\pi} \theta + \text{constant} \tag{13}$$

The constant vanishes if θ is measured from the zero equipotential line. The negative sign arises because circulating flow is clockwise when Γ is a positive number.

Vortex flow satisfies *continuity*, and therefore a stream function exists such that

$$u_r = \frac{1}{r} \frac{\partial \psi}{\partial \theta} = 0$$

$$u_\theta = -\frac{\partial \psi}{\partial r} = -\frac{\Gamma}{2\pi} \frac{1}{r}$$

By integration,

$$\psi = \frac{\Gamma}{2\pi} \log \frac{r}{a} \tag{14}$$

where $-(\Gamma/2\pi) \log (a)$ is the constant of integration.

Vortex flow satisfies *continuity* and is irrotational for all points in the field outside the circle $r = \epsilon$, where ϵ is arbitrarily small. Any stream-line forms the contour of a circular cylinder, and, therefore, vortex flow represents the true flow pattern of the circulatory flow about a cylinder when the velocity at infinity is zero.

4.7 CIRCULATORY FLOW ABOUT A CYLINDER IN A UNIFORM STREAM

If the stream functions of Sections 4.5 and 4.6 are added, the result-ing stream function will satisfy continuity, irrotationality, and the boundary conditions for the circulatory flow about a cylinder in a uni-form stream.

$$\psi = V_\infty y \left(1 - \frac{a^2}{r^2} \right) + \frac{\Gamma}{2\pi} \log \left(\frac{r}{a} \right) \tag{15}$$

The uniform stream is in the direction of the positive x-axis, and the circulatory flow is clockwise. The cylinder $r = a$ forms part of the zero streamline. The flow pattern is shown in Fig. 5.

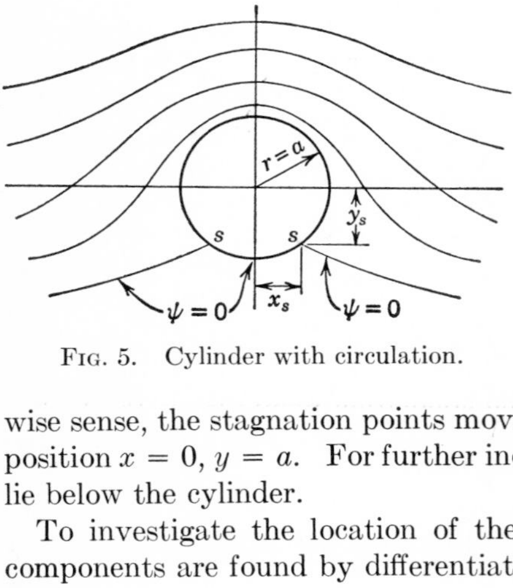

At points s, the zero stream-line intersects itself. Since the streamline is the direction of the velocity, it follows that the magnitude of the velocity at the points s is zero. These so-called *stagnation* points lie on the x-axis at $\pm a$ when the circulation is zero. As the cir-culation increases in the clock-wise sense, the stagnation points move down until they coincide at the position $x = 0$, $y = a$. For further increases in Γ, the stagnation points lie below the cylinder.

FIG. 5.   Cylinder with circulation.

To investigate the location of the stagnation points, the velocity components are found by differentiating Eq. 15.

$$u_r = \frac{1}{r} \frac{\partial \psi}{\partial \theta} = V_\infty \left(1 - \frac{a^2}{r^2} \right) \cos \theta$$

$$u_\theta = - \frac{\partial \psi}{\partial r} = - V_\infty \sin \theta \left(1 + \frac{a^2}{r^2} \right) - \frac{\Gamma}{2\pi} \frac{1}{r}$$

(16)

On the surface of the cylinder, $r = a$ and u_r vanishes. The resultant velocity is

$$u_\theta = -2V_\infty \sin\theta - \frac{\Gamma}{2\pi a}$$

For the stagnation value of θ, u_θ must vanish.

$$\sin\theta_s = -\frac{\Gamma}{4\pi a V_\infty}$$

Since $\sin\theta = y/r$, the stagnation position in cartesian coordinates is

$$y_s = -\frac{\Gamma}{4\pi V_\infty}$$

$$x_s = \pm\sqrt{a^2 - y_s^2} \tag{17}$$

From Eqs. 17, it is apparent that, as Γ becomes large, the stagnation points move downward until $(\Gamma/4\pi V_\infty)^2$ equals a^2. Under these conditions, the points coincide on the y-axis at $(0, -a)$. For $(\Gamma/4\pi V_\infty)^2 > a^2$,

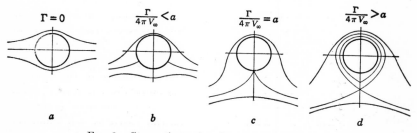

FIG. 6.   Stagnation points for several values of Γ.

Eqs. 17 no longer hold because the stagnation points leave the body. The position of the stagnation points for several values of Γ are shown in Fig. 6.

4.8 FORCE ON A CYLINDER WITH CIRCULATION IN A UNIFORM STREAM

The pressure at any point in the field of Section 4.7 may be found from Bernoulli's equation:

$$p = \text{constant} - \tfrac{1}{2}\rho V^2 \tag{18}$$

It is of interest to find the total force on a circle of radius r_1 as pictured in Fig. 7. To this end, the x- and y-components of the incremental force $\mathbf{n}p\,ds$ are integrated around the circle. Because of the symmetry of the flow pattern about a vertical axis through the center of the circle, the integral of the x-component of the incremental force over the left half of the circle will be equal and opposite to the integral over the right half; that is,

$$F_x = \int_0^{2\pi} - pr_1 \cos \theta \, d\theta = 0 \qquad (19)$$

It cannot be said, however, that F_y vanishes, because the flow is not symmetrical about the horizontal axis. The right- and left-hand quadrants of the lower half of the cylinder experience identical forces in the

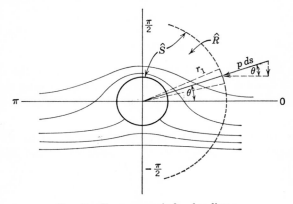

FIG. 7.   Force on a circle of radius r_1.

y-direction because of symmetry about a vertical axis. Similarly, the right- and left-hand quadrants of the upper half of the circle experience identical forces in the y-direction. The total force in the y-direction is therefore given by the expression

$$F_y = 2 \int_{-\pi/2}^{+\pi/2} - pr_1 \sin \theta \, d\theta \qquad (20)$$

The pressure is always directed towards the surface and contributes a negative increment of force when $\sin \theta$ is positive. Therefore, the integrand is given a negative sign.

The pressure is given by Eq. 18. Substituting this value in Eq. **20**,

$$F_y = \rho r_1 \int_{-\pi/2}^{+\pi/2} V^2 \sin \theta \, d\theta \qquad (21)$$

The constant term in Eq. 18 has been omitted because it makes no contribution to the integral. V^2 can be found from Eqs. 16.

$$V^2 = u_r{}^2 + u_\theta{}^2$$

$$V^2 = \underbrace{V_\infty{}^2 \left(1 - \frac{a^2}{r^2}\right)^2 \cos^2 \theta}_{(1)} + \underbrace{V_\infty{}^2 \left(1 + \frac{a^2}{r^2}\right)^2 \sin^2 \theta}_{(2)}$$

$$+ \underbrace{\frac{V_\infty \Gamma \sin \theta}{\pi r}\left(1 + \frac{a^2}{r^2}\right)}_{(3)} + \underbrace{\left(\frac{\Gamma}{2\pi r}\right)^2}_{(4)}$$

Since

$$\int_{-\pi/2}^{\pi/2} \cos^2 \theta \sin \theta \, d\theta = \int_{-\pi/2}^{\pi/2} \sin^3 \theta \, d\theta = \int_{-\pi/2}^{\pi/2} \sin \theta \, d\theta = 0$$

Eq. 21 can be written

$$F_y = \rho r_1 \int_{-\pi/2}^{\pi/2} \frac{V_\infty \Gamma}{\pi r_1}\left(1 + \frac{a^2}{r_1{}^2}\right) \sin^2 \theta \, d\theta = \frac{1}{2}\rho V_\infty \Gamma \left(1 + \frac{a^2}{r_1{}^2}\right) \quad (22)$$

If $r_1 = a$, the forces derived are those experienced by the cylinder with circulation in a uniform stream. Equations 19 and 22 become

$$F_x = 0$$
$$F_y = \rho V_\infty \Gamma \qquad\qquad (23)$$

4.9   KUTTA-JOUKOWSKI THEOREM

The forces in the example of Section 4.8 can readily be derived by the momentum theorem developed in Chapter 3. Equation 12 of that chapter, specialized to the case of steady flow, is repeated below

$$\mathbf{F} = \iint_{\hat{S}} \mathbf{V}\rho V_n \, d\hat{S} \qquad\qquad (24)$$

The control volume $\hat{R}$ enclosed by the control surface $\hat{S}$ is taken to be the region of unit thickness included between the dashed circle of radius r_1 and the cylinder of Fig. 7. Both the circle and the cylinder make up the surface $\hat{S}$, but only the circle need be considered in the integration because there is no momentum flux through the cylinder. From symmetry, it can be seen that the x-components of the force and the momentum flux in Eq. 24 are zero, and therefore only the y-components need be considered.

Let F_{r_1} and F_a represent the resultant forces at the outer and inner boundaries respectively of the region $\hat{R}$. Then from Eq. 24 the y-component is written

$$F_{r_1} + F_a = \iint_{\hat{S}} v\rho V_n \, d\hat{S}$$

or solving for the force $-F_a$ that the fluid exerts on the inner boundary:

$$-F_a = F_{r_1} - \iint_{\hat{S}} v\rho V_n \, d\hat{S} \tag{25}$$

Because only the outer boundary enters the momentum flux term, it appears that the force exerted by a fluid on a submerged body may be calculated by investigating conditions in the fluid at a great distance from the body. The x- and y-components of F_{r_1} have already been computed in Section 4.8. It remains only to find the resultant flux of momentum across the circle of radius r_1. V_n in the integral above is u_{r_1} which is given by Eq. 16

$$u_{r_1} = V_\infty \left(1 - \frac{a^2}{r_1{}^2} \right) \cos \theta \tag{16}$$

v is obtained by differentiating the stream function given by Eq. 15:

$$v = -\frac{\partial \psi}{\partial x} = -V_\infty \left(\frac{2a^2}{r^4} \, xy \right) - \frac{\Gamma}{2\pi} \frac{x}{r^2}$$

After replacing x and y with their values in polar coordinates, v on the circle $r = r_1$ becomes

$$v = -V_\infty \left(\frac{2a^2}{r_1{}^2} \cos \theta \sin \theta \right) - \frac{\Gamma}{2\pi} \frac{\cos \theta}{r_1} \tag{26}$$

Using Eqs. 16 and 26, the momentum flux through the circle of radius r_1 becomes

$$\iint_{\hat{S}} v\rho V_n \, d\hat{S}$$

$$= \rho r_1 V_\infty \left(1 - \frac{a^2}{r_1{}^2} \right) \int_0^{2\pi} \left[-V_\infty \frac{2a^2}{r_1{}^2} \cos^2 \theta \sin \theta - \frac{\Gamma}{2\pi} \frac{\cos^2 \theta}{r_1} \right] d\theta$$

The $\cos^2 \theta \sin \theta$ term makes no contribution and the $\cos^2 \theta$ term gives the result

$$\iint_{\hat{S}} v\rho V_n \, d\hat{S} = -\frac{\rho V_\infty \Gamma}{2} \left(1 - \frac{a^2}{r_1{}^2} \right) \tag{27}$$

Putting Eq. 27 and the expression for F_{r_1} given by Eq. 22 into Eq. 25

$$-F_a = \frac{\rho V_\infty \Gamma}{2}\left(1 + \frac{a^2}{r_1^2}\right) + \frac{\rho V_\infty \Gamma}{2}\left(1 - \frac{a^2}{r_1^2}\right)$$

$$-F_a = \rho V_\infty \Gamma = F_y \tag{28}$$

The force F_x in the x-direction is zero.

This result is identical to Eqs. 23, which were obtained by direct integration of the pressure over the boundary of the cylinder. By the momentum theorem, however, the computations involved are at a position in the fluid far removed from the body. The body influences these calculations only to the extent that it influences the flow pattern in the region in which computations are made.

The stream function for the flow about a circular cylinder with circulation in a uniform stream was built up by adding together the stream functions of the uniform flow, the doublet, and the vortex flow.

$$\psi = V_\infty r \sin\theta - \frac{\mu}{2\pi}\frac{\sin\theta}{r} + \frac{\Gamma}{2\pi}\log\left(\frac{r}{R}\right) \tag{29}$$

The stream function for the flow about cylinders having cross-sectional shapes other than circular may be built up by adding various distributions of source-sink pairs (a source and a sink of equal strength) to the uniform stream and vortex. The circular cylinder is a special example of a single source-sink pair in the form of a doublet at the origin.

In applying the momentum theorem we are interested in the flow pattern at a great distance from the origin. Now, viewed from infinity, any source-sink pair appears to be a doublet,* and, consequently, the source-sink pairs that determine the shape of the cylinder will, at infinity, contribute terms to the stream function of the nature of the middle term in Eq. 29. If the calculation for the force on a circle of radius r_1 as given by Eq. 22 and the calculation for the net momentum flux through the circle of radius r_1 as given by Eq. 27 are observed closely, it will be seen that the doublet portion of the flow pattern makes no contribution to either the momentum or the force when r_1 becomes large. Therefore, the shape of the cylinder cannot influence the resultant force as given by Eq. 28. This idea is embodied in the *Kutta-Joukowski theorem*, which may be stated:

The force per unit length acting on a right cylinder of any cross section whatever is equal to $\rho V \Gamma$ and acts perpendicular to **V**.

* See Problem 2 of Section 4.4, Problems.

If the cross section is an airfoil and $\mathbf{V}$ is the relative wind, the Kutta-Joukowski theorem is

$$L' = \rho V\Gamma$$
$$D' = 0$$

(30)

where L' and D' represent lift and drag per unit length, respectively.

4.10 BOUND VORTEX

It was shown in the last section that the force on a body is determined entirely by the circulation around it and by the free stream velocity. In an identical manner, it can be shown that the force on a vortex that is stationary with respect to the uniform flow is given by the Kutta-Joukowski law. The vortex that represents the circulation around the body departs in its characteristics from a true vortex in that it does not remain attached to the same fluid particles but instead it remains *bound* to a given set of space coordinates. This vortex that represents the circulatory flow around the wing is called a *bound vortex* in order to distinguish it from a true vortex, which cannot remain stationary with respect to the general flow.

Then, as far as resultant forces are concerned, a bound vortex of proper strength in a uniform stream is completely equivalent to a body with circulation in a uniform stream.

4.11 KUTTA CONDITION

The Kutta-Joukowski theorem states that the force experienced by a body in a uniform stream is equal to the product of the fluid density, stream velocity, and circulation and has a direction perpendicular to the stream velocity. In Section 4.1, it was stated that one and only one irrotational flow can be found that satisfies the boundary conditions at infinity and at the body, provided the circulation is specified. If the circulation is not specified, the conditions at infinity and the geometry of the body do not determine the flow pattern.

In order to find the force on a body that is submerged in a streaming fluid (or, equivalently, on a body moving through a stationary fluid), it is necessary to know the value of the circulation. Yet the theory indicates that the geometry of the body and the stream velocity do not determine the circulation.

The value of the circulation is fixed by an empirical observation. Experiments show that, for a body with a sharp trailing edge, the rear stagnation point moves to the trailing edge soon after the body has reached a steady velocity and that it remains there.* The value of the

* L. Prandtl-O. G. Tietjens, *Applied Hydro and Aero Mechanics*, Figs. 42–51, McGraw-Hill, New York, 1934.

circulation is fixed by this fact. The Kutta condition may be stated as follows:

A body with a sharp trailing edge which is moving through a fluid will create about itself a circulation of sufficient strength to hold the rear stagnation point at the trailing edge.

The influence of the circulation on the position of the rear stagnation point can be seen in Figs. 8–10. In Fig. 8, the flow pattern about a body for zero circulation is shown. Upstream of the rear stagnation point the velocity is in one direction, and downstream of this point the velocity is in the opposite direction. In Fig. 9, a pure clockwise circulatory flow about the airfoil is shown. At the point *a* in Fig. 8 the velocity of the noncirculatory flow has a value equal and opposite to the circulatory velocity at point *a* of Fig. 9. The two patterns have been superimposed in Fig. 10. The velocity at point *a* of Fig. 10 is zero, and therefore point *a* is a stagnation point. The clockwise circulation has served to move the rear stagnation point downstream. It is apparent that a certain value of the circulation will bring the rear stagnation point to the trailing edge, and this value, according to the Kutta condition, is the one that actually exists.

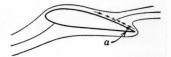

FIG. 8.   Flow with zero circulation.

FIG. 9.   Pure circulating flow.

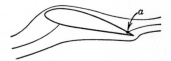

FIG. 10.   Flow with circulation.

Experiment also shows that associated with the establishment of the circulation is a formation of vorticity at the trailing edge in a direction opposite to that of the circulation. The strength of the shed vorticity is, in fact, equal and opposite to that of the circulation about the body. See Fig. 11.

FIG. 11.   Vorticity formation at trailing edge.

The formation of vorticity at the trailing edge is traceable to the viscosity of the fluid. This subject is treated in further detail later in the book.

The Kutta condition may be stated in other ways. In Fig. 8 it can be seen that, if the condition is not fulfilled, the velocities on the upper and lower surface near the trailing edge will be in opposite directions; that is, there will be a velocity discontinuity at the trailing edge. This will always occur unless the rear stagnation point is at the trailing edge. Then, if it is required that the velocity discontinuity at the trailing edge be zero, the Kutta condition will be fulfilled. This statement of the Kutta condition is useful in formulating thin-airfoil theory.

 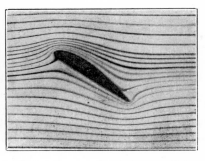

Photographs of the flow about an airfoil simulating the zero circulation condition. Courtesy of A. D. Moore, University of Michigan. The fluid mapping technique used in producing these photographs is described in an article by A. D. Moore, "Fields from Fluid Flow Mappers," *J. Applied Phys.*, Vol. 20, No. 8, pp. 790–804, August 1949.

The Thin Airfoil

CHAPTER 5

5.1 INTRODUCTION

The history of the development of airfoil shapes is long and involves many names in philosophy and the sciences.* By the beginning of the twentieth century, the methods of classical hydrodynamics had been successfully applied to airfoils, and it became possible to predict the lifting characteristics of certain airfoil shapes mathematically. These special shapes which lent themselves to precise mathematical treatment did not represent the optimum in airfoil performance, and workers in the field restored to experimental methods guided by theory † to determine the characteristics of arbitrarily shaped airfoils.

In 1929, the NACA began studying the characteristics of systematic series of airfoils in an effort to find those shapes which were best suited for specific purposes. Families of airfoils constructed according to a certain plan were tested and their characteristics recorded.‡ The airfoils were composed of a *thickness envelope* wrapped around a *mean camber line* in the manner shown in Fig. 1. The mean line lies halfway between the upper and lower surfaces of the airfoil and intersects the chord line at the leading and trailing edges. Any one family of airfoils has a mean line of a certain shape; the particular members of the family are partly distinguished by the maximum camber z_c of the mean line

---

* See *Historical Sketch*, by R. Giacomelli, Vol. 1 of *Aerodynamic Theory*, edited by W. F. Durand, California Institute of Technology, Pasadena, 1943.

† The theory that guided the NACA experiments was based chiefly on the work of Theodorsen, reported in *Theory of Wing Sections of Arbitrary Shape*, NACA TR 411, 1931, and by thin-airfoil theory, which forms the subject of the present chapter.

‡ Ira H. Abbott and Albert E. von Doenhoff, *Theory of Wing Sections, Including a Summary of Airfoil Data*, McGraw-Hill, New York, 1949.

and the distance x_c of the maximum camber behind the leading edge. The thickness envelope is wrapped around the mean camber line. A particular family of airfoils has the same general shape for the thickness envelope, and individual members of the family are distinguished in part by the value of the ratio of the maximum thickness, $t_{max.}$, to the chord. The numbering of the NACA airfoils and the geometry of the

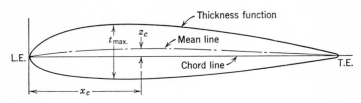

FIG. 1.   Construction of NACA airfoils.

mean lines and thickness functions are given in the literature that reports the results of the wind-tunnel tests on the various airfoils.* A brief illustration of the numbering system is given in Section 1 of Appendix C.

The lifting characteristics of an airfoil below the stall are negligibly influenced by viscosity. Further, the resultant of the pressure forces on the airfoil (magnitude, direction, and line of action) is only slightly influenced by the thickness function, provided that the ratio of maximum thickness to chord $t_{max.}/c$ is small, the maximum mean camber z_c is small, and the airfoil is operating at a small angle of attack. These three conditions are usually fulfilled in the normal operation of the usual types of airfoils. As a consequence, the overall lifting characteristics of an airfoil are well predicted by the thin-airfoil theory outlined in the following sections. In this approximate theory, viscosity is neglected and the airfoil is replaced with its mean camber line. The kinematic problem is resolved into one of finding a flow pattern that has one streamline coincident with the mean camber line. The bound vortex sheet described in Section 2.13 is used to construct the pattern. The pressure at various points along the camber line is given by the Kutta-Joukowski law and the overall lifting characteristics are determined from the integral of the pressure forces.

5.2 THE VORTEX SHEET IN THIN-AIRFOIL THEORY

The concept of the vortex sheet has already been introduced in Section 2.13. It was shown that, according to the law of Biot and Savart,

* *Ibid.*

the velocity induced at point P by an increment of sheet ds is given by

$$dV = \frac{\gamma}{2\pi} \frac{ds}{r} \tag{1}$$

where γ is the strength of the sheet per unit length. See Fig. 2. It was also stated that the velocity field induced by a vortex sheet satisfies *continuity* at every point. *Irrotationality* is satisfied at every point except at those that lie on the sheet. At these points the curl of the velocity is infinite. Further, the velocity is finite at every point in the field except at the edges of the sheet, where it is infinite. Finally, the velocity component parallel to the sheet has a discontinuity at the sheet equal in magnitude to the strength of the sheet at the point under consideration.

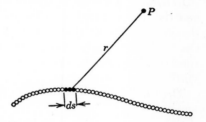

FIG. 2.   Vortex sheet as mean camber line.

In thin-airfoil theory, the airfoil is replaced with its mean camber line. The flow pattern is built up by placing a vortex sheet on the camber line and so adjusting its strength that the camber line becomes a streamline of the flow. Points on the camber line (and therefore on the vortex sheet) lie outside the field of flow. The velocity pattern, then, is composed of a uniform stream plus the field induced by the vortex sheet.

Continuity and *irrotationality* are satisfied at every point in the field. The velocity at infinity is that of the uniform stream because a vortex sheet can make no contribution at infinity. At the inner boundary (the camber line) the resultant of the uniform stream and the field induced by the sheet is parallel to the camber line.

According to the discussion of Chapter 4, in order to establish the uniqueness of an irrotational flow, it is necessary to specify not only the velocity at infinity and the direction of the velocity at the body but also the circulation around the body. It is apparent that the circulation around the sheet is simply the strength of the entire sheet. It follows, therefore, that for a sheet of given total strength there is only one distribution of vortex strength that will make the sheet a streamline when the field of the sheet is combined with the uniform stream. It is this distribution that is sought.

The circulation around the body is established by the Kutta condition. In Section 4.11 it was shown that the Kutta condition means that there can be no velocity discontinuity at the trailing edge. In terms of the vortex strength distribution along the mean camber line, the Kutta condition must be interpreted as fixing the strength of the vorticity at the trailing edge at zero. Therefore, the Kutta condition removes the difficulty of an infinite velocity at the trailing edge of the vortex sheet. The infinite velocity at the leading edge remains, which means that the flow pattern at the leading edge predicted by the theory cannot be correct.

In summary, it can be said that the resultant of the uniform stream and the field induced by a vortex sheet satisfies *continuity* and *irrotationality* and has a value at infinity equal to that of the uniform stream. One and only one distribution of vortex strength can be found of given total strength, which, when combined with a uniform stream, makes the vortex sheet a streamline.

The total strength of the sheet is fixed by the Kutta condition:

$$\gamma(\text{T.E.}) = 0 \tag{2}$$

In order for the resultant of the uniform stream and the velocity induced by the sheet to be parallel to the sheet, the normal components of the uniform stream and induced velocity must sum to zero. The geometry drawn out of scale for clarity, is shown in Fig. 3. It should

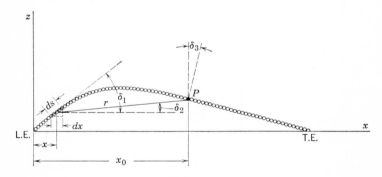

FIG. 3.   Field induced by vortex sheet.

be remembered that, for wings in common use, the maximum mean camber is of the order of 2 per cent of the chord. An increment of induced velocity is given by Eq. 1. The normal component of the increment is

$$dV_{in} = \frac{\gamma}{2\pi} \frac{ds}{r} \cos \delta_3 \tag{3}$$

Using the relations

$$r = \frac{x_0 - x}{\cos \delta_2}$$

$$ds = \frac{dx}{\cos \delta_1}$$

and integrating from the leading edge to the trailing edge,*

$$V_{i_n} = -\frac{1}{2\pi} \int_{\text{L.E.}}^{\text{T.E.}} \frac{\gamma \, dx}{x_0 - x} \frac{\cos \delta_2 \cos \delta_3}{\cos \delta_1} \tag{4}$$

The negative sign is used because clockwise circulation and outward along the normal to the upper surface are considered positive. The three angles δ_1, δ_2, and δ_3 are functions of x.

The component of the free stream normal to the mean camber line at P is given by

$$V_{\infty_n} = V_\infty \sin\left(\alpha - \tan^{-1}\frac{dz}{dx}\right)_0 \tag{5}$$

The subscript 0 on the angle indicates a chordwise station corresponding to the coordinate x_0. The angle of attack as shown in Fig. 4 is taken as

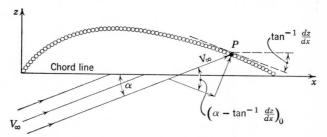

FIG. 4.   Boundary condition.

positive. dz/dx is the slope of the mean camber line with respect to the chord.

The sum of Eqs. 4 and 5 must be zero if the mean camber line is to be a streamline of the flow.

$$V_{i_n} + V_{\infty_n} = 0 \tag{6}$$

* The integral of Eq. 4 has an infinite integrand at $x = x_0$. The induced velocity is the *principal value* of this integral. For a discussion of the limiting process involved in taking the principal value of an integral see I. S. Sokolnikoff, *Advanced Calculus*, p. 347, first edition, McGraw-Hill, New York, 1939.

Integrals of this type occur frequently in the present and the following chapter. In each instance it is the principal value to which reference is being made.

The central problem of thin airfoil theory is to find a γ distribution that satisfies Eqs. 2 and 6. In the next section a simplification of Eq. 6 is introduced which leads to the concept of the planar wing.

5.3 PLANAR WING

The three angles δ_1, δ_2, and δ_3 in Eq. 4 are small if the maximum mean camber is small. This is the usual situation in practical airfoils, and to good approximation the cosines of the three angles can be set equal to unity. Equation 4 becomes

$$V_{in} = -\frac{1}{2\pi}\int_{\text{L.E.}}^{\text{T.E.}} \frac{\gamma\, dx}{x_0 - x} \tag{7}$$

But Eq. 7 represents the velocity induced on the x-axis by a vortex sheet lying on the x-axis. Therefore, the simplification introduced above is equivalent to satisfying boundary conditions on the x-axis instead of at the mean camber line.

The same order of approximation is made in Eq. 5, the additional assumption being that the angle of attack is small. Setting the sine and tangent equal to the angle, Eq. 5 becomes

$$V_{\infty_n} = V_\infty\left(\alpha - \frac{dz}{dx}\right) \tag{8}$$

The boundary condition at the airfoil corresponding to Eq. 6 becomes

$$\frac{1}{2\pi}\int_0^c \frac{\gamma\, dx}{x_0 - x} = V_\infty\left(\alpha - \frac{dz}{dx}\right)_0 \tag{9}$$

Equation 9 represents the condition of zero flow normal to the mean camber line. The condition is applied at the x-axis, however, instead of at the mean camber line.

This technique, referred to as the planar wing approximation, is used throughout thin-wing theory. It appears again in Chapter 6 in connection with the finite wing and in Chapter 11 in the development of supersonic wing theory.

5.4 PROPERTIES OF THE SYMMETRICAL AIRFOIL

The distribution that will satisfy Eqs. 2 and 9 will be found first for the case $dz/dx = 0$. This corresponds to a symmetrical airfoil or one in which the chord line and mean camber line are coincident. It is convenient to change coordinates by letting $x = (c/2)(1 - \cos\theta)$ where c is the chord of the airfoil. θ becomes the independent variable and θ_0 corresponds to x_0. Then the conditions to be satisfied are, from Eqs. 2 and 9:

$$\gamma(\pi) = 0 \tag{10}$$

$$\frac{1}{2\pi} \int_0^\pi \frac{\gamma \sin \theta \, d\theta}{\cos \theta - \cos \theta_0} = V_\infty(\alpha) \tag{11}$$

It can be readily verified that the γ distribution that satisfies both Eqs. 10 and 11 is *

$$\gamma = 2\alpha V_\infty \frac{1 + \cos \theta}{\sin \theta} \tag{12}$$

To verify that Eq. 12 satisfies Eq. 11, it is necessary to show that

$$\frac{1}{2\pi} \int_0^\pi \frac{2\alpha V_\infty(1 + \cos \theta)}{\cos \theta - \cos \theta_0} \, d\theta = V_\infty(\alpha)$$

This can be done with the help of the integral

$$\int_0^\pi \frac{\cos n\theta}{\cos \theta - \cos \theta_0} \, d\theta = \pi \frac{\sin n\theta_0}{\sin \theta_0} \tag{13}$$

This integral occurs several times in both thin-airfoil theory and finite-wing theory. An evaluation of it may be found in other textbooks on aerodynamics.†

That Eq. 12 satisfies Eq. 10 can be shown by evaluating the indeterminate form.

The lift per unit span per unit chordwise distance is given by

$$p = \rho V_\infty \gamma \tag{14}$$

The accuracy of the pressure distribution as given by Eqs. 14 and 12 is not good because of the assumptions of the theory. The overall lifting characteristics, however, are determined fairly well. The lift per unit span is given by

$$L' = \int_0^c p \, dx = \rho V_\infty \int_0^\pi 2\alpha V_\infty \frac{1 + \cos \theta}{\sin \theta} \frac{c}{2} \sin \theta \, d\theta \tag{15}$$

* A direct method for finding the γ distribution consists of transforming the flow about a circle into the flow about a flat plate by conformal mapping. The problem formulates to the *second type* of boundary value problem in potential theory. An account of it may be found in Chapter 2 of W. F. Durand's *Aerodynamic Theory*, Vol. 2.

† See H. Glauert, *Elements of Aerofoil and Airscrew Theory*, p. 92, Cambridge University Press, Cambridge, 1937; Richard von Mises, *Theory of Flight*, p. 208, McGraw-Hill, New York, 1945; T. von Kármán and J. M. Burgers, *General Aerodynamic Theory—Perfect Fluids*, in *Aerodynamic Theory*.

A sectional-lift coefficient c_l is defined by *

$$c_l = \frac{L'}{\frac{1}{2}\rho V_\infty^2 c} \tag{16}$$

After evaluating the integral, Eqs. 15 and 16 lead to a value of the sectional-lift coefficient given by Eq. 17

$$c_l = 2\pi\alpha \tag{17}$$

Thin-airfoil theory indicates that the sectional-lift coefficient for a symmetrical airfoil is directly proportional to the geometric angle of attack, where the geometric angle of attack is defined as the angle between the flight path and the chord line of the airfoil. Further, when the geometric angle of attack is zero, the lift coefficient is zero. A plot of Eq. 17 is shown in Fig. 5. The lift curve slope m_0 is equal to 2π.

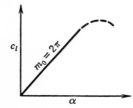

FIG. 5. Lift coefficient versus angle of attack.

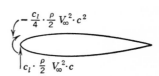

FIG. 6. Load system on an airfoil.

The dotted portion of the curve is not predicted by the theory, for it represents angles of attack above which viscosity effects on the lift cannot be neglected. On normal airfoils between 13° and 17° the flow separates from the airfoil, and the airfoil is said to be stalled. The moment of the lift about the leading edge of the airfoil is given by

$$M'_{\text{L.E.}} = -\int_0^c px\,dx$$

A stalling moment is taken as positive (clockwise in Fig. 6). Again using Eqs. 14 and 12 and defining a sectional-moment coefficient $c_{m\text{L.E.}} = M'_{\text{L.E.}}/\frac{1}{2}\rho V_\infty^2 c^2$, the value of the sectional-moment coefficient becomes

$$c_{m\text{L.E.}} = -\frac{\pi\alpha}{2} \tag{18}$$

or, in terms of the lift coefficient,

$$c_{m\text{L.E.}} = -\frac{c_l}{4} \tag{19}$$

* A discussion of dimensionless coefficients is given in Chapter 1.

The load system on the airfoil is shown in Fig. 6. If the load system is transferred to the right by an amount equal to $c/4$, it is apparent that the moment will vanish. This point must, therefore, be the center of pressure. The center of pressure for a symmetrical airfoil is located behind the leading edge by a distance equal to 25 per cent of the chord and is independent of the magnitude of the lift.

The lifting characteristics have now been completely determined in magnitude, direction, and line of action. Summarizing, for a symmetrical airfoil:

(a) The sectional lift coefficient is directly proportional to the geometric angle of attack and is equal to zero when the geometric angle of attack is zero.

(b) The lift curve slope m_0 equals 2π.

(c) The center of pressure is at the quarter chord for all values of the lift coefficient.

5.5 VORTICITY DISTRIBUTION FOR THE CAMBERED AIRFOIL

The method of determining the properties of a cambered airfoil is essentially the same as that for the symmetrical airfoil. However, because of the dependence of these properties on the mean-camber-line shape, the actual computations are more involved. The properties of the cambered airfoil must include those of the symmetrical airfoil as a special case. Again, the central problem is finding a γ distribution that satisfies Eqs. 2 and 9. Using the transformation

$$x = \frac{c}{2}(1 - \cos\theta)$$

Eqs. 2 and 9 become

$$\gamma(\pi) = 0 \tag{20}$$

$$\frac{1}{2\pi}\int_0^\pi \frac{\gamma\sin\theta\,d\theta}{\cos\theta - \cos\theta_0} = V_\infty\left(\alpha - \frac{dz}{dx}\right)_0 \tag{21}$$

The γ distribution that satisfies Eq. 21 may be represented as the sum of two parts. One part involves the shape of the mean camber line *and* the angle of attack and has the form of the γ distribution for the symmetrical airfoil as given by Eq. 12. This part is written

$$2V_\infty A_0\frac{1 + \cos\theta}{\sin\theta}$$

It will be shown later that $A_0 = \alpha$ when the airfoil is symmetrical; that is, when $dz/dx = 0$. The other part of the γ distribution depends only upon the shape of the mean camber line and is finite everywhere including the point at the leading edge. It is convenient to express this part as a Fourier series. Because we are interested in γ in the interval from 0 to π, the following sine series is adequate:

$$\sum_{n=1}^{\infty} B_n \sin n\theta$$

The total γ distribution is the sum of the two parts and may be written

$$\gamma = 2V_\infty \left[A_0 \frac{1 + \cos \theta}{\sin \theta} + \sum_{n=1}^{\infty} A_n \sin n\theta \right] \tag{22}$$

B_n has been replaced with $2V_\infty A_n$.

When $\theta = \pi$, $\gamma = 0$ for all values of the coefficients. Equation 20 is satisfied.

It remains to find the values of A_0 and A_n that will make Eq. 22 satisfy Eq. 21. To this end, Eq. 22 is substituted in Eq. 21, giving

$$\frac{1}{\pi} \int_0^\pi \frac{A_0(1 + \cos \theta)}{\cos \theta - \cos \theta_0} d\theta + \frac{1}{\pi} \int_0^\pi \sum_{n=1}^{\infty} \frac{A_n \sin n\theta \sin \theta}{\cos \theta - \cos \theta_0} d\theta = \left(\alpha - \frac{dz}{dx} \right)_0 \tag{23}$$

The first integral on the left-hand side of Eq. 23 is of the form of relation shown in Eq. 13. The second infinite series of integrals may also be evaluated by Eq. 13 if the trigonometric identity $\sin n\theta \cdot \sin \theta = \frac{1}{2}[\cos (n - 1)\theta - \cos (n + 1)\theta]$ is used. After performing these integrations and rearranging terms, Eq. 23 becomes

$$\frac{dz}{dx} = (\alpha - A_0) + \sum_{n=1}^{\infty} A_n \cos n\theta \tag{24}$$

The station subscript has been dropped for it is understood that Eq. 24 applies to any chordwise station. The coefficients A_0 and A_n must satisfy Eq. 24 if Eq. 22 is to represent the γ distribution that satisfies the condition of parallel flow at the mean camber line.

It will be observed that Eq. 24 has the form of the cosine series expansion of dz/dx. For a given mean camber line, dz/dx is a known function of θ, and, therefore, the values of A_0 and A_n may be written directly as

$$A_0 = \alpha - \frac{1}{\pi} \int_0^\pi \frac{dz}{dx} d\theta \tag{25}$$

$$A_n = \frac{2}{\pi} \int_0^\pi \frac{dz}{dx} \cos n\theta \, d\theta \tag{26}$$

Equations 25, 26, and 22 determine the γ distribution of the cambered airfoil in terms of the geometric angle of attack and the shape of the mean camber line. For zero camber $A_0 = \alpha$ and $A_n = 0$. Equation 22 becomes

$$\gamma = 2V_\infty \alpha \frac{1 + \cos \theta}{\sin \theta}$$

which was shown to be the γ distribution for the symmetrical airfoil in Section 5.4.

5.6 PROPERTIES OF THE CAMBERED AIRFOIL

The lift and moment coefficients for the cambered airfoil are found in the same manner as for the symmetrical airfoil.

$$c_l = \frac{1}{\frac{1}{2}\rho V_\infty^2 c} \int_0^c p \, dx$$

$$c_{m\text{L.E.}} = -\frac{1}{\frac{1}{2}\rho V_\infty^2 c^2} \int_0^c px \, dx$$

where p equals $\rho V_\infty \gamma$ and where γ is given by Eq. 22. After performing the integrations, the lift and moment coefficients become

$$c_l = 2\pi A_0 + \pi A_1 \tag{27}$$

$$c_{m\text{L.E.}} = -\frac{\pi}{2}\left(A_0 + A_1 - \frac{A_2}{2}\right) \tag{28}$$

The moment coefficient in terms of the lift coefficient may be written

$$c_{m\text{L.E.}} = -\frac{c_l}{4} + \frac{\pi}{4}(A_2 - A_1) \tag{29}$$

The load system on a cambered airfoil is shown in Fig. 7.

The center of pressure position behind the leading edge is found by dividing the moment about the leading edge by the lift.

C.P. behind L.E. $= \dfrac{c}{4} - \dfrac{\pi c}{4}\left(\dfrac{A_2 - A_1}{c_l}\right)$

$$\tag{30}$$

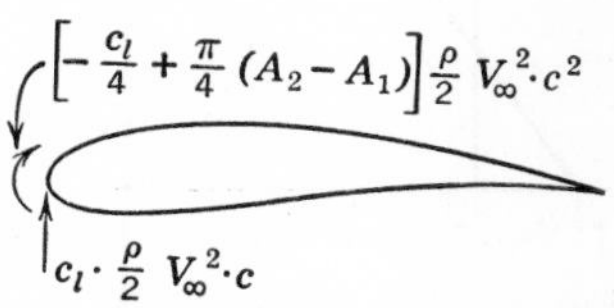

Fig. 7. Load system on a cambered airfoil.

From Eq. 26, it can be seen that A_1 and A_2 are independent of the angle of attack. They depend only on the shape of the mean camber line. Therefore the position of the center of pressure will vary as the lift coefficient varies. The line of action of the lift, as well as the magnitude, must be specified for each angle of attack.

It will be observed from Eq. 29 and Fig. 7 that, if the load system is transferred to a point behind the leading edge by a distance equal to 25 per cent of the chord, the moment coefficient about this point will be independent of angle of attack.

$$c_{m_{c/4}} = \frac{\pi}{4} (A_2 - A_1) \qquad (31)$$

Then the load system can be specified as a lift and a constant moment acting at the quarter chord. This is a simpler method of specifying the load system and is the one commonly employed. The point about which the moment coefficient is independent of the angle of attack is called the *aerodynamic center* of the section, and the moment coefficient about the aerodynamic center is given the symbol c_{mac}. Because this moment exists for all angles of attack, including the angle of attack that gives zero lift, it is frequently called the *zero-lift moment*. A moment in the absence of a resultant force is a couple. The zero-lift moment, therefore, is a couple. According to thin-airfoil theory, the aerodynamic center is at the quarter chord point, and, therefore, the moment coefficient about the aerodynamic center is given by Eq. 31. After A_2 and A_1 are replaced with their equivalents from Eq. 26, the c_{mac} becomes

$$c_{mac} = \frac{1}{2} \int_0^\pi \frac{dz}{dx} (\cos 2\theta - \cos \theta)\, d\theta \qquad (32)$$

The influence of the mean-camber-line shape on the c_{mac} will be shown later. For symmetrical airfoils, the c_{mac} is zero.

Replacing the coefficients A_0 and A_1 with their equivalents from Eqs. 25 and 26, the lift coefficient becomes

$$c_l = 2\pi \left[\alpha + \frac{1}{\pi} \int_0^\pi \frac{dz}{dx} (\cos \theta - 1)\, d\theta \right] \qquad (33)$$

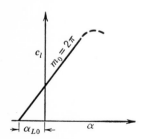

Fig. 8. Lift versus angle of attack for a cambered airfoil.

The lift coefficient varies linearly with the geometric angle of attack, and the slope of the lift curve m_0 is 2π. See Fig. 8. The lift coefficient, however, is not zero when the geometric angle of attack is zero, as for the symmetrical airfoil. The value of the geometric angle of attack which makes the lift coefficient zero is called the angle of zero lift and is given the symbol α_{L0}. From Eq. 33 the angle of zero lift is

$$\alpha_{L0} = -\frac{1}{\pi} \int_0^\pi \frac{dz}{dx} (\cos \theta - 1) \, d\theta \tag{34}$$

For symmetrical airfoils, the angle of zero lift is zero.

In Fig. 9, an airfoil is shown set at a geometric angle of attack equal to the angle of zero lift. A line on the airfoil parallel to the flight path

Fig. 9.   Orientation of zero lift.

V_∞ and passing through the trailing edge when the airfoil is set at the orientation of zero lift is called the zero-lift line of the airfoil. For symmetrical airfoils, the zero-lift line coincides with the chord line.

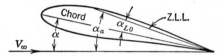

Fig. 10.   Absolute angle of attack.

The absolute angle of attack is defined as the angle included between the flight path and the zero-lift line and is given the symbol α_a. From Fig. 10,

$$\alpha_a = \alpha - \alpha_{L0} \tag{35}$$

The negative sign occurs because α_{L0} is itself a negative number on normal airfoils. From Eqs. 34 and 35, the absolute angle of attack is

$$\alpha_a = \alpha + \frac{1}{\pi} \int_0^\pi \frac{dz}{dx} (\cos \theta - 1) \, d\theta \tag{36}$$

Then Eq. 33 may be written

$$c_l = 2\pi \alpha_a \tag{37}$$

Summarizing, the theory of thin airfoils shows the cambered airfoil to have the following properties:

(a) $m_0 = 2\pi$.

(b) $\alpha_{L0} = -(1/\pi) \int_0^\pi (dz/dx)(\cos \theta - 1) \, d\theta$.

(c) Aerodynamic center is at $0.25c$ behind leading edge.

(d) $c_{mac} = \frac{1}{2}\int_0^\pi (dz/dx)(\cos 2\theta - \cos \theta)\, d\theta.$

Experimental results for several NACA airfoils are shown in Figs. 6, 7, and 8 of Appendix C.

5.7 INFLUENCE OF CAMBER ON α_{L0} AND c_{mac}

The influence of the shape of the mean camber line on α_{L0} and c_{mac} can be seen by evaluating the integrals of Eqs. 34 and 32 graphically. The expression for α_{L0}

$$\alpha_{L0} = -\frac{1}{\pi}\int_0^\pi \frac{dz}{dx}(\cos \theta - 1)\, d\theta$$

is put in terms of the independent variable x by using the relation

$$x = \frac{c}{2}(1 - \cos \theta)$$

For an airfoil of unit chord, α_{L0} becomes

$$\alpha_{L0} = +\frac{2}{\pi}\int_{L.E}^{T.E.} \frac{x\, dz}{\sqrt{x - x^2}}$$

and an integration by parts leads to the relation

$$\alpha_{L0} = \frac{1}{\pi}\left\{ z\,\frac{2x}{\sqrt{x - x^2}}\bigg]_{L.E.}^{T.E.} - \int_{L.E.}^{T.E.} \frac{z\, dx}{(1 - x)\sqrt{x - x^2}} \right\} \qquad (38)$$

The first expression on the right-hand side of Eq. 38 vanishes at both the leading and trailing edges. This statement may be verified by assuming a linear relation between x and z at the leading and trailing edges. In the same manner, it may be verified that the integrand of the second expression vanishes at the leading edge and becomes infinite at the trailing edge.

Let

$$f_1(x) = -\frac{1}{\pi}\frac{1}{(1 - x)\sqrt{x - x^2}}$$

Then the expression for α_{L0} becomes

$$\alpha_{L0} = \int_0^1 z f_1(x)\, dx \qquad (39)$$

To facilitate numerical integration, Glauert * has tabulated the function $f_1(x)$; the data appear in Fig. 11, Table A.

Though the integrand of Eq. 39 is infinite at the trailing edge, the integral is closed, and, following Glauert, a numerical integration is performed between $x = 0$ and $x = 0.95$. The integration is performed analytically between $x = 0.95$ and $x = 1$ by assuming a straight-line relation between x and z in the 0.05 interval at the trailing edge. The reader may verify that this portion of the airfoil contributes to α_{L0} an amount equal to $-2.87z'$ where z' is the value of z at $x = 0.95$.

From Eq. 39 and Table A of Fig. 11, it can be seen that α_{L0} will always be a negative number for an airfoil whose mean camber line lies above the chord line $(z > 0)$. Further, the or-

x	$f_1(x)$	x	$f_2(x)$
0.025	−2.09	0.025	+6.10
0.05	−1.54	0.05	+4.13
0.10	−1.18	0.10	+2.67
0.20	−1.00	0.20	+1.50
0.30	−0.99	0.30	+0.87
0.40	−1.08	0.40	+0.41
0.50	−1.27	0.50	0
0.60	−1.62	0.60	−0.41
0.70	−2.32	0.70	−0.87
0.80	−3.98	0.80	−1.50
0.90	−10.6	0.90	−2.67
0.95	−29.2	0.95	−4.13

Table A Table B

FIG. 11.   Tables for computing α_{L0} and c_{mac}. (Courtesy of H. Glauert, *The Elements of Airfoil and Airscrew Theory*, Cambridge University Press, Cambridge, 1947.)

dinates of the mean camber line in the vicinity of the trailing edge more powerfully influence the value of α_{L0} than the ordinates elsewhere. If the ordinates are made negative in the vicinity of the trailing edge, this portion of the airfoil will contribute positive increments to α_{L0}. By reflexing the trailing edge in this manner, α_{L0} can be made zero or positive. See Fig. 12.

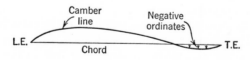

FIG. 12.   Reflexed trailing edge.

The influence of the shape of the mean camber line on c_{mac} is found in a similar manner. The expression for c_{mac} given by Eq. 32,

$$c_{mac} = \frac{1}{2} \int_0^\pi \frac{dz}{dx} (\cos 2\theta - \cos \theta) \, d\theta$$

* H. Glauert, *Elements of Aerofoil and Airscrew Theory*.

can be put in the form of Eq. 40 by using the identity $\cos 2\theta = 1 - 2 \times \sin^2 \theta$:

$$c_{mac} = -\frac{1}{2}\int_0^\pi \frac{dz}{dx}(\cos\theta - 1)\,d\theta - \int_0^\pi \frac{dz}{dx}\sin^2\theta\,d\theta \qquad (40)$$

The first integral is $(\pi/2)\alpha_{L0}$. The second integral is put in terms of the independent variable x by using the relation

$$x = \frac{c}{2}(1 - \cos\theta)$$

For an airfoil of unit chord, c_{mac} becomes

$$c_{mac} = \frac{\pi}{2}\alpha_{L0} - 4\int_0^1 \sqrt{x - x^2}\,dz$$

After integrating by parts,

$$c_{mac} = \frac{\pi}{2}\alpha_{L0} + 2\int_0^1 z\frac{1 - 2x}{\sqrt{x - x^2}}\,dx$$

By assuming a linear relation between x and z at the leading and trailing edges, it may be easily verified that the integrand is zero at both places. The expression $(1 - 2x)/\sqrt{x - x^2}$ is replaced with $f_2(x)$, and the expression for c_{mac} becomes

$$c_{mac} = \frac{\pi}{2}\alpha_{L0} + 2\int_0^1 zf_2(x)\,dx \qquad (41)$$

Glauert's tabulation of $f_2(x)$ appears in Table B of Fig. 11.

Equation 41 and Table B show that the c_{mac} of airfoils of the usual shape will be negative. The c_{mac} may be made zero or positive by reflexing the trailing edge.

Experimental values of the α_{L0} and c_{mac} for several NACA airfoils are shown in Figs. 7 and 8 of Appendix C.

The value of the c_{mac} plays an important role in the stability and balance of a wing in flight. This subject is discussed in the chapter on finite wings.

5.8 THE FLAPPED AIRFOIL

In the last section, it was shown that the portion of the mean camber line in the vicinity of the trailing edge powerfully influences the value of α_{L0}. It is on this fact that the aileron as a lateral-control device and the flap as a high-lift device are based. A deflection downward of a portion of the chord at the trailing edge effectively makes the ordinates of the mean camber line more positive in this region. As a consequence, α_{L0} becomes more negative and the lift at a given geometric angle of attack is increased. These results are shown in Fig. 13. The lift curve

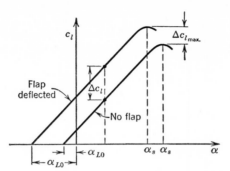

FIG. 13.   Gain in lift through flap deflection.

is displaced to the left as a result of an increase in α_{L0} negatively. The gain in lift at the given geometric angle of attack is shown as Δc_l. If the rear portion of the trailing edge is deflected upward, an opposite displacement of the lift curve results and the lift at a given geometric angle of attack is decreased.

The success of the flap as a high-lift device is based on the fact that, though the stalling angle α_s is reduced by the deflection of a flap, the reduction is not great enough to remove the gain arising from the shift of the curve as a whole. The increase in maximum lift coefficient, $\Delta c_{l_{\max}}$, is shown in Fig. 13.

The influence of small flap deflections on the section properties can be predicted by thin-airfoil theory.* Because all angles are small, it is sufficient to find the properties of a symmetrical airfoil at zero angle of

FIG. 14.   Airfoil with flap deflected.

attack with flap deflected. These may be added directly to the properties of the cambered airfoil at any angle of attack. In Fig. 14, the mean camber line of a symmetrical airfoil at zero angle of attack is shown

* H. Glauert, *A Theory of Thin Airfoils*, Aeronautical Research Committee, Reports and Memorandum 910, London, 1924; H. Glauert, *Theoretical Relationships for an Aerofoil with Hinged Flap*, Aeronautical Research Committee, Reports and Memoranda 1095, London, 1927.

with a trailing-edge flap deflected through an angle η. If the leading and trailing edges are connected by a straight line and if this is treated as a fictitious chord line, the problem reduces to that of a cambered airfoil at an angle of attack α'. See Fig. 15. Let E be the ratio of the flap

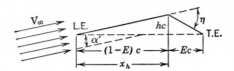

FIG. 15.   Geometry of flapped airfoil problem.

chord to the total chord. hc is the length shown in Fig. 15. From the leading edge to the hinge line, the slope of the mean camber line is $h/(1-E)$. From the hinge line to the trailing edge, the slope is $-h/E$. The formulas of Sections 5.5 and 5.6 apply directly. From Eqs. 25 and 26,

$$A_0 = \alpha' - \frac{1}{\pi} \int_0^\pi \frac{dz}{dx} \, d\theta$$

$$A_n = \frac{2}{\pi} \int_0^\pi \frac{dz}{dx} \cos n\theta \, d\theta$$

The integrals must be evaluated in two parts: from the leading edge to the hinge line θ_h, and from the hinge line to the trailing edge. A_0 becomes

$$A_0 = \alpha' - \frac{1}{\pi} \left[\frac{h}{1-E} \theta \right]_0^{\theta_h} - \frac{1}{\pi} \left[-\frac{h}{E} \theta \right]_{\theta_h}^{\pi}$$

After substituting in the limits and using the relations

$$\frac{h}{1-E} + \frac{h}{E} = \eta$$

$$\alpha' + \frac{h}{E} = \eta$$

the value of A_0 becomes

$$A_0 = \left(\frac{\pi - \theta_h}{\pi} \right) \eta \qquad (42)$$

In a similar manner, the values of A_n are found to be

$$A_n = \frac{2 \sin n\theta_h}{n\pi} \eta \qquad (43)$$

The values of c_l and c_{mac} are given by Eqs. 27 and 31, respectively.

$$c_l = 2\pi A_0 + \pi A_1$$

$$c_{mac} = \frac{\pi}{4}(A_2 - A_1)$$

Using the relations shown in Eqs. 42 and 43, the values of c_l and c_{mac} become

$$c_l = [2(\pi - \theta_h) + 2\sin\theta_h]\eta \tag{44}$$

$$c_{mac} = [\tfrac{1}{2}\sin\theta_h(\cos\theta_h - 1)]\eta \tag{45}$$

The lift coefficient and moment coefficient about the aerodynamic center vary linearly with the flap deflection. The magnitudes depend upon the parameter θ_h, which is related to the distance x_h of the hinge line behind the leading edge by the expression

$$x_h = \frac{c}{2}[1 - \cos\theta_h]$$

5.9 CONCLUDING REMARKS

In the preceding sections, the characteristics of a two-dimensional wing have been developed by an approximate theory that is based on potential flow over an airfoil of zero thickness. The lift curve slope, angle of zero lift, position of the aerodynamic center, and moment coefficient about the aerodynamic center show good agreement with experimental values for angles of attack that are not close to the stall. The pressure distribution given by the theory is inaccurate, especially near the leading edge. The prediction of the pressure distribution over a thick airfoil is an important problem in the design of laminar flow and high-speed airfoils, and a more accurate method of determining pressures must be resorted to when such designs are of interest.*

The theory cannot predict the maximum lift coefficient and profile drag coefficient, because the stall and drag of bodies is a viscosity effect. These phenomena are described in detail later in this book.

The results of thin-airfoil theory are compared with experiment in Appendix C. In particular, the reader's attention is called to Figs. 6, 7, and 8 of Appendix C.

* T. Theodorsen and I. E. Garrick, *General Potential Theory of Arbitrary Wing Sections*, NACA TR 452, 1933.

Finite Wing

CHAPTER 6

6.1 INTRODUCTION *

It was shown in Section 4.10, from momentum considerations, that a vortex that is stationary with respect to the general flow experiences a force of magnitude $\rho V \Gamma$ in a direction perpendicular to **V**. The Kutta-Joukowski theorem, which was derived in Chapter 4, states that the force experienced by unit span of a right cylinder of any cross section whatever is $\rho V \Gamma$ and it is directed perpendicular to **V**. Then we see immediately that a stationary two-dimensional vortex in a moving stream is the equivalent of a two-dimensional wing as far as the resultant forces are concerned.

Finite-wing theory also makes use of the airfoil-vortex analogy, but it is not possible to make the point vortex serve as the equivalent of unit span of a finite wing if it is desired to take into account tip effects or the variation in section properties in the spanwise direction. Before the vortex filament, which is the three-dimensional counterpart of the two-dimensional point vortex, can be made to serve as the equivalent of the finite wing, the analogy must be scrutinized more carefully and other details of the equivalence brought to light.

6.2 BOUND VORTICITY

To both the point vortex and the vortex sheet in the two-dimensional theory, all the properties of vorticity and vortex flow were ascribed except one. The vortex becomes the counterpart of the wing, provided

---

* The development of the theory of wings of finite span is mainly the work of Lanchester and Prandtl. An exposition of the theory was given by Prandtl in 1921 in NACA TR 116, *Applications of Modern Hydrodynamics to Aeronautics*. For a historical background to finite-wing theory the reader is referred to the article "Historical Sketch," by R. Giocomelli, in *Aerodynamic Theory*, Vol. 1, edited by W. F. Durand, California Institute of Technology, Pasadena, 1943.

that it is stationary in a moving fluid, and the vortex sheet in thin-airfoil theory is also taken to be stationary with respect to the general flow. A stationary vortex in a moving fluid violates the Helmholtz requirement that vorticity remain attached to the same fluid particles. Then, clearly, the analogy, though it is the equivalent of an actual physical case, cannot in itself have physical reality. Vorticity of this nature is termed *bound* vorticity, the adjective *bound* indicating that, unlike *true* or *free* vorticity, it does not remain attached to the same fluid particles but remains bound to a particular set of space coordinates. Thus, a *bound* vortex or a *bound* vortex sheet is the counterpart of unit span of a two-dimensional wing.

Another approach to the concept of bound vorticity makes its extension to the three-dimensional problem apparent. It has been noted that a force $\rho V\Gamma$ is associated with a stationary vortex in a moving fluid. This force should be thought of as having its origin outside the fluid. For example, a wing moving through the fluid is sustained by a lift $\rho V\Gamma$. This lift is simply the reaction to the force that the wing exerts on the fluid by virtue of its weight and inertia. Therefore, in the wing-vortex analogy, the force $-\rho V\Gamma$, which is associated with the bound vortex in a moving stream, is simply the force being applied to the fluid by the body. If an external force is applied impulsively in the fluid (for example, at the surface of a wing), vorticity will be created in the fluid. From the equations of motion, the law governing this action can be shown to be

$$\frac{\partial}{\partial t}\operatorname{curl}\mathbf{V} = \frac{\operatorname{curl}\mathbf{F}}{\rho}$$

where $\mathbf{F}$ represents the external force per unit volume that is introduced into the fluid. If a uniform force is applied impulsively throughout an unbounded region, vorticity will not be created because the curl of the force will be zero everywhere. If an impulsive force is applied uniformly throughout a finite region and allowed to decrease rapidly to zero at the edge of the region, the curl of the force will have a value at the edge and vorticity will be created there. It can be shown that if a uniform

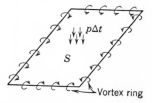

FIG. 1.   Formation of vortex ring.

impulsive pressure $p\Delta t$ is applied to a surface S, a vortex of strength Γ will be formed at the edges of S where

$$\Gamma = \frac{p\Delta t}{\rho}$$

The path connecting the axes of rotation of these fluid particles will form a vortex ring at the edge of S as shown in Fig. 1.*

Now consider a surface of span b and width c, illustrated in Fig. 2. Let an impulsive pressure $p\Delta t$ be applied intermittently on this surface. Vorticity will be created intermittently and, if the general body of fluid is at rest, vortex rings will tend to accumulate in the vicinity of the edges of the surface. These rings will not be motionless but will have

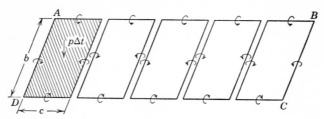

FIG. 2.   Intermittent application of impulse on a surface.

a motion that is dictated by the velocity field induced by all the vorticity present; that is, this vorticity, like all real vorticity, remains attached to the same fluid particles. The motion of the vortex rings caused by the vorticity itself will be referred to as the inherent motion of the vorticity.

Continuing the example, let the fluid have a general velocity V parallel to the plane upon which the impulsive pressure is being applied. Further, let the velocity V be large compared to the inherent velocity of the vortex rings. Then the rings will be carried downstream away from the plate with approximately a velocity V. Let the impulsive pressure $p\Delta t$ be applied every c/V sec. Then, after an interval of time, the rings will be arranged relatively to the surface S in the manner indicated in Fig. 2.

The only uncanceled vorticity is the rectangle $ABCDA$. Now let the chord length become very small. The interval between impulses c/V becomes very small, and this rapid succession of impulses in the limit as $c \rightarrow 0$ becomes a continuous application of impulse. Shrinking the chord to zero does not change the above picture, however, except to decrease the size of the rectangles. The only uncanceled vorticity still remains $ABCDA$.

The line AD is what we have termed *bound* vorticity. Actually, Helmholtz's theorem has not been violated, for the vorticity created

* A detailed account of the foundations of finite-wing theory has been given by J. M. Burgers in Vol. 2 of *Aerodynamic Theory*. The reader may find the development of the two equations cited in Chapter 3 of that volume.

along AD is carried downstream with the fluid. Because it is being continuously created at AD, the effect is that of a vortex filament that is bound to a fixed set of space coordinates while the general flow moves past it.

That the force per unit span along AD is $\rho V\Gamma$ follows immediately from the fact that the force at AD is simply equal to the impulse applied there each second. An impulsive force ($p\Delta tcb$) is applied every c/V sec. Therefore, in 1 sec, a total impulsive force of $(p\Delta tcbV)/c$ is applied.

$$F = p\Delta tcb\,\frac{V}{c}$$

$$F' = \frac{F}{b} = p\Delta tV = \rho V\Gamma$$

It is apparent that the strength of the vortex filaments AB, BC, and CD will be constant along their length and equal to the strength of the filament AD as long as the continuous application of impulse at AD is of constant strength. If the impulses vary in strength, as they would in oscillating-airfoil theory, it can be expected that uncanceled vortex filaments parallel to the wing span will occupy the entire space between the filament AD and the filament BC.

The explanation and the formulas given above are approximate, but they serve to illustrate the airfoil-vortex analogy as applied in finite-wing theory.

6.3 HORSESHOE VORTEX SYSTEM

From the theory that was briefly outlined in Section 6.2, we find that the vortex configuration that can be constructed to represent the finite wing consists of a bound vortex (line AD in Fig. 3) and two rectilinear vortex filaments trailing downstream from the tips of the bound vortex and joined at the opposite end by the vortex filament that was formed when the first impulse was applied. The bound vortex that represents the wing is called the *lifting line*, and the vortex filament BC is called the starting vortex. The latter is the vorticity that is shed at the trailing edge when the motion is

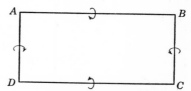

FIG. 3. Vortex system for constant spanwise load.

started. It should be remembered that, as long as the impulse which is being continuously applied along AD is of constant strength, no uncanceled vorticity will exist within $ABCD$. However, if the strength of the impulse being applied along AD varies with time, then the region enclosed by $ABCD$ will contain a series of vortex filaments that are parallel to AD. Under these conditions, the filaments AB and DC will not be of constant strength along their length.

Figure 3 represents the case of constant impulse applied along AD. If it is desired to apply along AD an impulse that is constant with time but varying in a spanwise direction, vortex filaments parallel to AB will trail downstream and fill the region $ABCD$. As an example, consider a wing that is symmetrically loaded and has a load which decreases as the tip is approached. To the original impulse applied along AD, add another impulse in a region having the same chordwise extent but shorter in the spanwise direction—for example, between E and F in Fig. 4. Then the impulse between E and F will be the sum of the original and the additional impulses, whereas the impulse along FA and ED will simply be the original impulse. The additional impulse added between E and F will create the vortex rectangle $EFGH$.

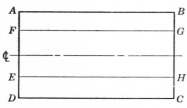

Fig. 4.   Effect of additional impulse applied between E and F.

This process can be continued indefinitely, resulting in a continuously varying distribution of impulse along AD and a continuous distribution of vortex filaments between DC and AB. As shown in Fig. 5, the lifting

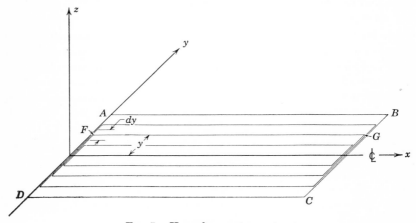

Fig. 5.   Horseshoe vortex system.

line and wake lie in the $z = 0$ plane; that is, the wing is taken to be a planar body, as discussed in Section 5.3. The strength $d\Gamma$ of any filament FG is infinitesimal, and it is related to the rate of change in strength of Γ along AD by the expression

$$d\Gamma = \frac{d\Gamma}{dy} dy \qquad (1)$$

6.4 THE FIELD OF FLOW—DOWNWASH AND INDUCED DRAG

In Sections 6.2 and 6.3 an equivalence was established between the horseshoe vortex system and the finite wing. The velocity in the neighborhood of the lifting line is composed of the uniform stream added vectorially to the velocities induced by the horseshoe vortex system. Because the vortex system is continuously expanding as the starting vortex line BC in Fig. 5 is swept downstream from the lifting line, the flow field is unsteady. After an interval of time, the starting vortex is so far removed from the lifting line that its influence in the vicinity of the latter is negligible and the flow field is no longer a function of time. Finite-wing analysis presumes that the motion has continued long enough so that the flow field is steady.

The inherent velocity of the wake will vary from point to point within it. As a result, the wake will form a warped surface behind the wing, and the velocity induced at the lifting line by elements of the wake will not necessarily be in a plane that is perpendicular to the lifting line. This effect is neglected in finite-wing analysis. It is assumed that the wake is flat and lies in a plane determined by the lifting line and the direction of motion. It should be observed that elements of the *flat* wake will induce velocities above and below the lifting line that have components in the spanwise direction. Therefore, the flow around unit span of a finite wing is nowhere strictly two-dimensional except in the plane of symmetry of a symmetrically loaded wing.

Physically, this deviation from two-dimensional flow can be seen by considering the velocity produced by the pressure difference between the upper and lower surfaces. At the tips, air flows from the high-pressure region beneath the wing into the low-pressure region above the wing. We can expect a span-wise component of velocity towards the wing tips on the under-

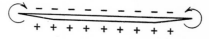

FIG. 6.   Flow over tips.

side of the wing and towards the plane of symmetry on the upperside. See Fig. 6.

The spanwise component of flow is neglected in the analysis that follows. Each unit span of the finite wing is treated as though the flow about it were two-dimensional.

Then, looking at a cross section of the finite wing, we see a stationary vortex representing the lifting line which is in the presence of a uniform stream V_∞ opposite to the direction of motion and a stream w perpendicular to the direction of motion. w is the velocity induced by the wake and is called the *downwash*. This is illustrated in Fig. 7.

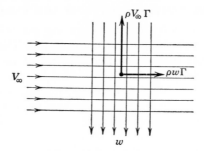

Fig. 7.   Downwash and induced drag.

According to the Kutta-Joukowski theorem, the vortex will experience a force $\rho V_\infty \Gamma$ perpendicular to V_∞ and a force $\rho w \Gamma$ perpendicular to w. Letting **V** represent the vector sum of V_∞ and w, we can see that the total force vector is $\rho V \Gamma$ and acts perpendicular to **V**. A cross section of the wing is drawn in Fig. 8. The geometric and absolute

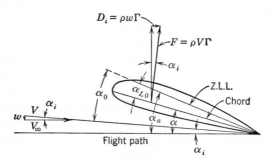

Fig. 8.   Fundamental diagram of finite-wing theory.

angles of attack and the angle of zero lift are defined in the same manner as they were for a section of an infinite wing. The vector sum of the flight velocity V_∞ and the downwash w is designated the *relative wind*. The angle between the relative wind and the zero-lift line of the wing is the angle that determines the force and is termed the effective angle of attack α_0. The section of the finite wing behaves just as though it were a section of an infinite wing set at an absolute angle of attack equal to α_0. Thus, for a finite wing section,

$$c_l = m_0 \alpha_0 \tag{2}$$

where m_0 has a theoretical value of 2π per radian. That the above formula reduces to the formula for the infinite wing

$$c_l = m_0 \alpha_a$$

can be verified by allowing the span to become infinite and the strength of the lifting line to become constant along its length. Then the wake vanishes and there is no downwash velocity w. Under these conditions, the relative wind and flight path become coincident, and

$$\alpha_0 = \alpha_a$$

The angle between the relative wind and flight path is called the induced angle of attack α_i because it arises as a result of the induced velocity w. α_0 and α_i are both measured from the relative wind. Therefore, the values of these parameters that are shown in Fig. 8 must have opposite signs. When the induced velocity is downward, as shown in Fig. 8, the induced angle of attack is itself a negative number. The relation between the induced angle and the induced velocity is given by

$$\alpha_i = \tan^{-1} \frac{w}{V_\infty} \simeq \frac{w}{V_\infty} \tag{3}$$

Lift and drag are defined as the components of the resultant force that are perpendicular and parallel to the *flight path*, respectively. From Fig. 7 and Fig. 8, it is apparent that

$$L' = \rho V \Gamma \cos \alpha_i = \rho V_\infty \Gamma$$

$$D'_i = -\rho V \Gamma \sin \alpha_i = -\rho w \Gamma$$

The primes indicate force components per unit span. The drag component carries the subscript i and is called the *induced drag*. The induced drag is a result of the backward bending of the resultant force vector by the induced velocity and must be added to the profile drag that arises from skin friction and separation. Profile drag is discussed in a later chapter. The induced drag can also be written

$$D'_i = -\frac{L'w}{V_\infty} = -L' \tan \alpha_i \simeq -L'\alpha_i \tag{4}$$

The induced drag coefficient c_{d_i} and lift coefficient c_l are related in the same manner.

$$c_{d_i} = -c_l \alpha_i \qquad (5)$$

The downwash velocity w is small compared to the flight velocity $\mathbf{V}_\infty$. The magnitude of the vector sum, therefore, does not vary significantly from the magnitude of $\mathbf{V}_\infty$. In the sections that follow, no distinction will be made between $|\mathbf{V}|$ and $|\mathbf{V}_\infty|$.

It is not convenient at all times to use the effective angle of attack in writing an expression for the lift coefficient

$$c_l = m_0 \alpha_0$$

It is more convenient to use the easily measurable absolute angle of attack α_a. This is permissible, provided that a new lift curve slope m is defined

$$c_l = m \alpha_a$$

m has a value less than 2π, and it is a function of the wake characteristics. The equation relating m to m_0 is found by employing the relation between the absolute and effective angles of attack. This relation is shown in Fig. 8.

$$\alpha_a = \alpha_0 - \alpha_i \qquad (6)$$

The fact that α_i is itself a negative number accounts for the negative sign in Eq. 6.

$$\frac{c_l}{m} = \frac{c_l}{m_0} - \alpha_i$$

$$m = \frac{m_0}{1 - m_0 \dfrac{\alpha_i}{c_l}} \qquad (7)$$

It will be shown later that α_i/c_l may be written in terms of the geometry and orientation of the wing.

6.5 FUNDAMENTAL EQUATION OF FINITE-WING THEORY

The main problem of finite-wing theory is the determination of the spanwise distribution of airloads on a wing of given geometry that is flying with a given speed and orientation in space. The analysis proceeds on the assumption that the flow about each unit span of the finite wing is two-dimensional and the resultant force experienced by each unit span is given by the Kutta-Joukowski theorem. The absolute angle of attack of any section is a known quantity in the problem. The lift per unit span or its equivalent, Γ, is the unknown. The fundamental equation of finite-wing theory in its simplest form relates the absolute and effective angles of attack. This relation has been given by Eq. 6.

$$\alpha_a = \alpha_0 - \alpha_i$$

The effective angle of attack is easily expressed in terms of Γ and the known quantities in the problem.

$$L' = \rho V \Gamma = m_0 \alpha_0 \frac{\rho}{2} V^2 c$$

$$\alpha_0 = \frac{2\Gamma}{m_0 V c} \tag{8}$$

The induced angle of attack equals w/V and the downwash w may also be expressed in terms of Γ. Then the fundamental equation will contain only the unknown Γ, and this is the equation that must be solved in order to determine the spanwise distribution of airloads.

In order to find the downwash induced at any point along the lifting line by the wake, the law of Biot and Savart as given in Section 2.12 is applied to the horseshoe vortex system. Let dw_{y_0y} be an increment of downwash induced at the point y_0 by an increment of vortex filament dx which originates at the lifting line at spanwise station y. See Fig. 9. The Biot-Savart law gives

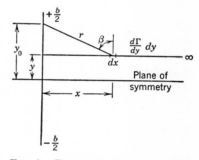

FIG. 9. Downwash induced by trailing vortex sheet.

$$dw_{y_0y} = \frac{d\Gamma}{4\pi} \frac{\cos \beta \, dx}{r^2}$$

Then the entire filament at y contributes a downwash equal to

$$w_{y_0y} = \frac{d\Gamma}{4\pi} \int_0^\infty \frac{\cos \beta \, dx}{r^2} = \frac{d\Gamma}{4\pi} \frac{1}{y_0 - y}$$

The strength $d\Gamma$ is given by Eq. 1.

$$d\Gamma = \frac{d\Gamma}{dy} dy$$

The downwash at y_0 resulting from the entire wake is found by integrating $w_{y_0 y}$ from one wing tip $-b/2$ to the other $+b/2$.

$$w_{y_0} = -\frac{1}{4\pi} \int_{-b/2}^{+b/2} \frac{d\Gamma/dy}{y_0 - y} \, dy \tag{9}$$

The negative sign is needed because $d\Gamma/dy$ is a negative number between zero and $+b/2$ and a positive number between $-b/2$ and zero.

Utilizing Eqs. 8, 9, and 3, the fundamental Eq. 6 takes the form

$$(\alpha_a)_{y_0} = \left(\frac{2\Gamma}{m_0 V c}\right)_{y_0} + \frac{1}{4\pi V} \int_{-b/2}^{+b/2} \frac{d\Gamma/dy}{y_0 - y} \, dy \tag{10}$$

The only unknown in the above integral differential equation is the circulation Γ. A solution of this equation for all spanwise stations y_0 solves the spanwise airload distribution problem.

6.6   THE ELLIPTICAL LIFT DISTRIBUTION

Equation 10 of the preceding section is readily solved if the Γ distribution is assumed to be known and the chord distribution $c(y)$ is taken as the unknown. This problem of finding a chord distribution that corresponds to a given circulation distribution simply involves the solution of an algebraic equation. A very important special case is the elliptical circulation distribution, for this represents the wing of minimum induced drag. The properties of wings of arbitrary plan forms that do not differ radically from the usual shapes are close to the properties of the elliptical wing. It is customary to write the properties of wings of arbitrary plan form in terms of the properties of the elliptical wing and a correction factor. In this section, the properties of a wing with an elliptical circulation distribution are investigated. The proof that such a wing has the minimum induced drag is delayed until Section 6.8.

If Γ_s represents the circulation in the plane of symmetry, the elliptical variation of circulation with span is written

$$\Gamma = \Gamma_s \sqrt{1 - \left(\frac{y}{b/2}\right)^2} \tag{11}$$

The downwash for an elliptical Γ distribution is found by substituting Eq. 11 in Eq. 9.

$$w_{y_0} = -\frac{\Gamma_s}{4\pi} \int_{-b/2}^{+b/2} \frac{\dfrac{d}{dy}\sqrt{1 - \left(\dfrac{y}{b/2}\right)^2}}{y_0 - y} \, dy$$

The integral is evaluated easily if the trigonometric substitution $y = (b/2) \cos \theta$ is made. The downwash becomes

$$w_{\theta_0} = \frac{-\Gamma_s}{2\pi b} \int_\pi^0 \frac{\dfrac{d}{d\theta} \sin \theta}{\cos \theta_0 - \cos \theta} \, d\theta$$

$$w_{\theta_0} = \frac{\Gamma_s}{2\pi b} \int_0^\pi \frac{\cos \theta \, d\theta}{\cos \theta_0 - \cos \theta}$$

The integral will be recognized as that which occurred so frequently in Chapter 5. The value of the integral was given as

$$\int_0^\pi \frac{\cos n\theta \, d\theta}{\cos \theta - \cos \theta_0} = \frac{\pi \sin n\theta_0}{\sin \theta_0} \tag{12}$$

The case at hand corresponds to $n = 1$. The value of the downwash becomes

$$w = \frac{-\Gamma_s}{2b} \tag{13}$$

Equation 13 indicates that the velocity induced at any point along the lifting line is constant if the Γ distribution is elliptical. Therefore, the induced angle of attack α_i will be constant along the span, and, if the absolute angles of attack of each spanwise station are the same, we can expect a constant effective angle of attack.

$$\alpha_0 = \alpha_a + \alpha_i$$

$$c_l = m_0 \alpha_0$$

$$c_{d_i} = -c_l \alpha_i$$

If the sectional-lift curve slopes are independent of span, the sectional-lift coefficients and induced-drag coefficients will be independent of span. Summarizing, for wings with an elliptical Γ distribution and a constant lift curve slope and absolute angle of attack, the nondimensional section properties will not vary along the span.

Under these conditions, the chord of the wing must vary elliptically, for

$$L' = \rho V \Gamma_s \sqrt{1 - \left(\frac{y}{b/2}\right)^2} = m_0 \alpha_0 \frac{\rho V^2}{2} c$$

$$c = \frac{2\Gamma_s}{m_0 \alpha_0 V} \sqrt{1 - \left(\frac{y}{b/2}\right)^2}$$

It should be observed that an elliptical chord distribution does not mean that the plan form of the wing is an ellipse. If m_0 and α_0 are not independent of span, then an elliptical Γ distribution requires that the product $m_0 \alpha_0 c$ vary elliptically with span.

The same conclusions could have been drawn by substituting Eqs. 13 and 11 into Eq. 10. This step leads to the expression

$$\alpha_a = \frac{2\Gamma_s}{m_0 V c} \sqrt{1 - \left(\frac{y}{b/2}\right)^2} + \frac{\Gamma_s}{2bV}$$

from which

$$c = \left[\frac{2\Gamma_s}{\left(\alpha_a - \dfrac{\Gamma_s}{2bV}\right) m_0 V}\right] \sqrt{1 - \left(\frac{y}{b/2}\right)^2}$$

The wing properties are found by integrating the section properties across the span. The wing-lift coefficient C_L is defined as the wing lift L divided by the dynamic pressure $\frac{1}{2}\rho V^2$ times the wing area S. Then, since the lift per unit span for a wing with an elliptical Γ distribution is

$$L' = \rho V \Gamma_s \sqrt{1 - \left(\frac{y}{b/2}\right)^2}$$

we can write the wing-lift coefficient

$$C_L = \frac{L}{\frac{1}{2}\rho V^2 S} = \frac{\displaystyle\int_{-b/2}^{+b/2} L' \, dy}{\frac{1}{2}\rho V^2 S} = \frac{\Gamma_s \pi b}{2VS} \tag{14}$$

The wing-lift coefficient and sectional-lift coefficient are equal when the sectional-lift coefficients are constant along the span.

$$C_L = \frac{1}{\frac{1}{2}\rho V^2 S} \int c_l \frac{\rho}{2} V^2 c \, dy = c_l \tag{15}$$

If Eq. 14 is solved for Γ_s and this value for Γ_s is used in Eq. 13, the expression for the downwash becomes

$$w = \frac{-C_L V}{\pi \, \mathcal{R}}$$

where $\mathcal{R}$ is the aspect ratio of the wing and is defined

$$\mathcal{R} = \frac{b^2}{S}$$

The induced angle of attack and induced-drag coefficient are given by

$$\alpha_i = \frac{w}{V} = -\frac{C_L}{\pi \, \mathcal{R}} \qquad (16)$$

$$C_{D_i} = c_{d_i} = -C_L \alpha_i = \frac{C_L{}^2}{\pi \, \mathcal{R}} \qquad (17)$$

The expression for the lift curve slope of a section of a finite wing (Eq. 7) may now be completed. The value of α_i / c_l is $-1 / \pi \mathcal{R}$. Therefore, Eq. 7 becomes

$$m = \frac{m_0}{1 + \dfrac{m_0}{\pi \, \mathcal{R}}} \qquad (18)$$

The induced-drag coefficient and lift curve slope for a wing of arbitrary plan form are given by

$$C_{D_i} = \frac{C_L{}^2}{\pi \, \mathcal{R}} (1 + \sigma) \qquad (19)$$

$$m = \frac{m_0}{1 + \dfrac{m_0}{\pi \, \mathcal{R}} (1 + \tau)} \qquad (20)$$

where σ and τ are small numbers. To prove that C_{D_i} is a minimum for an elliptical Γ distribution, it must be proved that σ is always positive. The values of σ and τ for arbitrary wings will be derived in the following sections.

6.7   GLAUERT'S SOLUTION OF THE FUNDAMENTAL EQUATION

In the last section, the fundamental equation Eq. 10 was solved by assuming the lift distribution to be known and inquiring what chord distribution corresponded to the given lift distribution. In this section, we assume that everything is known about the geometry of the wing and its speed and orientation in space, and we solve Eq. 10 for the Γ distribution.

$$\{\alpha_a\}_{y_0} = \left\{ \frac{2\Gamma}{m_0 V c} \right\}_{y_0} + \frac{1}{4\pi V} \int_{-b/2}^{b/2} \frac{d\Gamma/dy}{y_0 - y} \, dy \qquad (10)$$

Following Glauert,* we write Γ as a Fourier series. If we again make the trigonometric substitution $y = (b/2) \cos \theta$, Γ will be defined in the

* H. Glauert, *Aerofoil and Airscrew Theory*, Chapter 11, Cambridge University Press, Cambridge, 1947.

interval 0 to π, and either the sine or cosine terms in the series may be dropped. If a sine series is used, the boundary conditions which require that $\Gamma = 0$ at θ equals zero and π are both satisfied for all values of B_n.

$$\Gamma = \sum_{n=1}^{\infty} B_n \sin n\theta \tag{21}$$

The constants B_n are influenced by the sectional chord, lift curve slope, and flight speed. This may be seen by remembering that the lift per unit span, which may be written

$$L' = m_0 \alpha_0 \tfrac{1}{2}\rho V^2 c$$

is equal to $\rho V\Gamma$. Solving for Γ,

$$\Gamma = \frac{m_0 \alpha_0 c V}{2}$$

It is convenient to make the B_n's nondimensional by dividing each constant by $m_{0_s} c_s V/2$ and multiplying the entire series by the same factor. The subscript s represents sectional values in the plane of symmetry of the wing. The series for Γ is finally written

$$\Gamma = \frac{m_{0_s} c_s V}{2} \sum_{n=1}^{\infty} A_n \sin n\theta \tag{22}$$

where A_n of Eq. 22 is equal to B_n of Eq. 21 divided by $m_{0_s} c_s V/2$. If Eq. 22 is inserted in Eq. 10 and if the trigonometric substitution $y = (b/2) \cos \theta$ is made, Eq. 10 becomes

$$\{\alpha_a\}_{\theta_0} = \frac{(cm_0)_s}{(cm_0)_{\theta_0}} \sum_{n=1}^{\infty} A_n \sin n\theta_0 + \frac{m_{0_s} c_s}{4\pi b} \int_0^\pi \frac{\dfrac{d}{d\theta}\left(\displaystyle\sum_{n=1}^{\infty} A_n \sin n\theta\right) d\theta}{\cos \theta - \cos \theta_0} \tag{23}$$

After performing the differentiation and the integration with the aid of Eq. 12, Eq. 23 reduces to the algebraic form

$$\alpha_a = \frac{c_s m_{0_s}}{c m_0} \sum_{n=1}^{\infty} A_n \sin n\theta + \frac{m_{0_s} c_s}{4b} \sum_{n=1}^{\infty} n A_n \frac{\sin n\theta}{\sin \theta} \tag{24}$$

The above equation is applicable for all values of θ_0; that is, it can be applied to every spanwise station. For this reason the subscripts 0 have been omitted. The only unknowns occurring are the constants A_n. As many A_n's as desired may be solved for by applying Eq. 24 to an equal number of stations along the span. This procedure leads to a set of simultaneous algebraic equations that may be solved for the constants A_n. These values may then be substituted into Eq. 22, which yields the circulation and, therefore, the lift, as a function of span. This solves the spanwise lift distribution problem for wings of known geometry and orientation in space. It is pointed out that each change in angle of attack will change the sectional values of α_a and therefore will in general require a new solution of the simultaneous equations. In Section 6.9, it will be shown how the lift distribution for all angles of attack may be found by solving the simultaneous equations only twice.

6.8 WING AND SECTION PROPERTIES IN TERMS OF THE A_n'S OF GLAUERT'S SOLUTION

The expression for Γ was given by Eq. 22 of the last section as

$$\Gamma = \frac{m_{0s} c_s V}{2} \sum_{n=1}^{\infty} A_n \sin n\theta$$

and the expression for induced angle of attack is given by the last term on the right-hand side of Eq. 24

$$\alpha_i = - \frac{m_{0s} c_s}{4b} \sum_{n=1}^{\infty} n A_n \frac{\sin n\theta}{\sin \theta} \tag{25}$$

The sectional-lift coefficient and induced-drag coefficients are readily found by substituting the above relations in

$$c_l = \frac{\rho V \Gamma}{\frac{1}{2}\rho V^2 c}$$

$$c_{d_i} = - c_l \alpha_i$$

which gives these section characteristics in terms of the A_n's

$$c_l = \frac{m_{0s} c_s}{c} \sum_{n=1}^{\infty} A_n \sin n\theta \tag{26}$$

$$c_{d_i} = \frac{m_{0s}^2 c_s^2}{4bc} \left[\sum_{n=1}^{\infty} A_n \sin n\theta \right] \left[\sum_{n=1}^{\infty} n A_n \frac{\sin n\theta}{\sin \theta} \right] \tag{27}$$

The lift curve slope for a section of a finite wing was given by Eq. 7 as

$$m = \frac{m_0}{1 - (m_0 \alpha_i / c_l)}$$

and Eq. 20 as

$$m = \frac{m_0}{1 + (m_0 / \pi \, \mathcal{R})(1 + \tau)}$$

Equations 25 and 26 establish the value of τ as

$$\tau = +\frac{\pi c}{4 c_m} \frac{\sum\limits_{n=1}^{\infty} n A_n \, (\sin n\theta / \sin \theta)}{\sum\limits_{n=1}^{\infty} A_n \sin n\theta} - 1 \qquad (28)$$

where c_m is the mean chord of the wing. The wing-lift coefficient is related to the integral of Eq. 26

$$C_L = \frac{\displaystyle\int_{-b/2}^{+b/2} c_l \tfrac{1}{2}\rho V^2 c \, dy}{\tfrac{1}{2}\rho V^2 S}$$

In performing the integration, a change in the order of the summation and integration signs will show that all terms in the summation are zero except $n = 1$. The value of C_L becomes

$$C_L = \frac{m_{0s} c_s \pi b}{4S} A_1 \qquad (29)$$

In a similar fashion, the wing-drag coefficient is related to the integral of Eq. 27

$$C_{D_i} = \frac{\displaystyle\int_{-b/2}^{+b/2} c_{d_i} \tfrac{1}{2}\rho V^2 c \, dy}{\tfrac{1}{2}\rho V^2 S}$$

A term-by-term multiplication of the two infinite series involved in c_{d_i} will show that each term in the integrand of C_{D_i} is of the form

$$A_n A_m \sin n\theta \sin m\theta$$

The integrals of these terms vanish for all values of m and n except $m = n$. The value of C_{D_i} is given by

$$C_{D_i} = \frac{m_{0s}{}^2 c_s{}^2 \pi}{16S} \sum_{n=1}^{\infty} n A_n{}^2 \qquad (30)$$

The value of C_{D_i} for a wing of arbitrary shape has been given by Eq. 19 as

$$C_{D_i} = \frac{C_L{}^2}{\pi R} (1 + \sigma)$$

To prove that the induced-drag coefficient for an elliptical wing

$$C_{D_i} = \frac{C_L^2}{\pi \, \mathcal{R}}$$

is a minimum, it must be shown that σ is a positive number. By using Eq. 29, Eq. 30 may be written

$$C_{D_i} = \frac{C_L^2}{\pi \, \mathcal{R}} \sum_{n=1}^{\infty} n \left(\frac{A_n}{A_1}\right)^2 \qquad (31)$$

This relation establishes the value of σ as

$$\sigma = 2 \left(\frac{A_2}{A_1}\right)^2 + 3 \left(\frac{A_3}{A_1}\right)^2 + \cdots \qquad (32)$$

Because all the terms in Eq. 32 are squared, σ is necessarily positive, which proves the assertion that the induced-drag coefficient for an elliptical wing is the minimum.

A discussion of the other properties of the finite wing, namely, the center of pressure and angle of zero lift of the wing, is deferred to Section 6.11.

6.9 THE TWISTED WING—BASIC AND ADDITIONAL LIFT

It is frequently desirable to twist a wing so that the sectional geometric angles of attack are not all equal. It will be shown later that the stall characteristics and the moment coefficient about the aerodynamic center of the wing may be controlled in this fashion. If the geometric angles of attack at various spanwise stations are unequal, the wing is said to have *geometric twist*. Specifically, if the wing is so twisted that the geometric angle of attack at the wing tip is less than the geometric angle of attack at the wing root, the wing is said to have geometric *washout*. Wings with the opposite twist have *washin*.

A wing has *aerodynamic twist* if the absolute angles of attack are not the same at every spanwise station. Aerodynamic washout and washin are defined analogously to geometric washout and washin. Wings with zero geometric twist will have aerodynamic twist if the angles of zero lift of the sections are not the same. On the other hand, a difference in angles of zero lift can be compensated by the proper amount of geometric twist, so that a wing of varying section can be geometrically twisted until the aerodynamic twist is reduced to zero. The α_a on the left-hand side of Eq. 24 will be different for different spanwise stations if the wing has aerodynamic twist. In Fig. 10, a typical section is drawn. In addition to the angles and lines already defined, the zero-lift line of the wing (Z.L.L.W.) has been drawn in. Z.L.L.W. will be an average, weighted in a certain fashion to be described later, of the Z.L.L.'s of the sections. When the flight path is in the direction of Z.L.L.W., the total lift on the wing is zero. Under these conditions, the lift at the various spanwise stations is not zero but has a value corresponding to the angle of attack α_{ab}, where α_{ab} is the angle between Z.L.L.W. and the Z.L.L. of the station under consideration. The lift

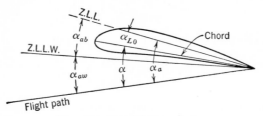

FIG. 10.   Zero-lift line of wing.

that the spanwise station has when the total lift on the wing is zero is called the *basic lift*. The integral of the basic lift from one wing tip to the other is zero.

In addition to the basic lift, each spanwise station will have a lift corresponding to the angle of attack α_{aW}, where α_{aW} is the angle between the flight path and Z.L.L.W. This lift is called the *additional lift*. The lift coefficient at any spanwise station in terms of the basic and additional lift coefficients is written

$$c_l = c_{l_b} + c_{l_a} \tag{33}$$

The basic lift coefficient depends upon the twist of the wing and is independent of the angle of attack of the wing α_{aW}. The additional lift coefficient is independent of the wing twist and is directly proportional to α_{aW}. Then the above equation may be written

$$c_l = c_{l_b} + C_L c_{l_{a1}} \tag{34}$$

where c_{l_b} and $c_{l_{a1}}$ are functions of the wing geometry and are completely independent of α_{aW}. To show this, we rewrite the left-hand side of Eq. 24 so that the sectional angle of attack is split into two parts.

$$\alpha_{aW} + \alpha_{ab} = \frac{c_s m_{0s}}{cm_0} \sum_{n=1}^{\infty} A_n \sin n\theta + \frac{m_{0s} c_s}{4b} \sum_{n=1}^{\infty} n A_n \frac{\sin n\theta}{\sin \theta}$$

For the special case of $\alpha_{aW} = 0$, we apply the above equation to several stations along the span and solve for an equal number of the coefficients.

These values of the coefficients are designated A_{nb}. Then for the general case with $\alpha_{aW} \neq 0$, the series is written

$$\alpha_{aW} + \alpha_{ab}$$

$$= \left[\frac{c_s m_{0s}}{cm_0} \sum_{n=1}^{\infty} (A_n - A_{nb}) \sin n\theta + \frac{m_{0s}c_s}{4b} \sum_{n=1}^{\infty} n(A_n - A_{nb}) \frac{\sin n\theta}{\sin \theta} \right]$$

$$+ \left[\frac{c_s m_{0s}}{cm_0} \sum_{n=1}^{\infty} A_{nb} \sin n\theta + \frac{m_{0s}c_s}{4b} \sum_{n=1}^{\infty} nA_{nb} \frac{\sin n\theta}{\sin \theta} \right] \quad (35)$$

Because α_{ab} is exactly equal to the second bracket on the right-hand side of Eq. 35, α_{aW} must equal the first bracket. α_{aW} is not a function of span, and, therefore, when the equation

$$\alpha_{aW} = \frac{c_s m_{0s}}{cm_0} \sum_{n=1}^{\infty} (A_n - A_{nb}) \sin n\theta + \frac{m_{0s}c_s}{4b} \sum_{n=1}^{\infty} n(A_n - A_{nb}) \frac{\sin n\theta}{\sin \theta}$$

is applied to several stations along the span and values of $(A_n - A_{nb})$ are solved for, these coefficients will be directly proportional to α_{aW}. Thus, the c_l distribution along the span is split into two series, one of which involves the coefficients A_{nb} that are independent of α_{aW} and the other of which involves the coefficients $(A_n - A_{nb})$ that are directly proportional to α_{aW}. The wing-lift coefficient C_L is also proportional to α_{aW} and is zero when α_{aW} is zero. Therefore, the sectional-lift coefficient may be written as shown in Eq. 34. $c_{l_{a1}}$ may be interpreted as the sectional-lift coefficient of the *untwisted wing* when the wing-lift coefficient is unity.

To find the distribution of sectional-lift coefficient for any value of the wing-lift coefficient, we may solve Glauert's Eq. 24, using two values of α_{aW}. Then two values of c_l for each spanwise station will be known, and if they are used in the left-hand side of Eq. 34, c_{l_b} and $c_{l_{a1}}$ may be computed. With c_{l_b} and $c_{l_{a1}}$ known as functions of span, Eq. 34 may again be employed to find the c_l distribution for any desired value of C_L.

The spanwise distribution of induced drag can be found by means of Eq. 5.

$$c_{d_i} = -c_l \alpha_i$$

α_i is given by Eq. 6, which may be written

$$\alpha_i = \alpha_0 - \alpha_a = \frac{c_l}{m_0} - \frac{c_l}{m}$$

With these relations, the expression for the induced-drag coefficient becomes

$$c_{d_i} = c_l^2 \left(\frac{m_0 - m}{m_0 m} \right) \tag{36}$$

6.10 FIRST-ORDER EFFECT OF DEVIATION FROM AN ELLIPTIC DISTRIBUTION

It has been observed that the additional lift of a finite wing lies approximately halfway between a distribution proportional to the chord and an elliptic distribution.*

$$L'_a = \frac{1}{2} \left[\frac{L}{S} c + \frac{4L}{\pi b} \sqrt{1 - \left(\frac{y}{b/2} \right)^2} \right] \tag{37}$$

If we use the relation

$$c_{l_{a1}} = \frac{L'_a}{qcC_L}$$

in Eq. 37, an expression giving $c_{l_{a1}}$ as a function of span follows immediately

$$c_{l_{a1}} = \frac{1}{2} \left[1 + \frac{4}{\pi} \frac{c_m}{c} \sqrt{1 - \left(\frac{y}{b/2} \right)^2} \right] \tag{38}$$

Schrenk's approximation gives a clear picture of the influence of taper on the spanwise lift distribution. The dotted lines in Fig. 11 are

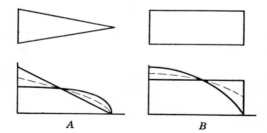

A   B

FIG. 11.   Schrenk approximation for additional lift.

drawn halfway between an elliptical distribution and a distribution proportional to the chord.

It can be seen that the effect of taper is to increase the load in the outboard portion above that which would occur if the lift were propor-

* Otto Schrenk, *A Simple Approximation Method for Obtaining the Spanwise Lift Distribution*, NACA TM 948, 1940.

tional to the chord. For stress-analysis purposes, the assumption of a lift distribution proportional to chord is unconservative if the ratio of the tip chord to the root chord is less than $\frac{1}{2}$.

6.11 ADDITIONAL CHARACTERISTICS OF THE FINITE WING

Methods of calculating the spanwise distributions of lift and drag and the values of the lift and drag coefficients for the finite wing have been discussed in previous sections. The angle of zero lift of the wing,

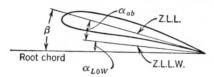

FIG. 12.   Angle of zero lift of wing.

α_{LOW}, is defined by Fig. 12, and its value was found by equating the integral of the basic lift distribution to zero. Thus,

$$c_{l_b} = m\alpha_{ab} = m(\beta + \alpha_{LOW})$$

$$\int_{-b/2}^{+b/2} m(\beta + \alpha_{LOW})qc\, dy = 0$$

$$\alpha_{LOW} = -\frac{\displaystyle\int_{-b/2}^{b/2} m\beta c\, dy}{\displaystyle\int_{-b/2}^{b/2} mc\, dy} \tag{39}$$

The fore and aft location of the center of pressure of a finite wing is needed for design purposes. It is to be expected that the center of pressure location of the wing will be a weighted average of the center of pressure locations of the wing sections. The center of pressure of a finite wing is specified in the same manner as for a section. The load and moment of the load about the aerodynamic center of the wing are given, and these completely define the load system. The aerodynamic center of a finite wing is defined as the fore and aft location about which the moment coefficient of the load is independent of angle of attack. The moment coefficient about the aerodynamic center is given the symbol C_{MAC}. If the C_{MAC} and position of the aerodynamic center are specified, the center of pressure can be found for any value of the lift coefficient C_L.

In order to find the aerodynamic center of a wing, we must find the chordwise location about which the moment coefficient is independent of angle of attack. To this end, the moment of the load is found about an arbitrary reference line that is perpendicular to the plane of symmetry and passes through the leading edge of the root chord. See Fig. 13.

The line of aerodynamic centers is a line connecting the aerodynamic centers of the sections. The sectional load systems are taken as acting

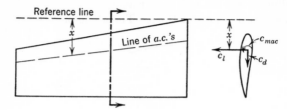

Fig. 13. Moment about reference line.

along the line of aerodynamic centers. If we neglect the moment resulting from the drag, the total moment about the reference line is given by the expression

$$M_{RL} = \int_{-b/2}^{b/2} (-c_l x + c_{mac}c)qc\,dy$$

If c_l is replaced with its equivalent $c_{l_b} + C_L c_{l_{a1}}$ the moment coefficient about the reference line can be written

$$C_{M_{RL}} = \frac{M_{RL}}{qc_m S} =$$

$$\underbrace{\int_0^1 -c_{l_b}\frac{cx}{c_m^2}d\left(\frac{y}{b/2}\right)}_{C_{M_{lb}}} + \underbrace{C_L\int_0^1 -c_{l_{a1}}\frac{cx}{c_m^2}d\left(\frac{y}{b/2}\right)}_{C_{M_{la}}} + \underbrace{\int_0^1 c_{mac}\left(\frac{c}{c_m}\right)^2 d\left(\frac{y}{b/2}\right)}_{C_{M_s}}$$

$C_{M_{la}}$ is the only component of the moment coefficient that depends on the angle of attack of the wing. If the position of the reference line is so chosen that $C_{M_{la}}$ vanishes, then that position will be the aerodynamic center. Obviously, the aerodynamic center of the wing is at the centroid of the additional lift. The position X of the aerodynamic center behind the leading edge of the root chord is given by

$$X_{AC} = \frac{\int_0^1 c_{l_{a1}}cx\,d\left(\frac{y}{b/2}\right)}{\int_0^1 c_{l_{a1}}c\,d\left(\frac{y}{b/2}\right)} \tag{40}$$

The moment coefficient about the aerodynamic center is the C_{MAC}. Then, if the reference line to which x is measured is chosen through the centroid of the additional lift, the value of C_{MAC} is given by

$$C_{MAC} = \int_0^1 - c_{l_b} \frac{cx}{c_m{}^2} d\left(\frac{y}{b/2}\right) + \int_0^1 c_{mac} \left(\frac{c}{c_m}\right)^2 d\left(\frac{y}{b/2}\right) \tag{41}$$

The C_{MAC} is an average of the sectional c_{mac}'s weighted according to the chord squared plus a term determined by the twist and sweep of the wing.

6.12 STABILITY AND TRIM OF WINGS

A wing is said to be statically stable if a small disturbance from equilibrium sets up forces that tend to return the wing to equilibrium. In Fig. 14, a wing cross section is shown with the load system acting at the aerodynamic center. Considering the section as a rigid body, any unbalanced moments will cause the section to rotate about its center of gravity (C.G.). If the C.G. is behind the aerodynamic center, any additional increment of lift that may arise from a disturbance of the section will cause a moment in the direction of stall. The attending angle of attack increase results in a further increase in lift, which, in turn, increases the moment, etc. It can be concluded, then, that a wing whose center of gravity is behind the aerodynamic center is unstable. By the same argument, it can be seen that a wing whose C.G. is in front of the aerodynamic center is stable.

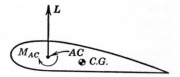

FIG. 14.   Load system on rigid body.

For most wing configurations, the C.G. lies behind the aerodynamic center, and stability must be achieved by placing a horizontal stabilizer behind the wing. From Fig. 15, it can be seen that the tail contributes

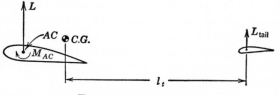

FIG. 15.   Tail stabilizer.

a stabilizing moment when the wing-tail configuration is disturbed from equilibrium, and, by a proper adjustment of the tail area and tail length l_t, this stabilizing moment can easily be made to outweigh the destabilizing effect of the wing.

If an airplane is to be constructed without a tail, it is necessary for stability reasons that the aerodynamic center be behind the C.G.

Stability is not the entire consideration. For steady equilibrium flight, the airplane must be trimmed; that is, the pitching moments must vanish. The stable wing shown in Fig. 16 will trim only if the

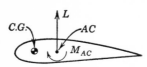

FIG. 16. Stable wing that can be trimmed.

M_{AC} is positive. Under these conditions, the negative moment of the airload about the C.G. will be counterbalanced by the M_{AC}. From Eq. 41, the C_{MAC} is composed of two parts; one part arises from the sectional c_{mac}'s, and the other from the basic lift. It was shown, in Chapter 5, that the moment coefficient about the aerodynamic center of a wing section which has a mean camber line that is concave downward is always negative. Sections with positive c_{mac} can be formed by reflexing the trailing edge. On normal airfoils without reflexed trailing edges the contribution to the C_{MAC} of the sectional moments will be negative.

The contribution to the C_{MAC} of the basic lift may be either positive or negative, depending upon the twist and sweep of the wing. Consider the sweptback wing shown in Fig. 17. The direction of sweep of a wing is determined by the inclination of the line of aerodynamic centers. Presume that the wing is set at $C_L = 0$ so that the lift acting at any section is the basic lift. Then, if the wing is washed out at the tips, the lift acting on the outboard sections will be down, whereas the lift acting on the in-

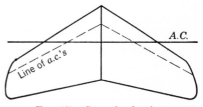

FIG. 17. Sweptback wing.

board sections will be up. This is a consequence of the fact that the integral of the basic lift must be zero. The moment about the aerodynamic center of basic lift so distributed will be positive.

By the same argument, it can be shown that a combination of sweepforward and washin at the tips will also result in a positive contribution to the C_{MAC} by the basic lift.

In summary, the C_{MAC} of a wing may be made positive by reflexing the trailing edges of the wing sections or by providing the proper amount of twist and sweep.

The combination of sweepback and washout is useful in flying wing design.   The sweepback moves the aerodynamic center of the wing rearward, thereby facilitating the stability condition which requires that the C.G. lie in front of the aerodynamic center.   The combination of sweepback and washout obtains a positive C_{MAC}, the necessary condition for trim.

6.13   APPROXIMATIONS IN PRANDTL LIFTING LINE THEORY

In this section the approximations of Prandtl lifting line theory will be pointed out in the light of a more general treatment of the subject.

The arguments of Sections 6.2 and 6.3 can be extended to apply to the lifting surface by the simple device of arranging elementary lifting lines one after the other over the chordwise extent of the wing.   From each lifting line trails the horseshoe vortex system appropriate to the spanwise lift distribution along it.   The resulting configuration appears as shown in Fig. 18.   The portion of the $z = 0$ plane represented by the

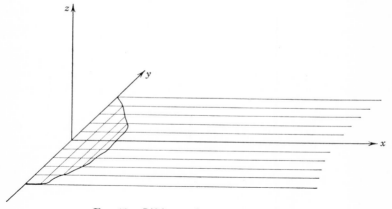

FIG. 18.   Lifting surface model of a wing.

wing is covered with a lattice of vortex filaments extending in the spanwise and chordwise directions.   The *wake* part of the $z = 0$ plane for the case of steady flow contains only chordwise filaments.   The problem is to find a vorticity distribution in the $z = 0$ plane such that the induced flow will cancel the component of the free stream normal to the wing.   The Kutta condition at the trailing edge must also be fulfilled. These boundary conditions are the same as those imposed in the theory of the planar two-dimensional wing of Chapter 5.

In addition to contracting the lifting surface to a lifting line at the quarter chord position, the Prandtl lifting line theory contains other approximations that may be seen by considering the fundamental formula of the Prandtl theory as given by Eq. 6.

$$\alpha_a = \alpha_0 - \alpha_i \tag{6}$$

Equation 6 is based on the idea that any section of a finite wing behaves as though it were a section of a two-dimensional wing in the presence of the free stream plus the velocity induced by the trailing vortices. The velocity w_T from the trailing vortices is given by

$$w_T = V_\infty \alpha_i \tag{42}$$

We shall show that α_0 is proportional to the velocity w_L induced at the $\frac{3}{4}$ chord position by a two-dimensional lifting line. We recall that α_0 when used with the two-dimensional lift curve slope determines the sectional lift

$$2\pi\alpha_0 \tfrac{1}{2}\rho V_\infty^2 c = \rho V_\infty \Gamma$$

from which

$$V_\infty \alpha_0 = \frac{\Gamma}{2\pi} \frac{1}{c/2} \tag{43}$$

The right-hand side of Eq. 43 will be recognized as the velocity induced by a two-dimensional vortex filament of strength Γ at a position removed from the filament by $\frac{1}{2}$ chord. For a lifting line at the $\frac{1}{4}$ chord, the induced velocity then is the value at the $\frac{3}{4}$ chord point.

$$w_L = -V_\infty \alpha_0 \tag{44}$$

The negative sign occurs because a positive α_0 provides a negative induced velocity at the $\frac{3}{4}$ chord position.

The fundamental equation of Prandtl theory is simply a statement of the familiar boundary condition of no flow normal to the wing. This can be seen by substituting Eqs. 42 and 44 into 6 and obtaining

$$V_\infty \alpha_a + w_L + w_T = 0$$

At any point D on the $\frac{3}{4}$ chord line shown in Fig. 19, the lifting line ABC will induce a flow quite different from that of the two-dimensional filament EF assumed in the Prandtl theory. The difference is attributable both to the geometry and to the fact that Γ is varying along the lifting line. For infinite aspect ratio, zero sweep wings EF and ABC coincide and there is no spanwise variation in Γ. If the sweep is small EF and ABC will be nearly coincident. If, in addition, the aspect ratio is large, the spanwise variation in Γ is weak enough in the region near D so that assuming it constant at the value Γ_D is approximately correct.

For low-aspect ratio wings with large amounts of sweep, the Prandtl

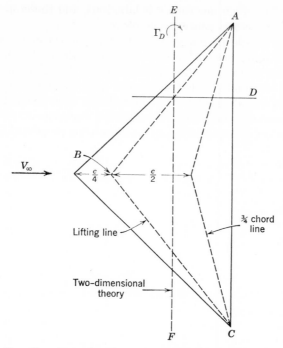

FIG. 19.   Approximations in Prandtl lifting line theory.

lifting line theory can be improved by calculating the induced flow from the true lifting line, taking into account its sweep and Γ variation along the span. This has been done by Weissinger,[*] and results of the theory applied to a large number of planforms may be found in the NACA literature.[†]

6.14   CONCLUDING REMARKS

The preceding sections are intended to show the basis of finite-wing theory and some of the approaches used in solving the spanwise lift distribution problem. The potential flow about a finite wing is more closely approximated by using a surface distribution of vorticity in the portion of the $z = 0$ plane occupied by the wing and its wake.[‡] For supersonic flow, a surface theory of this nature is feasible to apply, and details are discussed in Chapter 11. In the low-speed regime, however,

[*] J. Weissinger, *The Lift Distribution of Swept Back Wings*, NACA TM 1120, 1947.

[†] John De Young and Charles W. Harper, *Theoretical Symmetric Span Loading at Subsonic Speeds for Wing Having Arbitrary Planform*, NACA TR 921, 1948.

[‡] J. Weissinger, *The Lift Distribution of Swept Back Wings*.

the application of surface theory is laborious, and therefore one of the lifting line theories is generally employed.

Finally, it should be remembered that those properties of the wing that depend upon viscosity effects are not predicted by the theory of the preceding sections. These include profile drag and the maximum lift or stall. On highly swept supersonic wing configurations operating at low speed a leading edge flow separation is observed well below the stall that must also be charged to the fluid viscosity.

The influence of compressibility on finite-wing properties is discussed in Chapter 11.

Introduction to
Compressible Fluids

CHAPTER 7

7.1 SCOPE

The object of Chapters 7 through 11 is to describe the changes that occur in the aerodynamic characteristics of bodies in high-speed flight. In the preceding chapters, the basic concepts of the flow of a perfect fluid past solid bodies were studied. The agreement with theory and the discrepancies between the theory and experiments were pointed out. Some of these discrepancies result from treating the fluid as non-viscous. Others arise as a consequence of assuming air to be incompressible.

The similarity parameter * characterizing compressible flows is the Mach number, which is the ratio of the airspeed to the speed of sound. Whereas incompressible fluid considerations are a good approximation to low Mach number flows, as the Mach number increases density variations throughout the flow become greater and greater and the approximation involved in taking the density constant becomes poorer and poorer.

Since air is both viscous and compressible, the flow will depend on Mach number, Reynolds number, and other similarity parameters to be defined in Chapter 14. It is permissible, however, to postulate that the effect of viscosity is confined to a thin boundary layer (except where flow separation occurs) so that the main flow is approximately dependent only on Mach number. Accordingly, the analysis in these chapters shall in the main be limited to compressible nonviscous flows; experimental tests demonstrate the extent to which viscosity alters these results.

* Similarity parameters are discussed in Chapter 1 and Appendix A.

123

The physical quantities that were considered constant in previous chapters and now must be treated as variables are density and temperature. The two additional unknowns require additional equations for the solution of compressible flow problems and these are obtained from empirical information associated with energy concepts and the behavior of an ideal gas. The empirical principles are described briefly in Chapter 8 and the necessary mathematical equations are developed from them. In Chapters 9 and 10 the equations are manipulated to expose the nature of subsonic and supersonic flow. The section on compressibility is concluded with an introduction to wing theory in Chapter 11.

In Chapters 2 and 3 the principles of conservation of mass and momentum, which apply to elements of fixed identity, were formulated in terms of *field* properties. The resulting equations are perfectly general and apply whether the fluid is compressible or not. From these conservation principles the equations of continuity, equilibrium, irrotationality, and the associated concepts of stream function and velocity potential were derived. The remainder of this chapter is devoted to a brief discussion of each of the derived relationships from the viewpoint of compressible flow application.

7.2 EQUATION OF CONTINUITY—STREAM FUNCTION

The equation of continuity for the general case of unsteady, compressible flow is given by Eq. 9 of Chapter 2.

$$\operatorname{div} \rho \mathbf{V} = -\frac{\partial \rho}{\partial t} \tag{1}$$

It may be readily verified, by expansion into cartesian form, that Eq. 1 may be written

$$\operatorname{div} \mathbf{V} = -\frac{1}{\rho}\frac{\mathfrak{D}\rho}{\mathfrak{D}t} \tag{2}$$

For ρ constant, the substantial derivative is zero, and Eq. 2 takes the familiar form of incompressible-flow theory.

A stream function for two-dimensional steady compressible flows may be defined, provided that the density ρ is included in the definition. In accordance with the argument of Section 2.6 a parameter ψ' can be found such that the speed at any point in the flow is given by

$$|\mathbf{V}| = \frac{1}{\rho}|\operatorname{grad} \psi'| \tag{3}$$

and the direction of the velocity is given by the family of curves

$$\psi' = \text{constant} \tag{4}$$

The component of velocity in any direction s is given by differentiating the stream function at right angles to the left.

$$V_s = \frac{1}{\rho} \cdot \frac{\partial \psi'}{\partial n} \tag{5}$$

where the direction of n is normal to that of s.

7.3 IRROTATIONALITY—VELOCITY POTENTIAL

The rotation vector $\boldsymbol{\omega}$ defined in Chapter 2 does not involve density, and, therefore, the three components of rotation for a compressible fluid are given by

$$\omega_x = \frac{1}{2}\left(\frac{\partial w}{\partial y} - \frac{\partial v}{\partial z}\right)$$

$$\omega_y = \frac{1}{2}\left(\frac{\partial u}{\partial z} - \frac{\partial w}{\partial x}\right) \tag{6}$$

$$\omega_z = \frac{1}{2}\left(\frac{\partial v}{\partial x} - \frac{\partial u}{\partial y}\right)$$

In the absence of viscosity, the rotation of a fluid particle that was originally at rest is always zero. Therefore,

$$\text{curl } \mathbf{V} = 0 \tag{7}$$

For irrotational velocity fields, a scalar ϕ exists such that

$$\mathbf{V} = \text{grad } \phi \tag{8}$$

or, in cartesian form

$$u = \frac{\partial \phi}{\partial x}$$

$$v = \frac{\partial \phi}{\partial y} \tag{9}$$

$$w = \frac{\partial \phi}{\partial z}$$

The existence and implications of the existence of a velocity potential ϕ were shown in Chapter 2. The compressibility of the fluid in no way alters that discussion.

7.4 EQUATION OF EQUILIBRIUM—BERNOULLI'S EQUATION

Euler's equation, which expresses the dynamic equilibrium of an incremental mass $\rho\,\Delta x\,\Delta y\,\Delta z$ of a nonviscous fluid, was derived in Chapter 3 and is repeated below:

$$\frac{\mathfrak{D}\mathbf{V}}{\mathfrak{D}t} + \frac{\text{grad } p}{\rho} = 0 \tag{10}$$

In the derivation of Euler's equation, no assumptions regarding the compressibility of the fluid were made. Therefore, Eq. 10 is the equation of motion of a compressible, nonviscous fluid.*

In Section 3.4, the dot product of terms in Euler's equation with an increment of streamline **ds** led to the result

$$d\frac{V^2}{2} + \frac{dp}{\rho} + dU = 0 \tag{11}$$

Equation 11 will be referred to as the equilibrium equation in differential form. It holds for any nonviscous flow whether it is compressible or not. If ρ is constant, an integration of Eq. 11 leads to the familiar form of Bernoulli's equation. If ρ is variable, a relation between ρ and p must be found before the middle term can be integrated.

7.5 NONSUPERPOSITION OF COMPRESSIBLE FLOWS

In Chapter 4, it was shown that the irrotationality condition in terms of the stream function leads to the Laplace equation

$$\nabla^2\psi = 0 \tag{12}$$

and, similarly, the equation of continuity in terms of the velocity potential leads to the Laplace equation

$$\nabla^2\phi = 0 \tag{13}$$

Thus, the velocity field is completely determined by a linear differential equation with one dependent variable, the scalar ϕ or ψ. Therefore, solutions can be added (superimposed) to form new solutions, and, in this way, complicated flows can be analyzed as the sum of a number of simple flows. For instance, in Section 4.5, the flow around a circular cylinder was obtained by superimposing a uniform flow and a doublet, which is itself a superposition of source and sink flow.

* A derivation of the equations of motion for a viscous compressible flow is given in Appendix B.

An analogous procedure is not fruitful when the density is a variable. For a compressible flow, the irrotationality condition in terms of the stream function leads to (z-component)

$$\mathrm{curl}_z \mathbf{V} = -\frac{\partial}{\partial x}\left(\frac{1}{\rho}\frac{\partial \psi'}{\partial x}\right) - \frac{\partial}{\partial y}\left(\frac{1}{\rho}\frac{\partial \psi'}{\partial y}\right) = 0 \tag{14}$$

Similarly, the equation of continuity in terms of the velocity potential leads to (steady flow)

$$\mathrm{div}\,\rho\mathbf{V} = \frac{\partial}{\partial x}\left(\rho\frac{\partial \phi}{\partial x}\right) + \frac{\partial}{\partial y}\left(\rho\frac{\partial \phi}{\partial y}\right) = 0 \tag{15}$$

Because ρ is a function of both ϕ and ψ', Eqs. 14 and 15 are nonlinear, and, therefore, it is not possible to add solutions as in the incompressible case. This fact complicates the precise analysis of compressible flows.

In the subsonic range, compressible flow problems are solved by reducing them to equivalent incompressible flow problems through a suitable transformation of variables. For the flow over *thin* wings and bodies in the supersonic range, the nonlinear flow equation can be approximated by a linear form and the method of superposition again applies.

The Energy Relations

CHAPTER 8

8.1 INTRODUCTION

The concept of energy was introduced in Chapter 3 in the derivation of Bernoulli's equation for incompressible flow. In that chapter, energy was identified with mechanical work. Accordingly, the force terms in the steady flow Euler equation were multiplied by an increment of the path length along a streamline and after integration, assuming ρ to be a constant, Bernoulli's equation resulted:

$$p + \tfrac{1}{2}\rho V^2 = H \tag{1}$$

A decrease in kinetic energy per unit volume, according to Eq. 1, is accompanied by an equal increase in pressure energy so that the sum of the two energies is conserved. Thus, mechanical energy is conserved. Equation 1 represents simply one more implication of the principle of conservation of momentum expressed by Euler's equation.

When the gas is compressible, mechanical energies are *not* conserved and it is no longer possible to deduce an energy relation from the momentum principle. An entirely separate empirical fact, the first law of thermodynamics, must be introduced. *Intrinsic energy*, a concept derived from the first law, enters the energy balance. Furthermore, the first law encompasses other energies in addition to mechanical work, thereby generalizing the energy conservation principle. The energy forms of interest in aerodynamics are thermal and mechanical. The laws governing the transfer from one form to the other are derived and applied in this and the following chapters to problems of practical importance.

Intrinsic energy involves temperature, a gas characteristic that has not been considered so far. To relate temperature to density and pres-

128

sure requires another empirical fact, *the equation of state*, which is discussed in Section 8.2, together with other characteristics of an ideal gas.

In Sections 8.3 and 8.4 the first law of thermodynamics is formulated and used to develop an equation which expresses conservation of energy for a gas in motion. The use of the energy equation with and without viscous dissipation and heat addition is illustrated by examples. In Section 8.5 the notion of *reversibility* is introduced, and special relations among temperature, pressure, and density are derived for adiabatic reversible flows.

The direction in which an energy exchange may proceed is governed by the second law of thermodynamics, also an empirical observation. The second law is formulated in terms of *entropy* in Section 8.6.

Finally, for the special case of adiabatic reversible flows, the relation between density and pressure developed from the first law is introduced into the momentum equation and the integration of the momentum equation is carried out. The resulting energy equation is called Bernoulli's equation for compressible flow. However, unlike its counterpart for incompressible flow, the compressible Bernoulli equation stands as an independent energy relation that cannot be deduced from momentum considerations.

The thermodynamics concepts are stated in summary form in the present chapter. For details, the reader is referred to texts on thermodynamics.*

8.2 CHARACTERISTICS OF AN IDEAL GAS—EQUATION OF STATE

The table on p. 130 lists various quantities used in this chapter, together with the units in which they are measured. In aerodynamics, it is convenient to measure thermal energy in foot pounds, thereby avoiding the confusion of converting between mechanical and thermal units.

In the table, the first 12 quantities represent characteristics of the gas. In contrast, the last two, heat and work, represent energies in transit and are not characteristics of the gas. The gas characteristics may be directly observable, they may be quantities defined in terms of observable characteristics, or they may be quantities deduced from experiment. The *state* of a gas is fixed when all its characteristics have definite values. It will be seen later that not all of the characteristics are independent, and therefore the *state* of the gas may be fixed by specifying a limited number of characteristics.

* See, for example, Max Planck, *Treatise on Thermodynamics*, Dover Publications, New York, 1945; Mark Zemansky, *Heat and Thermodynamics*, McGraw-Hill, New York, 1943.

Table of Symbols *

SYMBOL	NAME	UNITS
p	Pressure	lb/ft^2
ρ	Density	$slugs/ft^3$
$v = 1/\rho$	Specific volume	$ft^3/slug$
T	Absolute temperature	degrees Rankine
u	Specific intrinsic energy	ft-lb/slug
e	Specific internal energy	ft-lb/slug
h	Specific enthalpy	ft-lb/slug
S	Specific entropy	ft-lb/slug ° R
c_p	Constant pressure specific heat	ft-lb/slug ° R
c_v	Constant volume specific heat	ft-lb/slug ° R
R	Gas constant	ft-lb/slug ° R
γ	Specific heat ratio c_p/c_v	
° R	Degrees Rankine	
° F	Degrees Fahrenheit	
$\hat{R}$	Control volume fixed in the field	
$\hat{S}$	Control surface fixed in the field	
$\hat{R}_1$	Control volume moving with the fluid	
$\hat{S}_1$	Control surface moving with the fluid	
q	Heat transfer per unit mass	ft-lb/slug
w	Work transfer per unit mass	ft-lb/slug

* In previous chapters, u, v, and w have been used to denote the cartesian components of velocity. In this chapter, u, v, and w have the meanings given in the table and the symbol **V** is used to indicate velocity.

In addition to the thermodynamic characteristics listed in the table, there are mechanical characteristics such as displacement and velocity that determine the potential and kinetic energies of the gas as a whole. In the following material, the term *state* is used to mean the thermodynamic state. The thermodynamic characteristics are described briefly in the following paragraphs.

1. EQUATION OF STATE AND THE GAS CONSTANT R. The ideal * or thermally perfect gas obeys the equation of state

$$p = \rho RT \tag{2}$$

where the gas constant R depends on the molecular weight of the gas being considered. For a gas of fixed composition, R is constant. For air, based on 21 per cent oxygen and 79 per cent nitrogen by volume

$$R = 1715 \text{ ft-lb/slug° R}$$

* The molecular model of an ideal gas has been described in Section 1.2.

At the extremely high temperatures encountered in very high Mach number flight, dissociation, ionization, and the formation of new compounds cause the average molecular weight of air to decrease with an attending rise in the gas constant R.   In this text, R will be considered to have the constant value given above unless stated otherwise.

The state of a gas of given molecular weight (and therefore all its thermodynamic characteristics) is, according to Eq. 2, fixed when any two of the three variables p, ρ, T are known.

2. INTRINSIC ENERGY AND CONSTANT VOLUME SPECIFIC HEAT.   The intrinsic energy is a characteristic deduced from experiment and is discussed in Section 8.3 in connection with the first law of thermodynamics.   Because intrinsic energy is determined by the state of the gas, it may be written *

$$u = u(v, T)$$

$$du = \left(\frac{\partial u}{\partial v}\right)_T dv + \left(\frac{\partial u}{\partial T}\right)_v dT$$

The Joule-Thomson experiments show that for an ideal gas

$$\left(\frac{\partial u}{\partial v}\right)_T = 0$$

and therefore the intrinsic energy depends only on temperature.   By definition, the constant volume specific heat is

$$c_v \equiv \left(\frac{\partial u}{\partial T}\right)_v = \left(\frac{\partial u}{\partial T}\right)_p \tag{3}$$

so that a change in intrinsic energy is given by:

$$\Delta u = \int_{T_1}^{T_2} c_v \, dT \tag{4}$$

Because c_v is defined in terms of characteristics u and T, it is itself a characteristic of the gas.   For temperatures less than $1000°$ R, c_v for air is practically constant and has the value

$$c_v = 4285 \text{ ft-lb/slug}° \text{ R}$$

For the very high temperatures encountered in hypersonic flight, c_v can

---

* The notation $\left\{\dfrac{\partial u}{\partial v}\right\}_T$ indicates that u has been differentiated with respect to v while holding T constant.   Note that if the subscript T had been omitted, the notation would not specifically indicate that the quantity being differentiated is an explicit function of v and T.

rise to several times the value indicated above. Unless stated otherwise, c_v in this text will be treated as a constant

3. ENTHALPY AND CONSTANT PRESSURE SPECIFIC HEAT. The enthalpy h is a characteristic defined as

$$h = pv + u \tag{5}$$

Also by definition, the constant pressure specific heat is

$$c_p \equiv \left(\frac{\partial h}{\partial T}\right)_p = \left(\frac{\partial h}{\partial T}\right)_v \tag{6}$$

The last equality follows from the Joule-Thomson law above. Equations 2, 4, and 5 show the enthalpy to be a function only of temperature. Therefore

$$dh = \left\{\frac{\partial h}{\partial T}\right\}_p dT = \left\{\frac{\partial h}{\partial T}\right\}_v dT$$

so that a change in enthalpy is given by

$$\Delta h = \int_{T_1}^{T_2} c_p \, dT \tag{7}$$

c_p is a characteristic of the gas because it is defined in terms of the characteristics h and T. For temperatures less than $1000°$ R, c_p for air is practically constant and has the value

$$c_p = 6000 \text{ ft-lb/slug}° \text{ R}$$

The comments made about c_v concerning its variation with temperature also apply to c_p.

It should be noted that an absolute value of intrinsic energy u is not defined, and therefore it is appropriate to speak only of changes in intrinsic energy as indicated in Eq. 4. Because h is defined in terms of u, an absolute value of h does not exist either.

4. RELATION BETWEEN THE GAS CONSTANT AND THE SPECIFIC HEATS. From the definition of enthalpy, Eq. 5

$$\frac{dh}{dT} = p\frac{dv}{dT} + v\frac{dp}{dT} + \frac{du}{dT}$$

$$\left\{\frac{dh}{dT}\right\}_p = p\left\{\frac{dv}{dT}\right\}_p + \left\{\frac{du}{dT}\right\}_p$$

Using Eqs. 6, 2, and 3 in the above,

$$c_p = R + c_v \tag{8}$$

5. RATIO OF SPECIFIC HEATS.   The specific heat ratio

$$\gamma = \frac{c_p}{c_v} \qquad (9)$$

occurs frequently in compressible flow theory.   For air, at 520° R

$$\gamma = 1.4$$

γ is close to this value for temperatures under 1000° R.   As the temperature rises γ decreases towards unity.   In this text γ will be assumed equal to 1.4 unless stated otherwise.

8.3   FIRST LAW OF THERMODYNAMICS

The principle of conservation of energy, like that of momentum stated in Section 3.3, applies to a group of particles of fixed identity. In thermodynamic terminology, the group of particles of fixed identity is called a system and everything outside the group of particles is called the surroundings of the system.   The first law of thermodynamics stems from the fundamental experiments of Joule which demonstrated that heat and work are entities of the same kind.   If a system goes through a succession of states such that the initial and final states are the same, then the net heat transferred across the boundary is equal to the net work transferred across the boundary.   Adopting the standard convention that work transferred out of the system and heat transferred into the system are positive, the first law may be formulated:

$$\oint (\delta q - \delta w) = 0 \qquad (10)$$

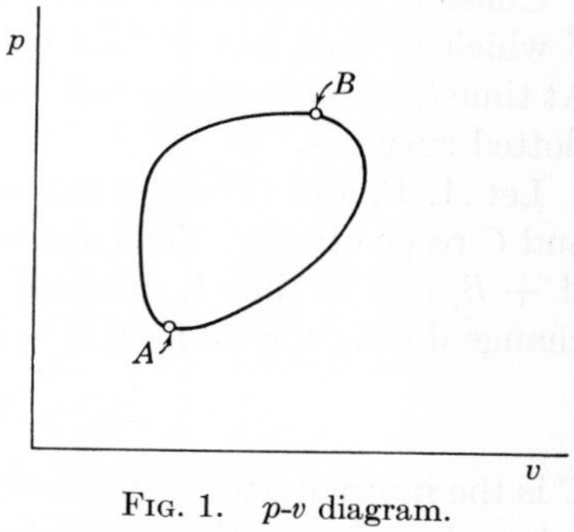

where the line integral represents a succession of state changes in which the initial and final states are identical, and δq and δw represent increments in the quantities.   As indicated in Section 8.2, the state of an ideal gas is completely determined by the two variables p and v.   Therefore, Eq. 10 applies to a succession of states represented by the locus of points from A to B to A in the p-v diagram of Fig. 1.

FIG. 1. p-v diagram.

Because by the first law the line integral around a closed path is zero, the line integral of $\delta q - \delta w$ between any two states A and B depends only on A and B and therefore a new gas characteristic e is defined.*

$$\Delta e = e_B - e_A = \int_A^B (\delta q - \delta w) \qquad (11)$$

e is called the internal energy of the gas. The absolute value of e is not defined but the difference in internal energy Δe between any two states A and B can be found by measuring the net heat and work transfers across the boundaries of the system as the system changes from state A to state B by any path whatever.

The rate of increase of energy within the elementary volume ΔR enclosed by the surface ΔS may be written

$$\frac{d}{dt}(\rho e)\,\Delta R = \left[\frac{\delta}{\delta t}(\rho q) - \frac{\delta}{\delta t}(\rho w)\right]\Delta R = \left[\frac{\delta q'}{\delta t} - \frac{\delta w'}{\delta t}\right]\Delta S \qquad (12)$$

where q' and w' are defined, respectively, as the heat and work transfer per unit area in ft lbs/ft^2. Applied to the volume $\hat{R}_1$ enclosed by the surface $\hat{S}_1$ Eq. 12 becomes

$$\frac{d}{dt}\iiint_{\hat{R}_1} \rho e\, d\hat{R}_1 = \frac{\delta}{\delta t}\iint_{\hat{S}_1} (q' - w')\, d\hat{S}_1 \qquad (13)$$

where $\hat{R}_1$ comprises particles of fixed identity, independent of the time.

The conversion to field representation of the conservation of energy principle follows the procedure used in Section 3.3 in which the same conversion was made of the conservation of momentum principle.

Consider the control surface $\hat{S}$ in Fig. 2. At time t, the control surface $\hat{S}$ which is fixed in the fluid contains a definite set of fluid particles. At time t_1, these particles will have moved to the region enclosed by the dotted curve $\hat{S}_1$.

Let A, B, and C be the internal energy of the fluid in regions A, B, and C respectively. Then at time t, the particles have internal energy $A + B_t$ and at time t_1, internal energy $B_{t_1} + C$. The internal energy change during the interval $t_1 - t$ is:

$$(B_{t_1} - B_t) + (C - A) \qquad (14)$$

C is the internal energy of the fluid that has passed out of $\hat{S}$ during the interval, and A is the internal energy of the fluid that has entered $\hat{S}$

---

* The mathematical argument has been elaborated in connection with the derivation of the velocity potential in Section 2.11.

† The notation $\dfrac{d}{dt}$ is to be interpreted as a derivative in the ordinary sense.

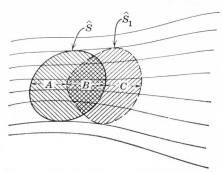

FIG. 2.   Conversion to field representation.

during the interval.   The time rate of change of internal energy is given
by the limit of expression 14 as $t_1 \to t$

$$\lim_{t_1 \to t} \left(\frac{B_{t_1} - B_t}{t_1 - t} + \frac{C - A}{t_1 - t} \right) \tag{15}$$

In the limit as $t_1 \to t$, $\hat{S}_1$ coincides with $\hat{S}$ and the first term in expression 15 becomes the time rate of change of internal energy of the fluid in region $\hat{R}$ enclosed by $\hat{S}$.   This is written as the integral

$$\frac{\partial}{\partial t} \iiint_{\hat{R}} e\rho \, d\hat{R}$$

The second term in expression 15 is the energy flux through $\hat{S}$, outward being counted positive.   In integral form, the second term is written

$$\iint_{\hat{S}} e\rho V_n \, d\hat{S}$$

The conservation of energy principle Eq. 13 is finally written

$$\frac{\partial}{\partial t} \iiint_{\hat{R}} e\rho \, d\hat{R} = - \iint_{\hat{S}} e\rho V_n \, d\hat{S} + \frac{\delta}{\delta t} \iint_{\hat{S}} (q' - w') \, d\hat{S} \tag{16}$$

All terms in the above equation are field properties.   The heat transfer term can be written in terms of the temperature gradient at the surface and the work transfer term in terms of general surface stresses.   Equation 16 can then be reduced to a differential equation relating field properties at each point in the fluid.   This analysis has been carried out in Appendix B, Section 6.

In the next section, a useful form of Eq. 16 is derived for a special case.

8.4 STEADY FLOW ENERGY EQUATION

For steady flow, the conservation of energy principle, Eq. 16, applied to a fixed control volume is

$$\iint_{\hat{S}} e\rho V_n \, d\hat{S} = \frac{\delta}{\delta t} \iint_{\hat{S}} q' \, d\hat{S} - \frac{\delta}{\delta t} \iint_{\hat{S}} w' \, d\hat{S} \qquad (17)$$

The net energy flux out of the fixed control volume $\hat{R}$ shown in Fig. 3 is equal to the rate of heat transfer into the control volume minus the

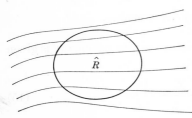

rate of work transfer out of the control volume. The terms of Eq. 17 are interpreted below.

1. INTERNAL ENERGY FLUX. In the flow processes treated in this text internal energy is stored in the gas by thermodynamic and mechanical means. Associated with the thermodynamic state of the gas is an intrinsic energy u as described

FIG. 3.   Control volume.

in Section 8.2.   For our purposes we may consider the intrinsic energy to be stored in the random molecular motion and other microscopic properties of the gas.   From Eq. 4, assuming c_v constant

$$u = c_v T + u_0 \qquad (18)$$

The constant u_0 is added because the zero level of intrinsic energy is undefined.

The mechanical storage consists of kinetic energy of the ordered motion $V^2/2$ and potential energy $+gz$ arising from the position of the system within the gravitational field.   The total internal energy is

$$e = c_v T + u_0 + \frac{V^2}{2} + gz \qquad (19)$$

The value of e given by Eq. 19 is substituted into the left side of Eq. 17 and integrated around the closed contour $\hat{S}$.   The constant u_0 can make no contribution to the integral, and in the problems we are concerned with $+gz$ changes so slightly over the contour $\hat{S}$ that its contribution is essentially zero.   The left-hand side of Eq. 17 becomes:

$$\iint_{\hat{S}} \left(\frac{V^2}{2} + c_v T \right) \rho V_n \, d\hat{S} \qquad (20)$$

2. RATE OF HEAT TRANSFER. If a temperature gradient exists across the control surface there will be a rate of heat transfer that is easily expressed in integral form. This has been done in Appendix B, Section 6. Heat may also be transferred to the control volume at a specific rate by a combustion process. In this chapter the total rate of heat addition to the fluid inside the control surface will be designated $M\dot{q}$ where M is the mass within the control volume and q is the heat transferred per unit mass.

The thermal conductivity of air is small and unless temperature gradients are large, the heat transfer can frequently be considered negligible. This circumstance arises when the control surface lies outside regions of viscous dissipation like the boundary layer of bodies or shock waves.* If the rate of heat transfer across the control surface is zero, the flow is *adiabatic*.

3. WORK RATE. Pressure and shearing stresses at the control surface boundary lead to a work rate that has been developed in detail in Appendix B. There may also be a work rate through the control surface if a propeller, turbine, or other device is present. Work of this nature will be called machine work w_m and the work rate is given the symbol $M\dot{w}_m$.

In many applications involving viscous dissipation it is possible to choose the control surface in such a way that the surface shearing stresses can be neglected. This leads to a great simplification in formulating the work rate due to surface stresses. Under these conditions, the surface stress is entirely pressure and the work rate for an increment of surface $d\hat{S}$ is $pV_n\,d\hat{S}$, or for the entire control surface

$$\iint_{\hat{S}} \frac{p}{\rho} \rho V_n \, d\hat{S} \tag{21}$$

The steady flow energy equation applied to a fixed control volume is written by substituting expressions 20 and 21 and $\dot{Q}$ and $\dot{W}_m$ in Eq. 17.

$$\iint_{\hat{S}} \left(\frac{V^2}{2} + c_v T + \frac{p}{\rho} \right) \rho V_n \, d\hat{S} = \dot{Q} - \dot{W}_m \tag{22}$$

$\dot{Q}$ and $\dot{W}_m$ represent rates of heat and work transfer respectively.

It is understood that the control surface must be chosen in such a way that the surface shearing stresses may be neglected. Using the equation of state $p/\rho = RT$ and the relation $c_v + R = c_p$, the energy equation can be simplified further to read

$$\iint_{\hat{S}} \left(\frac{V^2}{2} + c_p T \right) \rho V_n \, d\hat{S} = \dot{Q} - \dot{W}_m \tag{23}$$

* See Section 1.5.

Three applications of Eq. 23 are given below.

Illustrative Example 1

A turbo machine is indicated schematically in Fig. 4. Air enters the machine at 520° R with a speed of 500 ft/sec. The enthalpy drop across the machine is 60,000 ft-lb/slug and the exhaust velocity is 1000 ft/sec. Heat is added at the rate of 0.5×10^6 ft-lb/slug of air. How much work per slug of air passing through the machine is delivered to the compressor?

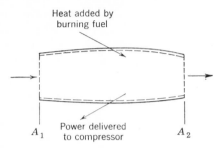

FIG. 4. Application of energy equation to a flow with heat and work transfer.

Solution. Choose a control surface indicated by the dotted line in Fig. 4 and assume the exit and entrance conditions are steady and uniform over the areas A_1 and A_2 respectively. Equation 23 for this case may be written:

$$\left(\frac{V^2}{2} + c_pT\right)_2 (\rho VA)_2 - \left(\frac{V^2}{2} + c_pT\right)_1 (\rho VA)_1 = \dot{Q} - \dot{W}_m$$

From conservation of mass the flux into the machine $(\rho VA)_1$ is equal to the mass flux out $(\rho VA)_2$. Dividing through by the mass flux and rearranging:

$$\frac{\dot{W}_m}{\rho VA} = \frac{\dot{Q}}{\rho VA} + \left(\frac{V_1^2}{2} - \frac{V_2^2}{2}\right) + c_p(T_1 - T_2)$$

The left-hand side of the equation is the work per unit mass.

$$\text{work per unit mass} = 0.5 \times 10^6 + \frac{500^2}{2} - \frac{1000^2}{2} + 60,000$$

$$= 185,000 \text{ ft-lb/slug}$$

Illustrative Example 2

The shock wave at the nose of the wedge shown in Fig. 5 is a region in which viscous dissipation results in a change of flow properties. If the wedge is traveling through sea level air at a speed of 2000 ft/sec, and the temperature of the air behind the shock is 705° R, what is the speed of the air behind the shock measured relative to the shock?

Solution. Let the axis of reference be attached to the wedge. Then sea level air appears to approach the shock at a uniform steady velocity of 2000 ft/sec. Choose a control surface whose lateral sides coincide with streamlines,

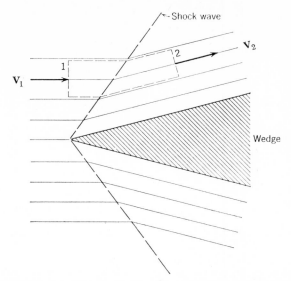

FIG. 5.   Application of energy equation to a flow in which viscous dissipation occurs.

as shown in Fig. 5.   Assuming viscosity effects to be small everywhere except at the shock itself, there will be no heat conducted across the control surface and Eq. 23 may be written

$$\left(\frac{V^2}{2} + c_p T\right)_1 (\rho V A)_1 = \left(\frac{V^2}{2} + c_p T\right)_2 (\rho V A)_2$$

Using the conservation of mass principle and rearranging:

$$\frac{V_2{}^2}{2} = c_p(T_1 - T_2) + \frac{V_1{}^2}{2}$$

or, after substituting in the numbers

$$V_2 = 1330 \text{ ft/sec}$$

where V_2 is an average value across A_2.   Because of the two-dimensional nature of the problem, V_2 has the same value no matter where the control surface is chosen.   Therefore, it is correct to identify V_1 as the velocity upstream of the shock and V_2 the velocity downstream of the shock.

An essential feature of the application of Eq. 23 illustrated above is the fact that viscous dissipation within the control volume is permissible.   It is only required that shearing stresses and heat transfer across the control surface be zero.   Within the boundary layer, where viscous dissipation is general, a control surface that satisfies these requirements cannot be drawn.   On the other hand, in flows containing isolated regions of viscous dissipation, a control surface approximately satisfying the above requirements is easily drawn.

Illustrative Example 3

As a final example of the application of Eq. 23, consider a flow in which viscous dissipation and heat conduction are everywhere zero. Such a flow is approximated by the region outside the boundary layer of a body moving through air at constant speed, as shown in Fig. 6. The control surface in the

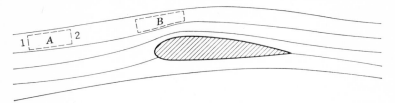

FIG. 6.   Application of energy equation to reversible flow.

figure has equal values of $c_p T + V^2/2$ over faces 1 and 2. Because the control surface could have been drawn anywhere on the stream tube, for example at B, it follows that $c_p T + V^2/2$ *has the same value at every point on the stream tube, or in the limit, on a streamline.* This result could have been obtained in a mathematical fashion by applying the divergence theorem to Eq. 23.

Next, the question of variation of $c_p T + V^2/2$ from streamline to streamline can be settled by observing that the flow at infinity has uniform temperature and speed. Therefore, the sum must have the same value for each streamline at infinity. Since there can be no variation along streamlines, it follows that

$$c_p T + \frac{V^2}{2} = \text{constant} \tag{24}$$

is satisfied *at every point in the flow.*

Flows in which the viscous dissipation and heat conduction are everywhere zero are in the category of *reversible* processes, described in the next section.

8.5   REVERSIBILITY

Let a system of particles of fixed identity exchange energy with its surroundings. If the process can be reversed so that the system of particles and its surroundings are restored in all respects to their initial conditions, the exchange process is said to be reversible.

For example, consider the process shown schematically in Fig. 7. Let heat flow from surroundings A to system B. As a consequence,

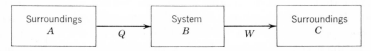

FIG. 7.   Schematic diagram of thermodynamic system and surroundings.

system B does work on surroundings C. If the work can be recovered from C to pump the heat back from B to A in such a manner that A, B, and C all return to their original conditions, the process is reversible.

The possibility of devising a process of the type outlined above cannot be settled by a theoretical proof. It is a fact of experience that a reversible process *has never been devised*, and this empirical observation is embodied in the second law of thermodynamics which is stated in Section 8.6.

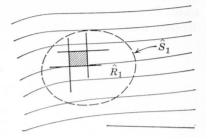

All fluid flow processes are irreversible as a result of viscosity effects and heat conduction. For example, consider the system of particles of fixed identity contained in the control volume $\hat{R}_1$ of Fig. 8.

FIG. 8.   Control volume.

Viscous dissipation resulting from shearing stresses at the surface and heat conduction through the surface $\hat{S}_1$ are responsible for the fact that the system and surrounding flow can never, after an ellapsed interval, return to their original conditions. This is true no matter how small the volume $\hat{R}_1$. Therefore, it is true for every vanishingly small subsystem within $\hat{R}_1$. Then it may be said, if there are any viscosity or heat transfer effects *within or on* the surface $\hat{S}_1$, the system will undergo an irreversible change of state.

If the control surface of Fig. 8 lies outside the boundary layer and contains no shock wave the requirement for reversibility is very nearly met. Under these conditions, special relations exist among the thermodynamic variables p, ρ, and T that are useful in the following chapters. They may be derived from the momentum and energy equations in the following manner:

The energy equation (24) is satisfied at every point in an adiabatic reversible flow. Therefore, its differential form may be written

$$c_p \, dT + V \, dV = 0 \tag{25}$$

The first term is the differential of the enthalpy which may be written from Eqs. 5 and 4 as

$$c_p \, dT = p \, dv + v \, dp + c_v \, dT \tag{26}$$

Equations 25 and 26 give the result

$$p \, dv + c_v \, dT + \frac{dp}{\rho} + d\frac{V^2}{2} = 0 \tag{27}$$

The differential form of the equilibrium equation for a nonviscous fluid (gravity neglected) is given by Eq. 11 of Chapter 7.

$$d\frac{V^2}{2} + \frac{dp}{\rho} = 0$$

Therefore, the sum of the first two terms of Eq. 27 are independently zero. Replacing p with its equivalent from the equation of state and dividing through by T leads to

$$R\frac{dv}{v} + c_v\frac{dT}{T} = 0$$

$$d\log v^R T^{c_v} = 0$$

$$\frac{T^{c_v}}{\rho^R} = \text{constant} \tag{28}$$

Using Eqs. 8 and 9, which relate the gas constant to the specific heats, the following relations may be deduced from Eq. 28.

$$\left.\begin{aligned} \frac{T}{\rho^{\gamma-1}} &= C \\[2ex] \frac{p}{\rho^{\gamma}} &= C_1 \\[2ex] \frac{T}{p^{(\gamma-1)/\gamma}} &= C_2 \end{aligned}\right\} \tag{29}$$

Equations 29 hold for adiabatic reversible flows.

8.6 SECOND LAW OF THERMODYNAMICS

The irreversibility of real fluid flow processes suggests that there are limitations on the direction in which energy exchanges can take place. The second law of thermodynamics defines the direction in which a state change can occur, and when formulated in terms of *entropy* it provides a quantitative measure of the degree of irreversibility.

Consider a system of particles of fixed identity enclosed by the surface $\hat{S}_1$. According to the first law

$$\delta q = de + \delta w \tag{30}$$

Internal energy depends on the state of the gas, but the heat and work transfers are not characteristics of the gas. If the equation is divided by the temperature we shall show that, under specialized circumstances, the ratio $\delta q/T$ is the differential of a quantity that depends only on the state of the gas. This quantity is called the *entropy*. The statement may be demonstrated by considering the system of fluid particles within the surface $\hat{S}_1$ along the stream tube shown in Fig. 9. The work transfer across the surface arises in general from machine work, w_m, and the work done by the surface pressure and shearing stresses. We assume w_m to be zero and the fluid to be nonviscous, so that only normal stresses exist at the surface. The work of the normal stresses can be written in simple form. The pressures on the lateral faces are normal to the flow direction and therefore do no work. At face 2, the pressure stress is in the direction of the displacement and

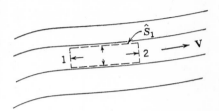

FIG. 9.   Control surface.

therefore positive work is done at the rate $p_2 A_2 V_2$ (work/sec). The flow rate at face 2 is $\rho_2 V_2 A_2$ (mass/sec). Therefore the work per unit mass at face 2 is $+p_2/\rho_2$. Similarly, the work per unit mass at face 1 of the boundary is $-p_1/\rho_1$. For the entire boundary, the work transfer at the surface is the sum of these two terms, which in the limit for small amounts of work is written

$$\delta w = \frac{p_2}{\rho_2} - \frac{p_1}{\rho_1} = d\frac{p}{\rho} \qquad (31)$$

The differential of internal energy is written from Eq. 19 (gravity neglected)

$$de = c_v \, dT + d\frac{V^2}{2} \qquad (32)$$

Substituting Eqs. 31 and 32 into 30 and dividing through by T yields

$$\frac{\delta q}{T} = \frac{1}{T}\left(d\frac{V^2}{2} + \frac{dp}{\rho}\right) + c_v \frac{dT}{T} - \frac{p}{\rho T}\frac{d\rho}{\rho}$$

The term in the parenthesis must vanish in a nonviscous fluid if equilibrium is satisfied and the remainder can be written

$$\frac{\delta q}{T} = d[\log T^{c_v} - \log \rho^R] \qquad (33)$$

Thus $\delta q/T$ becomes an exact differential of the thermodynamic variables T and ρ.

The assumption that allowed the work term to be written in differential form was precisely the assumption of reversibility. Therefore

$\delta q/T$ is an exact differential of state variables *only* if the flow is reversible. Under these conditions, $\delta q/T$ is defined as the differential of the entropy.

$$dS = \left(\frac{\delta q}{T}\right)_{\text{reversible}}$$

$$S_2 - S_1 = \oint_1^2 \left(\frac{\delta q}{T}\right)_{\text{reversible}} \tag{34}$$

Like internal energy, the entropy has no absolute base, and therefore we can give values only to entropy changes unless an arbitrary base is assigned.

From Eqs. 33 and 34, the change in entropy ΔS between states 1 and 2 is

$$\Delta S = \oint_1^2 \left\{\frac{\delta q}{T}\right\}_{\text{reversible}} = \log\left(\frac{T_2}{T_1}\right)^{c_v}\left(\frac{\rho_1}{\rho_2}\right)^R \tag{35}$$

The second law of thermodynamics is a completely independent physical principle and is one of the empirical laws on which aerodynamics is based. It may be stated in terms of entropy change in the following fashion:

$$\Delta S - \oint_1^2 \frac{\delta q}{T} \geq 0 \tag{36}$$

Let a system of particles at state 1 exchange energy with its surroundings and pass into state 2. From the initial and final states, ΔS can be computed using Eq. 35. Its value will always be equal to or greater than $\oint_1^2 \delta q/T$. The equal sign corresponds to a reversible process.

For adiabatic processes, the entropy rule reduces to

$$\Delta S \geq 0 \tag{37}$$

If the process is adiabatic and reversible

$$\Delta S = 0 \tag{38}$$

Such processes are called *isentropic*.

8.7 BERNOULLI'S EQUATION FOR ISENTROPIC COMPRESSIBLE FLOW

At each point in an isentropic flow, the energy relation given by Eq. 24 must be satisfied.

$$c_p T + \frac{V^2}{2} = c_p T_1 + \frac{V_1^2}{2} \tag{39}$$

Station 1 is a position at which all flow properties are assumed known.
From the last of Eqs. (29)

$$\frac{T}{p^{(\gamma-1)/\gamma}} = \frac{T_1}{p_1^{(\gamma-1)/\gamma}} \qquad (40)$$

Substituting Eq. 40 in Eq. 39 and replacing T_1 with $p_1/\rho_1 R$ from the
equation of state:

$$\left(\frac{c_p}{R}\frac{p_1^{1/\gamma}}{\rho_1}\right) p^{(\gamma-1)/\gamma} + \frac{V^2}{2} = \frac{c_p}{R}\frac{p_1}{\rho_1} + \frac{V_1^2}{2}$$

Finally, from Eqs. 8 and 9

$$\frac{c_p}{R} = \frac{c_p}{c_p - c_v} = \frac{\gamma}{\gamma - 1} \qquad (41)$$

and the energy equation in terms of p and V becomes:

$$\left(\frac{\gamma}{\gamma - 1}\frac{p_1^{1/\gamma}}{\rho_1}\right) p^{(\gamma-1)/\gamma} + \frac{V^2}{2} = \frac{\gamma}{\gamma - 1}\frac{p_1}{\rho_1} + \frac{V_1^2}{2} \qquad (42)$$

Equation 42 is called Bernoulli's equation for compressible flow, and,
unlike its incompressible counterpart, it cannot be deduced from the
conservation of momentum principle.* It can be obtained by integrating the differential form of the momentum equation *provided* we use
the relation between p and ρ given by the second of Eqs. 29:

$$\frac{p}{\rho^\gamma} = \frac{p_1}{\rho_1^\gamma} \qquad (43)$$

But Eq. 43 was derived from the first law of thermodynamics. Therefore, its use in integrating the momentum equation makes the result a
consequence of the first law. The derivation is carried out starting with
Eq. 11 of Chapter 7, gravity omitted.

$$d\frac{V^2}{2} + \frac{dp}{\rho} = 0 \qquad (44)$$

Using Eq. 43,

$$\int \frac{dp}{\rho} = \left(\frac{\gamma}{\gamma - 1}\frac{p_1^{1/\gamma}}{\rho_1}\right) p^{(\gamma-1)/\gamma} \qquad (45)$$

* It will be recalled that Eq. 39 is valid for adiabatic flows whereas Eq. 42 has
the additional restriction of isentropy. For this reason, Eq. 39 is frequently referred
to as the strong form of the energy equation and Eq. 42 as the weak form.

Substituting Eq. 45 in Eq. 44 and integrating

$$\frac{V^2}{2} + \left(\frac{\gamma}{\gamma - 1} \frac{p_1^{1/\gamma}}{\rho_1}\right) p^{(\gamma-1)/\gamma} = \text{constant}$$

Evaluating the constant from the known conditions at station 1

$$\frac{V^2}{2} + \left(\frac{\gamma}{\gamma - 1} \frac{p_1^{1/\gamma}}{\rho_1}\right) p^{(\gamma-1)/\gamma} = \frac{V_1^2}{2} + \frac{\gamma}{\gamma - 1} \frac{p_1}{\rho_1} \qquad (46)$$

Equations 46 and 42 are identical.

8.8 STATIC AND STAGNATION VALUES

The pressure, density, and temperature of a gas at rest were discussed in Section 2 of Chapter 1. The same interpretation of these properties applies to a gas in motion providing the measuring instrument moves with the gas. For example, in Eq. 39, in order to measure T the thermometer must move with the speed $\mathbf{V}$. Relative to the thermometer, the gas is at rest and the temperature recorded will be the stream or *static* value. The same argument applies to the pressure in Eq. 42. Whenever the terms temperature, pressure or density are used without a modifying adjective, the *static* value is implied.

To arrive at the meaning of *stagnation* value, we must visualize a hypothetical flow in which the ordered velocity is reduced to zero isentropically. The position of zero ordered velocity is called a stagnation point and the values of the gas characteristics at a stagnation point are called *stagnation* values. Stagnation values will be given a subscript or superscript (0). If station 1 in Eqs. 39 and 42 is a stagnation point, then the two equations would be written:

$$c_p T + \frac{V^2}{2} = c_p T_0 \qquad (47)$$

$$\left(\frac{\gamma}{\gamma - 1} \frac{p_0}{\rho_0}\right)\left(\frac{p}{p_0}\right)^{(\gamma-1)/\gamma} + \frac{V^2}{2} = \frac{\gamma}{\gamma - 1} \frac{p_0}{\rho_0} \qquad (48)$$

The stagnation pressure, density, and temperature in an isentropic flow have the same values at every point in the flow. In a nonisentropic flow, the stagnation values vary from point to point.

The restriction of isentropy for constant *stagnation temperature* T_0 may be lightened from the following consideration. Equation 39 applies to adiabatic flows with viscous dissipation provided T, $\mathbf{V}$, T_1, and $\mathbf{V}_1$ are interpreted as average values over a properly constructed control surface, as explained in Section 8.4. Therefore, it follows that Eq.

47 applies to adiabatic irreversible flows with the terms interpreted as averages.

Illustrative Example 4

Find the stagnation temperature, pressure, and density at every point in the flow of Illustrative Example 2. Assume an entropy rise across the shock of 156 ft-lb/slug ° R.

Solution. Only two points need to be considered because the entropy, and therefore the stagnation values, change only across the shock. Upstream of the shock:

$$V_1 = 2000 \text{ ft/sec}$$

$$p_1 = 2116 \text{ lb/ft}^2$$

$$\rho_1 = 0.002378 \text{ slugs/ft}^3$$

$$T_1 = 520° \text{ R}$$

From Eq. 47: * $T_1{}^0 = T_1 + \dfrac{V_1{}^2}{2c_p} = 853° \text{ R}$

From Eq. 29: $\dfrac{T_1}{\rho_1{}^{\gamma-1}} = \dfrac{T_1{}^0}{(\rho_1{}^0)^{\gamma-1}}$

$$\rho_1{}^0 = \rho_1 \left(\frac{T_1{}^0}{T_1}\right)^{1/(\gamma-1)} = 0.0082$$

$$p_1{}^0 = \rho_1{}^0 R T_1{}^0 = 12,000 \text{ lb/ft}^2$$

Downstream of the shock:

$$T_2 = 705° \text{ R}$$

$$T_2{}^0 = T_1{}^0 = 853° \text{ R}$$

$$\Delta S = 156 \text{ ft-lb/slug ° R}$$

From Eq. 35: $\rho_2 = \rho_1 \left(\dfrac{T_2}{T_1}\right)^{c_v/R} \dfrac{1}{\exp \dfrac{\Delta S}{R}} = 0.00463 \text{ slugs/ft}^3$

From Eq. 29: $\rho_2{}^0 = \rho_2 \left(\dfrac{T_2{}^0}{T_2}\right)^{1/(\gamma-1)} = 0.00745 \text{ slugs/ft}^3$

From Eq. 2: $p_2{}^0 = \rho_2{}^0 R T_2{}^0 = 10,900 \text{ lb/ft}^2$

---

* When subscripts are used to denote positions in the fluid, the symbol 0 indicating stagnation value is appended as a superscript.

Some Applications
of One-Dimensional
Compressible Flow

CHAPTER 9

9.1 INTRODUCTION

In one-dimensional flow theory the ordered velocity is assumed to be unidirectional, and the equations that describe the flow may be written as though the flow consists of one component only. As a result, the theory is simplified greatly and it is possible to deduce relatively simple relations that expose the fundamental nature of compressible flow.

Many important flow phenomena approximate one-dimensional flow sufficiently closely to make the theory developed here applicable. In the first two sections the speed of sound is defined and the isentropic flow parameters are expressed in terms of Mach number. Application is made to the basic one-dimensional flow represented by the Laval Nozzle in Section 9.6. The last two sections deal with the influence of friction and heat addition in one-dimensional flows.

9.2 SPEED OF SOUND

Consider the propagation of a disturbance of infinitesimal proportions through a fluid that is at rest. The geometry of the disturbance, that is, whether it is plane or spherical, does not influence the following argument. It will be shown in Chapter 10 that, because the disturbance is infinitesimal, the compression or expansion of the fluid as the disturbance passes through it is accomplished reversibly. The speed with which such a disturbance travels through a fluid is established by the properties of the fluid. Because a sustained sound is simply a succession of small disturbance of this nature, the speed with which a small disturbance travels is called the speed of sound. In contrast, a large

148

disturbance such as an explosion wave does not compress the fluid reversibly as it passes through the fluid, and the speed of propagation is
very different from that of sound. The speed of propagation of large
disturbances is treated in the next chapter.

The speed with which a spherical sound wave is propagated through a
fluid is the same as that with which a plane sound wave is propagated.
For simplicity, the plane wave is treated. Consider a portion of a plane
wave contained within the cylinder shown in Fig. 1. Let the wave be
traveling to the left with a velocity u, and let it be required to find the
relation between the speed of propagation u and the properties of the
fluid. In order to make the flow steady, attach the axis of reference to
the wave so that the wave is stationary
and the fluid passes through it from left to
right. In the adiabatic isentropic flow
through a tube of constant cross section, a
continuous change in the properties of the
fluid does not occur because nothing about

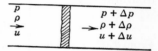

Fig. 1.   Plane wave in a tube.

the system will promote such a change. However, a discontinuity in
the flow properties may be premised; the mechanism by which a discontinuity develops is discussed in the next chapter. The point of view
is taken that the wave is a region at which discontinuities in the flow
properties occur. Upstream of the wave, the fluid velocity, pressure,
and density have the constant values u, p, and ρ, respectively. Downstream of the wave the properties are also constant and equal to
$u + \Delta u$, $p + \Delta p$, and $\rho + \Delta \rho$. The properties upstream and downstream of the wave are related by the equations of continuity and
momentum which, when applied to the example illustrated in Fig. 1,
become

$$\rho u = (\rho + \Delta\rho)(u + \Delta u)$$
$$p - (p + \Delta p) = (\rho + \Delta\rho)(u + \Delta u)^2 - \rho u^2 \tag{1}$$

Upon expanding, and using the *continuity* relation in the *momentum*
equation, Eqs. 1 become

$$\frac{\Delta u}{u} = -\frac{\Delta\rho}{\rho} - \frac{\Delta\rho\,\Delta u}{\rho u}$$

$$u\,\Delta u = -\frac{\Delta p}{\rho}$$

If the second of the above equations is divided by the first, there
results

$$u^2 = \frac{-\Delta p}{-\Delta\rho - \Delta\rho(\Delta u/u)} \tag{2}$$

For very small discontinuities, u^2 approaches the value of the ratio of the change in pressure across the wave to the change in density. In the limit, u becomes the velocity of sound a and we have from Eq. 2

$$a = \sqrt{\frac{dp}{d\rho}} \tag{3}$$

Because the process is isentropic, the density and pressure are related by

$$\frac{p}{\rho^\gamma} = c$$

from which

$$\frac{dp}{d\rho} = \gamma \frac{p}{\rho} \tag{4}$$

From Eqs. 3 and 4,

$$a = \sqrt{\gamma \frac{p}{\rho}} \tag{5}$$

and, by using the equation of state,

$$a = \sqrt{\gamma R T} \quad \text{Isentropic} \tag{6}$$

Equation 6 shows that the speed of sound is a function only of the temperature, that is, of the intrinsic energy of the gas. For air, Eq. 6 becomes

$$a = 49.1 \sqrt{T} \tag{7}$$

where T is in degrees Rankine.

The speed of sound in a flow that is nonisentropic is given by Eqs. 5 and 6. However, Eq. 3 has no meaning because p is not a function of ρ alone.

In the atmosphere, since the temperature decreases with height (up to 35,000 ft altitude) so does the speed of sound. Figure 2 is a plot of the temperature and speed of sound with altitude; the data are taken from NACA observations.*

The variation of the speed of sound with velocity in a high speed flow may be seen by using the energy equation developed in the last chapter:

$$c_p T + \frac{V^2}{2} = c_p T_0 \tag{8}$$

---

* William S. Aiken, Jr., *Standard Nomenclature for Air Speeds with Tables and Charts for Use in Calculation of Air Speed*, NACA Report **837**, 1946.

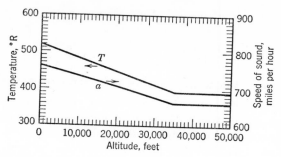

FIG. 2. Temperature and speed of sound versus altitude. (Courtesy of W. S. Aiken, *Standard Nomenclature for Airspeeds with Tables and Charts*, NACA TN 1120.)

After replacing T and T_0 with $a^2/\gamma R$ and $a_0{}^2/\gamma R$ respectively and using the relation

$$\frac{c_p}{\gamma R} = \frac{c_p}{\gamma(c_p - c_v)} = \frac{1}{\gamma - 1}$$

Equation 8 becomes

$$\frac{V^2}{2} + \frac{a^2}{\gamma - 1} = \frac{a_0{}^2}{\gamma - 1} \tag{9}$$

The local speed of sound decreases from a_0 at $V = 0$ to zero at the speed

$$V_m = \sqrt{\frac{2}{\gamma - 1}}\, a_0 \tag{10}$$

V_m is, therefore, the speed that is approached as the temperature approaches absolute zero. A plot of a/a_0 versus V/a_0 for air, where $\gamma = 1.4$, is shown in Fig. 3. Setting $V = a^*$ in Eq. 9, we see that for a speed equal to the speed of sound

$$a^* = \sqrt{\frac{2}{\gamma + 1}}\, a_0 = 0.913 a_0 \tag{11}$$

for air; that is, a^*, which is the speed of sound corresponding to a Mach number of unity, bears a definite relation to a_0. It is often convenient to express the right side

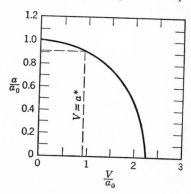

FIG. 3. Variation of speed of sound with velocity.

of Eq. 9 in terms of a^* instead of a_0. Thus

$$\frac{V^2}{2} + \frac{a^2}{\gamma - 1} = \frac{a_0^2}{\gamma - 1} = \frac{\gamma + 1}{2(\gamma - 1)} a^{*2} = \frac{V_m^2}{2} \tag{12}$$

9.3 ISENTROPIC FLOW RELATIONS IN TERMS OF MACH NUMBER

It was stated in Chapter 1 that if pressure changes within a flow are great enough the elasticity of the fluid must be considered, together with the viscosity and the density, as physical properties entering into the derivation of similarity parameters governing the flow. The elasticity is defined as the change in pressure per unit change in specific volume, that is, $\rho \, dp/d\rho$. Hence by the analysis of Section 9.2 the elasticity is given by ρa^2, and so we may take a the speed of sound as a physical property, which along with the density determines the elasticity. The dimensional analysis of Appendix A led to the definition of the Mach number.

$$M = \frac{V}{a} \tag{13}$$

The importance of Mach number in the analysis of compressible flow can be demonstrated by introducing the speed of sound into Bernoulli's equation for isentropic compressible flow developed in Chapter 8. Equation 48 of that chapter may be put in the form

$$\left(\frac{p}{p_0}\right)^{(\gamma-1)/\gamma} = 1 - \frac{\gamma - 1}{2} V^2 \frac{\rho_0}{\gamma p_0} = 1 - \frac{\gamma - 1}{2} \frac{V^2}{a_0^2} \tag{14}$$

where $a_0^2 = \gamma p_0/\rho_0$ is the speed of sound at a stagnation point. To put this equation in terms of the Mach number we multiply and divide the last term by a^2, and since the term a^2/a_0^2 can be written

$$\frac{a^2}{a_0^2} = \frac{T}{T_0} = \frac{p}{p_0} \frac{\rho_0}{\rho} = \left(\frac{p}{p_0}\right)^{(\gamma-1)/\gamma} \tag{15}$$

Equation 14 becomes

$$\frac{p}{p_0} = \left[1 + \frac{\gamma - 1}{2} M^2\right]^{-\gamma/(\gamma-1)} \tag{16}$$

From Eqs. 15 and 16,

$$\frac{\gamma - 1}{2} M^2 + 1 = \frac{a_0^2}{a^2} \tag{17}$$

which becomes, by Eq. 15,

$$\frac{T}{T_0} = \left[1 + \frac{\gamma - 1}{2} M^2\right]^{-1} \tag{18}$$

From Eqs. 16 and 18 and the equation of state,

$$\frac{\rho}{\rho_0} = \frac{p/RT}{p_0/RT_0} = \frac{pT_0}{p_0T} = \left[1 + \frac{\gamma-1}{2}M^2\right]^{-1/(\gamma-1)} \tag{19}$$

From Eqs. 16, 18, and 19 it can be seen that the Mach number uniquely determines the static to stagnation ratios of all the flow parameters. Because these relations were derived from Eq. 14, they hold only for isentropic flows. However, it is readily shown that Eqs. 17 and 18 may be derived from Eq. 47 of Chapter 8 and therefore Eqs. 17 and 18 apply to irreversible adiabatic flows. To show this, we may begin with Eq. 47 of Chapter 8

$$c_pT + \frac{V^2}{2} = c_pT_0 \tag{20}$$

If we employ the relations

$$T = \frac{p}{\rho R}$$

$$\frac{c_p}{R} = \frac{c_p}{c_p - c_v} = \frac{\gamma}{\gamma - 1}$$

Equation 20 becomes

$$\frac{\gamma}{\gamma - 1}\frac{p}{\rho} + \frac{V^2}{2} = \frac{\gamma}{\gamma - 1}\frac{p_0}{\rho_0} \tag{21}$$

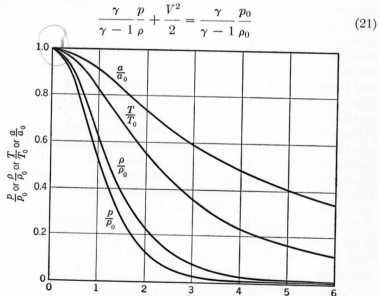

FIG. 4.   Ratio of static to stagnation values of the flow parameters versus Mach number.

After dividing through by a^2 and rearranging,

$$\frac{\gamma - 1}{2} M^2 + 1 = \frac{a_0{}^2}{a^2}$$

which becomes, through the use of Eq. 6,

$$\frac{T}{T_0} = \left(1 + \frac{\gamma - 1}{2} M^2\right)^{-1}$$

Curves of the static to stagnation ratios versus Mach number have been drawn in Fig. 4. The data are tabulated at the end of the book in Table 2 for the subsonic range and Table 3 for the supersonic range.

9.4 MEASUREMENT OF FLIGHT SPEED (SUBSONIC)

The measurement of flight speed at low speeds where Bernoulli's equation for *incompressible* flow is valid is easily achieved by means of a pitot-static tube.

However, as the speed of flight increases, two main difficulties arise: (1) measurement of p and p_0 (as given by the pitot-static tube) now determines, according to Eq. 16, the Mach number instead of the airspeed; (2) the flow interference due to adjacent parts of the aircraft grows rapidly with the Mach number so that the *position error* also increases. If the Mach number is obtained by means of pitot tube measurements of p and p_0, the speed can be computed, if we can obtain the speed of sound. The easiest way to do this is to measure the stagnation temperature T_0 by means of a thermometer. Then, knowing the Mach number, compute the ambient temperature T by Eq. 18. The speed of flight then follows from the formula $V = Ma$.

Since compressibility effects on the aerodynamic characteristics are a function of Mach number, an indispensable instrument for high-speed aircraft is the *machmeter*. Equation 16 is the fundamental equation on which this device operates; p and p_0 are measured by means of a pitot tube, and through complicated linkages the deflection on a dial gage is made proportional to the Mach number.

The above method is applicable only to the measurement of subsonic speeds. At supersonic speeds, a shock wave forms ahead of the pitot tube, and the isentropic formulas derived in the present chapter are not applicable.

9.5 ISENTROPIC ONE-DIMENSIONAL FLOW

In a channel with a small rate of change of cross section or between nearly parallel streamlines, the velocity components normal to the mean flow direction are small compared to the total velocity. As a consequence, the flow may be analyzed as though it were one-dimensional. This means that the flow parameters are constant in planes that are normal to the mean flow direction. In many practical problems, the conditions for one-dimensional flow are very nearly fulfilled.

Simple considerations of the equilibrium and continuity equations for isentropic flow lead to important conclusions regarding the nature of isentropic subsonic and supersonic flows. The flow through the stream-tube of Fig. 5 is such as to obey the continuity equation

$$\rho V A = \text{constant} \qquad (22)$$

as long as the angle between the streamlines is small enough so that we may consider the flow substantially one-dimensional.

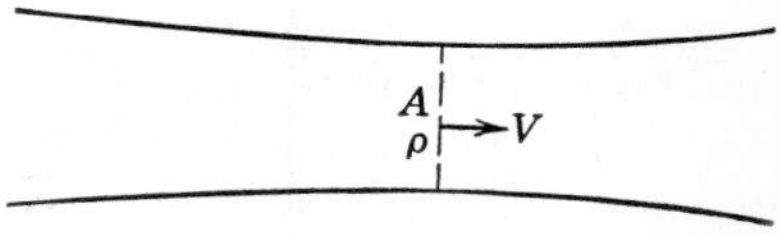

FIG. 5.   Stream tube.

Taking the logarithmic derivative, Eq. 22 becomes

$$\frac{dV}{V} + \frac{d\rho}{\rho} + \frac{dA}{A} = 0 \qquad (23)$$

The differential form of the equilibrium equation, gravity neglected, is given by Eq. 11 of Chapter 7

$$d\frac{V^2}{2} + \frac{dp}{\rho} = 0 \qquad a^2 = \frac{dp}{d\rho}$$

and may be written

$$V \, dV + \frac{d\rho}{\rho} \frac{dp}{d\rho} = V \, dV + a^2 \frac{d\rho}{\rho} = 0$$

By substituting for $d\rho/\rho$ from Eq. 23 we get

$$V \, dV - a^2 \left(\frac{dV}{V} + \frac{dA}{A} \right) = 0$$

and, after dividing through by a^2 and collecting terms,

$$\frac{dV}{V} (M^2 - 1) = \frac{dA}{A}$$

After introducing ds, the element of length along a streamline, the above equation becomes

$$(M^2 - 1) \frac{1}{V} \frac{dV}{ds} = \frac{1}{A} \frac{dA}{ds} \qquad (24)$$

Three cases must be considered. They are:

1. $M < 1$. dV/ds and dA/ds are then opposite in sign. Hence a subsonic flow decelerates $(dV/ds < 0)$ in an expanding channel $(dA/ds > 0)$ and accelerates in a converging channel.

2. $M > 1$. In this case dA/ds and dV/ds have the same sign. Hence a supersonic flow accelerates in an expanding channel and decelerates in a converging channel. Thus the behavior of the supersonic airstream is opposite to that of a subsonic.

3. $M = 1$. In this case $dA/ds = 0$ or $dV/ds = \infty$. The latter equation is ruled out on physical grounds. Then we see that sonic flow is not possible in a converging or expanding channel. We can rule out the large section of a channel (see Fig. 6, station B) by remembering

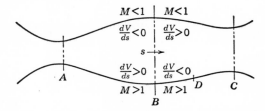

Fig. 6.   Nature of subsonic and supersonic flow in a channel.

that a supersonic flow accelerates and a subsonic flow decelerates in an expanding channel; hence it could never reach sonic speed at the end of a divergence. We conclude, therefore, that the *sonic flow can occur only at a constriction* (throat), such as station A in Fig. 6.

9.6   THE LAVAL NOZZLE

We shall here develop the one-dimensional *Laval nozzle* equations for isentropic flow through channels of varying cross section. They follow simply from the continuity relation Eq. 22 and the relation between V and p/p_0 given by Eq. 14. Let m be the rate of mass flow. Then, from continuity,

$$m = \rho V A = \rho_0 V A \frac{\rho}{\rho_0} = \rho_0 V A \left(\frac{p}{p_0}\right)^{1/\gamma}$$

after substituting for V from Eq. 14

$$\frac{m}{A} = \sqrt{\frac{2\gamma}{\gamma - 1} p_0 \rho_0 \left(\frac{p}{p_0}\right)^{2/\gamma} \left[1 - \left(\frac{p}{p_0}\right)^{(\gamma-1)/\gamma}\right]} \qquad (25)$$

This is known as the St. Venant equation.

It is convenient to write Eq. 25 in terms of the ratio of the area at a point to the *critical area*, A^*, that is, the throat area corresponding to sonic speed for the given mass flow. Introducing $M = 1$ in Eq. 30, the *critical value* of the pressure ratio is   16

$$\left(\frac{p}{p_0}\right)^* = \left(\frac{\gamma + 1}{2}\right)^{-\gamma/(\gamma-1)}$$

Substituting this value in Eq. 25

$$\frac{m}{A^*} = \sqrt{\gamma\left(\frac{2}{\gamma + 1}\right)^{(\gamma+1)/(\gamma-1)} p_0 \rho_0}$$

whence

$$\left(\frac{A}{A^*}\right)^2 = \frac{\gamma - 1}{2} \frac{\left(\dfrac{2}{\gamma + 1}\right)^{(\gamma+1)/(\gamma-1)}}{\left[1 - \left(\dfrac{p}{p_0}\right)^{(\gamma-1)/\gamma}\right]\left(\dfrac{p}{p_0}\right)^{2/\gamma}} \qquad (26)$$

Substituting for p/p_0 in terms of M from Eq. 16,

$$\left(\frac{A}{A^*}\right)^2 = \frac{1}{M^2}\left[\frac{2}{\gamma + 1}\left(1 + \frac{\gamma - 1}{2} M^2\right)\right]^{(\gamma+1)/(\gamma-1)} \qquad (27)$$

These are the fundamental equations connecting pressure ratio and Mach number with area ratio. They are plotted in Fig. 7 and the numerical data are tabulated in Tables 2 and 3 at the end of the book. Several features of these curves will be noted. The curves consist of a subsonic and a supersonic branch, so that A/A^* is double-valued except at $M = 1$ and at

$$\frac{p}{p_0} = \left(\frac{2}{\gamma + 1}\right)^{\gamma/(\gamma-1)} = 0.528$$

(for air). Since isentropic flow must follow these curves, in order to obtain subsonic flow in one part of the channel and supersonic in another, a throat of area A^* must intervene. If a throat of area A^* does not occur in the channel the flow remains supersonic or subsonic throughout.

Downstream of a throat of area A^* the flow can either accelerate supersonically or decelerate subsonically, depending on the pressure ratio at the exit of the channel. This fact is demonstrated by the curves of Fig. 8. Curves 1 and 4 show completely subsonic and completely supersonic flows, respectively; the area does not reach A^* for the mass

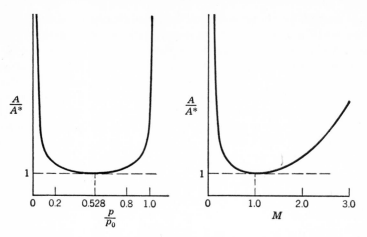

Fig. 7.   Area ratio versus pressure ratio and Mach number.

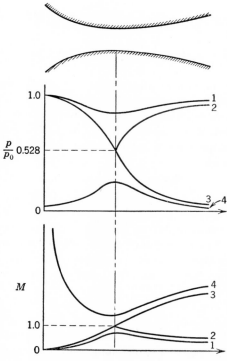

Fig. 8.   Laval nozzle.

flows involved in these cases. For the remaining curve, which branches at the throat into a subsonic and a supersonic branch ending at 2 and 3, respectively, the throat area has the critical value A^*. Curves 1, 2, and 3, are possible flows from a reservoir for the end pressure ratios indicated on the right. For 2 and 3, the maximum speed at the throat is sonic. Flow 4 must have a throat of area A^* somewhere upstream, since otherwise supersonic flow would never have been reached. It is clear that exit pressure ratios in the range between points 2 and 3 cannot be obtained isentropically. It will be shown in the next chapter that these flows involve shock waves.

9.7 ONE-DIMENSIONAL FLOW WITH FRICTION AND HEAT ADDITION

Extensions of the analysis of Section 9.5 lead to an indication of the effects of friction and heat addition on the one-dimensional flow of a compressible fluid. In Fig. 9 is indicated a portion of stream tube in a one-dimensional steady flow. The dotted line represents a fixed control surface on which are acting pressure and shearing stresses as indicated. The shearing stress is assumed to act only on the lateral faces and has an average value τ. The area over which the shear stress acts is f. The pressure stress on the lateral faces is taken to be the average of the pressure stresses on the normal faces. The heat per unit mass added between stations 1 and 2 is q. The equations that determine the flow are:

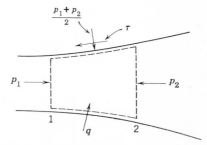

FIG. 9. Stream tube in one-dimensional steady flow.

1. Conservation of Mass

$$\rho_2 V_2 A_2 - \rho_1 V_1 A_1 = 0$$

$$\Delta(\rho V A) = 0$$

2. Conservation of Momentum

$$\rho_2 V_2{}^2 A_2 - \rho_1 V_1{}^2 A_1 = p_1 A_1 - p_2 A_2 - \tau f + \left(\frac{p_1 + p_2}{2}\right)(A_2 - A_1)$$

$$\rho V A \, \Delta V = -\Delta(pA) - \tau f + \frac{p_1 + p_2}{2} \Delta A$$

3. Conservation of Energy

$$\left(c_p T_2 + \frac{V_2{}^2}{2}\right) - \left(c_p T_1 + \frac{V_1{}^2}{2}\right) = q$$

$$\Delta\left(c_p T + \frac{V^2}{2}\right) = q$$

4. Equation of State

$$\frac{p_2}{\rho_2 T_2} = \frac{p_1}{\rho_1 T_1}$$

$$\Delta\left(\frac{p}{\rho T}\right) = 0$$

Ignoring higher order effects, the four equations above may be expanded to read

$$\frac{\Delta\rho}{\rho} = -\frac{\Delta V}{V} - \frac{\Delta A}{A} \tag{28}$$

$$\frac{\Delta p}{\rho} = -V\,\Delta V - \frac{\tau f}{\rho A} \tag{29}$$

$$\frac{\Delta T}{T} = \frac{q}{c_p T} - \frac{V\,\Delta V}{c_p T} \tag{30}$$

$$\frac{\Delta\rho}{\rho} = \frac{\Delta p}{p} - \frac{\Delta T}{T} \tag{31}$$

Equation 29 can be written

$$\frac{p}{\rho}\frac{\Delta p}{p} = -V\,\Delta V - \frac{\tau f}{\rho A}$$

and using the relation $a^2 = \gamma p/\rho$

$$\frac{\Delta p}{p} = -\frac{\gamma}{a^2}V\,\Delta V - \frac{\gamma}{a^2}\frac{\tau f}{\rho A} \tag{32}$$

Equating expressions 28 and 31 and eliminating $\Delta T/T$ and $\Delta p/p$ with Eqs. 30 and 32, respectively, leads to

$$-\frac{\gamma}{a^2}V\,\Delta V - \frac{\gamma}{a^2}\frac{\tau f}{\rho A} - \frac{q}{c_p T} + \frac{V\,\Delta V}{c_p T} = -\frac{\Delta V}{V} - \frac{\Delta A}{A}$$

$$\frac{\Delta V}{V}\left(-\gamma M^2 + 1 + \frac{V^2}{c_p T}\right) = \frac{\gamma}{a^2}\frac{\tau f}{\rho A} + \frac{q}{c_p T} - \frac{\Delta A}{A} \tag{33}$$

Using the relation $T = a^2/\gamma R$ in the left-hand side of Eq. 33 leads to the final result

$$\frac{\Delta V}{V} = \frac{1}{M^2 - 1} \left\{ \frac{\Delta A}{A} - \frac{q}{c_p T} - \frac{\gamma \tau f}{\rho A a^2} \right\}$$ (34)

This equation shows that the convergence of the stream tube ($\Delta A < 0$), friction, and heat addition cause acceleration of a subsonic flow and deceleration of a supersonic flow. Further, in the presence of heat addition or friction, sonic flow is reached in a slightly divergent channel, rather than at the throat.*

The postulation of one-dimensional viscous flow is to a certain extent anomalous, since in channel flow friction acts at the walls and destroys the one-dimensional nature of the flow. No difficulty arises, however, if we assume fully developed flow in the sense that velocity profiles remain similar so that cross components of the velocity do not exist; then each elementary stream tube is subject to the above analysis. Although no direct measurements exist to bear out this assumption, the measurements of Keenan and Neumann † and of Froessel ‡ indicate that departures from one-dimensionality are not of great importance in fully developed high-speed flow through a tube.

9.8 HEAT ADDITION TO A CONSTANT AREA DUCT

Quantitative relations for the flow changes across a frictionless constant area duct resulting from the introduction of heat are of interest in the study of aerothermodynamic powerplants. The subject is treated here because it represents a simple application of the conservation principles applied to one-dimensional diabatic flow.§ The conservation equations set down at the beginning of the last section when specialized to constant area frictionless flow may be written:

$$\rho_1 V_1 = \rho_2 V_2$$ (35)

$$p_1 - p_2 = \rho_2 V_2{}^2 - \rho_1 V_1{}^2$$ (36)

* For the detailed analysis the reader is referred to N. P. Bailey, "The Thermodynamics of Air at High Velocity," *J. Aero. Sci.*, Vol. 11, pp. 227–238, 1944.

† J. H. Keenan and E. Neumann, *Friction in Pipes at Subsonic and Supersonic Velocity*, NACA TN 963, 1945.

‡ W. Froessel, *Flow in Smooth Pipes Above and Below Sound Velocity*, NACA TM 844, 1938.

§ In an actual combustion chamber the cross-sectional areas will vary and frictional effects will not be entirely absent. Also, the introduction of fuel changes the mass flow slightly and the products of combustion will have some effect on the gas constant R. However, all of these effects are small enough to make the results of this analysis applicable as a guide to the behavior of a combustion chamber.

$$c_p T_1 + \frac{V_1{}^2}{2} + q = c_p T_2 + \frac{V_2{}^2}{2} \qquad (37)$$

$$\frac{p_1}{\rho_1 T_1} = \frac{p_2}{\rho_2 T_2} \qquad (38)$$

Stations 1 and 2 in Eqs. 35 through 38 refer to the exit and entrance of the constant area duct shown in Fig. 10.

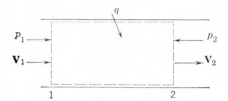

FIG. 10.   Constant area duct.

Eliminating density from Eqs. 35 and 38

$$\frac{p_1}{R T_1} V_1 = \frac{p_2}{R T_2} V_2$$

$$p_1 \frac{M_1}{\sqrt{T_1}} = p_2 \frac{M_2}{\sqrt{T_2}}$$

$$\frac{p_2}{p_1} = \frac{M_1}{M_2} \sqrt{\frac{T_2}{T_1}} \qquad (39)$$

From Eq. 36

$$p_1 - p_2 = \frac{p_2}{R T_2} V_2{}^2 - \frac{p_1}{R T_1} V_1{}^2$$

$$p_1(1 + \gamma M_1{}^2) = p_2(1 + \gamma M_2{}^2)$$

$$\frac{p_2}{p_1} = \frac{1 + \gamma M_1{}^2}{1 + \gamma M_2{}^2} \qquad (40)$$

Equating the expressions for p_2/p_1 given by Eqs. 39 and 40 and solving for the temperature ratio

$$\frac{T_2}{T_1} = \frac{M_2{}^2}{M_1{}^2} \left\{ \frac{1 + \gamma M_1{}^2}{1 + \gamma M_2{}^2} \right\}^2 \qquad (41)$$

From Eq. 37

$$T_1 \left(c_p + \frac{V_1{}^2}{2T_1} + \frac{q}{T_1} \right) = T_2 \left(c_p + \frac{V_2{}^2}{2T_2} \right)$$

$$T_1 \left(1 + \frac{\gamma R}{2c_p} M_1{}^2 + \frac{q}{c_p T_1} \right) = T_2 \left(1 + \frac{\gamma R}{2c_p} M_2{}^2 \right)$$

$$\frac{T_2}{T_1} = \frac{1 + [(\gamma - 1)/2]M_1{}^2 + (q/c_p T_1)}{1 + [(\gamma - 1)/2]M_2{}^2} \tag{42}$$

Equating the expressions for T_2/T_1 given by Eqs. 41 and 42

$$\frac{M_1{}^2 \left\{ 1 + \frac{\gamma - 1}{2} M_1{}^2 \right\}}{(1 + \gamma M_1{}^2)^2} + \frac{M_1{}^2}{(1 + \gamma M_1{}^2)^2} \frac{q}{c_p T_1} = \frac{M_2{}^2 \left\{ 1 + \frac{\gamma - 1}{2} M_2{}^2 \right\}}{(1 + \gamma M_2{}^2)^2} \tag{43}$$

By defining a function $\phi(M)$ as follows

$$\phi(M) = \frac{M^2 \left\{ 1 + \frac{\gamma - 1}{2} M^2 \right\}}{(1 + \gamma M_1{}^2)^2}$$

Equation 43 can be written:

$$\phi(M_2) = \phi(M_1) + \frac{M_1{}^2}{(1 + \gamma M_1{}^2)^2} \frac{q}{c_p T_1} \tag{44}$$

A knowledge of the entrance Mach number and temperature and the heat per unit mass added between entrance and exit is sufficient to compute the exit Mach number from Eq. 44. The pressure and temperature ratios can then be computed from Eqs. 40 and 41, respectively. The Mach number and static characteristics at the exit can be used to

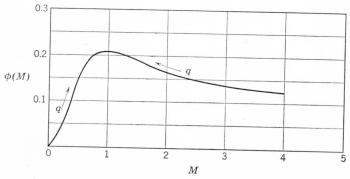

FIG. 11.   Heat addition diagram.

calculate the stagnation characteristics at the exit. In this manner, all exit characteristics can be found.

A plot of $\phi(M)$ is shown in Fig. 11.

The figure indicates that heat added subsonically will raise the Mach number and heat added supersonically will lower it. This conclusion was found in the qualitative analysis of Section 9.7. At any Mach number, there is a critical amount of heat that will drive the stream Mach number to unity. This is the condition for *thermal choking*. Heat added in excess of the critical amount will cause a decrease in mass flux through the duct.

Waves

CHAPTER 10

10.1 ESTABLISHMENT OF A FLOW FIELD

The disturbance caused by a body that is in motion through a fluid is propagated throughout the fluid with the velocity of sound. The speed of sound in an incompressible flow (ρ = constant) must be infinite according to the expression $a^2 = dp/d\rho$, and therefore the pressure variations in the fluid caused by the motion of the body are felt instantaneously at all points in the fluid. It follows that when the speed of motion of a body is much less than the speed of sound, the flow will closely resemble in all details that of an incompressible fluid, and the flow will be deflected well ahead of the body, as shown in Fig. 1.

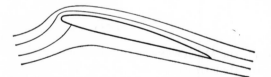

FIG. 1.   Subsonic flow about an airfoil.

As the speed of the body increases, it is clear that the pressure variations move upstream more and more slowly in relation to the body. If the body is moving faster than the speed of sound, it cannot make its presence known to the fluid ahead of it, and the mechanism for bending the streamlines ahead of the body no longer exists. Because of the possible existence of shock waves to be described later in this chapter, the foregoing statement holds only for thin sharp-nosed bodies.

Figure 2 is a diagram of a needle moving to the left with a supersonic velocity V. At times t_A, t_B, and t_C, the needle is at points A, B, and C, respectively. When the needle passes through A, a spherical sound wave is propagated outward from A with a velocity a. By the time the needle has reached point C, the wave originating at A has traveled a distance $a\overline{AC}/V$, where $\overline{AC}/V$ is the time required for the needle to move from A to C. Similarly, a wave originating at B will have traveled a distance $a\overline{BC}/V$ by the time the needle has arrived at C.

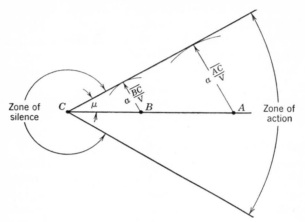

Fig. 2.   Wave formation from a point disturbance.

It is apparent that the wave fronts will have a common tangent that makes an angle $\mu = \sin^{-1}(a/V)$ with the positive x-axis. The tangent or line of wave fronts is called a Mach wave and the angle is called the Mach angle

$$\mu = \sin^{-1}\frac{1}{M} \tag{1}$$

The fluid outside the Mach wave has received no signal from the needle, for disturbances that travel at the velocity of sound cannot be communicated beyond the Mach wave boundary. Von Kármán has referred to this phenomenon as the *rule of forbidden signals*. He has called the region ahead of the Mach wave the *zone of silence* and the region behind the Mach wave the *zone of action*.*

From Eq. 1, it can be seen that as the Mach number decreases towards unity, the Mach angle becomes larger and larger, finally becoming 90° as the Mach number reaches unity. For Mach numbers less than unity, the waves travel ahead of the body and Eq. 1 has no meaning.

* T. von Kármán, "Supersonic Aerodynamics—Principles and Applications," *J. Aero. Sci.*, July 1947.

The above description is independent of whether the flow is two- or three-dimensional; that is, the body may be a razor blade or needle parallel to the flow. The Mach wave will be conical in the latter case and wedge-shaped in the former.

10.2 MACH WAVES

It was shown in the last section that the fluid surrounding a cone or wedge that is moving at a supersonic velocity can be divided into two parts. The part ahead of the Mach wave can receive no signals from the body. Consequently, any deflection of the stream due to the presence of the body must begin at the Mach wave. In the preceding treatment, it was specified that the cone or wedge be extremely thin; that is, the deflection of the stream due to the body is infinitesimal. If the deflection is finite the line of wave fronts is a *shock wave* rather than a Mach wave. The subject of shocks is discussed in Section 10.5. It is the purpose of this section to derive some quantitative relations between the infinitesimal flow deflection through a Mach wave and the flow parameters. It is understood that the changes in the flow parameters through a Mach wave will also be infinitesimal.

Consider the wall shown in Fig. 3 which changes its direction by an amount $d\theta$ at the point A. If the fluid is to follow the wall, then its

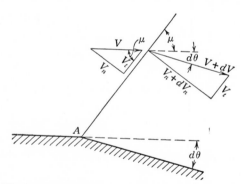

FIG. 3. Mach wave accompanying an infinitesimal flow deflection.

direction will also change by $d\theta$ at the point A. The disturbance to the flow will not be felt ahead of the Mach line originating at A. This case is comparable to that of a wedge moving through a fluid at rest if the axis of reference is attached to the wedge. It is different from the wedge case in that the flow deflection is in the opposite sense. The wall is assumed to extend to infinity in a direction normal to the plane of the paper. If the only bend in the wall is at the point A, then all of the turning will occur at the Mach line springing from A. The two-dimensional nature of the problem dictates that the turning must be identical at all points on the wave from A to infinity. Therefore, the change in flow properties across the wave must be the same at all points along the wave.

Because there is no pressure differential along the wave, the tangential component of the velocity cannot change in crossing the wave. This follows from considerations of continuity and equilibrium and is proved in the next section. Thus the change in the velocity of the fluid in crossing the wave results entirely from the change in the component of the velocity normal to the wave. The changes in the magnitude and direction of the velocity are functions of the change in the normal component, and, therefore, they are related to each other. The rate of change of magnitude with direction is found in the following manner.

The magnitude of the velocity or speed is given by

$$V = \sqrt{V_n{}^2 + V_t{}^2} \tag{2}$$

Because V_t is constant, the differential of the speed is

$$dV = \frac{V_n}{V} dV_n \tag{3}$$

The direction of the velocity referred to the direction of the wave may be observed from Fig. 3 to be

$$\tan^{-1} \frac{V_n}{V_t} \tag{4}$$

The change in direction is the differential of Eq. 4. Calling this $d\theta$,

$$d\theta = \frac{V_t}{V^2} dV_n \tag{5}$$

The rate of change of speed with deflection angle is obtained by dividing Eq. 3 by Eq. 5:

$$\frac{dV}{d\theta} = V \frac{V_n}{V_t} \tag{6}$$

From Fig. 3, $(V_n/V_t) = \tan \mu$, and since $\sin \mu = 1/M$ Eq. 6 may be written

$$\frac{dV}{d\theta} = \frac{V}{\sqrt{M^2 - 1}} \tag{7}$$

The above is a scalar equation that relates change in speed to change in the velocity direction. From Fig. 3 it can be seen that an increase in speed is associated with a clockwise change in direction, and therefore the positive sense must be counted clockwise. The flow about a wedge corresponds to a deflection opposite to that shown in Fig. 3. For such deflections the speed of the stream is decreased.

The pressure variation dp across the Mach wave is found with the aid of the differential form of the equilibrium equation (Eq. 11 of Chapter 7 with gravity neglected)

$$V\,dV + \frac{dp}{\rho} = 0$$

$$\frac{dV}{V} = -\frac{dp}{V^2 \rho} \tag{8}$$

The relation $a^2 = \gamma(p/\rho)$ is used to remove ρ in Eq. 8. Thus

$$\frac{dV}{V} = -\frac{1}{\gamma M^2}\frac{dp}{p} \tag{9}$$

Substituting Eq. 9 in Eq. 7,

$$\frac{dp}{d\theta} = -\frac{\gamma M^2}{\sqrt{M^2-1}}\,p \tag{10}$$

Because $dp/d\theta$ is a negative number, flow deflection as shown in Fig. 3 is accompanied by a decrease in pressure; that is, the fluid has been expanded. The Mach wave in this case is an expansion wave. For the flow about a wedge, the deflection causes a compression of the fluid. For this situation the Mach wave is a compression wave. An expansion of the fluid is accompanied by an increase in velocity and a decrease in pressure; a compression of the fluid is accompanied by a decrease in velocity and an increase in pressure.

It must be remembered that the relations derived in this section are valid only for infinitesimal flow deflections. The disturbance caused by the deflection is infinitesimal and the condition of isentropy here assumed is valid.

10.3 LARGE AMPLITUDE WAVES

Important concepts can be gained by a qualitative consideration of the sequence of events for waves of large amplitude. Consider a wave traveling to the right and having a distribution of pressure as shown in Fig. 4. As the wave passes through the fluid, the fluid is compressed from d to e, expanded from e to f, and compressed back to ambient again from f to g. Regions de and fg are the compressive portions of the wave, and region *ef* is the expansive portion. If the wave is traveling to the left instead of to the right, the compressive and expansive portions are interchanged.

A fluid element in the compressive portions *de* or *fg* is in the presence of a pressure gradient that will accelerate the element in the direction of the wave, that is, from left to right. A fluid element in the expansive portion *ef* will be accelerated from right to left. Then if we observe the velocity of a fluid element as the symmetrical wave shown in Fig. 4 passes over it, the element will accelerate from rest to the maximum velocity *u* as the portion of the wave from *d* to *e* passes over it, decelerate from *u* to rest in the presence of the portion from *e* to *o*, decelerate to the minimum value −*u* in the presence of the portion from *o* to *f*, and accelerate again to zero velocity from *f* to *g*.

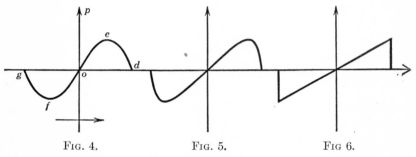

Fig. 4.   Fig. 5.   Fig 6.

Figs. 4, 5, and 6.   Development of a shock wave.

Therefore, it can be seen that the wave is propagated relatively to a fluid that is in motion. If we consider the velocity of sound relative to the moving fluid to be approximately constant, the *absolute* velocity of propagation of the wave will be *a* at points *d*, *o*, and *g*; *a* + *u* at point *e*; and *a* − *u* at point *f*. Hence, the disturbance at *e* will travel faster than the disturbance at *d*. Consequently, the compression portion of the wave *de* will steepen as shown in Fig. 5. A similar argument applies to the compressive portion *fg*. On the other hand, because the disturbance at *e* is traveling faster than the disturbance at *f*, the expansion portion *ef* will flatten out. After a short interval of time the compression portions become infinitely steep, as shown in Fig. 6; in other words, these portions have built up from waves of finite amplitude to *shock waves*.* Riemann predicted this behavior mathematically in 1860 and

---

* If the velocity of sound relative to the moving fluid is considered to be a variable, the effect described will be intensified. Equation 15 of Chapter 9 shows that the velocity of sound is proportional to the $(\gamma - 1)/2\gamma$ power of the pressure. Therefore, the velocity of sound will be the maximum at *e* and the minimum at *f*.

showed that the time required for a finite compression wave to build up into a shock is very small.

This different behavior of expansion and compression regions is illustrated graphically in Fig. 7 for a double wedge moving at a supersonic speed to the left. The analysis of the previous section shows that a compression forms where the flow turns into itself, that is, at A and C. At B, where the flow turns away from itself, an expansion forms. By the above reasoning, the compression waves formed at A and C remain

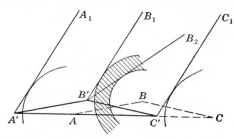

Fig. 7. Expansion and compression waves formed by a double wedge in supersonic flight.

sharp as they propagate outward along the lines $\overline{A'A_1}$ and $\overline{C'C_1}$. These lines, therefore, represent shock waves. On the other hand, the expansion wave formed at B becomes less steep as it propagates, and by the time the body reaches the position $A'B'C'$ the expansion formed at B is bounded by the lines $\overline{B'B_1}$ and $\overline{B'B_2}$, the former representing the Mach direction for the flow along $\overline{A'B'}$, the latter that for the flow along $\overline{B'C'}$.

10.4 PRANDTL-MEYER FLOW

The flow deflection at point B' in Fig. 7 is such that the fluid expands as it turns. It was shown in the last section that an expansion wave (a disturbance through which the fluid is expanded) of finite amplitude becomes less steep as it is propagated outward. As the fluid passes through the wave bounded by $\overline{B'B_1}$ and $\overline{B'B_2}$, the flow parameters change gradually from their values upstream of $\overline{B'B_1}$ to their values downstream $\overline{B'B_2}$. The finite change in properties can be considered as being accomplished by an infinite number of infinitesimal changes across a series of Mach waves lying within the fan $B_1B'B_2$. The relation between speed change and flow deflection across any one of these infinitesimal waves has been given by Eq. 7, which may be written in the form

$$d\theta = \frac{\sqrt{M^2 - 1}}{V} dV \tag{11}$$

The total deflection through the fan is the integral of Eq. 11. To perform the integration, $\sqrt{M^2 - 1}/V$ must be expressed in terms of V. This expression can be written

$$\frac{\sqrt{M^2 - 1}}{V} = \sqrt{\frac{1}{a^2} - \frac{1}{V^2}} \tag{12}$$

The speed of sound a can be written in terms of the speed of the stream by using the energy relation as given by Eq. 9 of Chapter 9.

$$\frac{V^2}{2} + \frac{a^2}{\gamma - 1} = \frac{a_0{}^2}{\gamma - 1} \tag{13}$$

We solve for a in Eq. 13 and substitute this value in Eq. 12. Then

$$\frac{\sqrt{M^2 - 1}}{V} = \frac{\dfrac{\gamma + 1}{2} V - \dfrac{a_0{}^2}{V}}{\sqrt{\left(\dfrac{1 - \gamma^2}{4}\right) V^4 + \gamma a_0{}^2 V^2 - a_0{}^4}} \tag{14}$$

By means of Eq. 14, $d\theta/dV$ in Eq. 11 can be expressed entirely in terms of V and the integration can be performed. Let $\theta = 0$ be the flow direction that corresponds to a Mach number of unity; that is, $V = a^*$. Then the deflection θ from this flow direction is given by

$$\theta = \int_{a^{*2}}^{V^2} \frac{\left(\dfrac{\gamma + 1}{4}\right) d(V^2)}{\sqrt{\left(\dfrac{1 - \gamma^2}{4}\right) V^4 + \gamma a_0{}^2 V^2 - a_0{}^4}}$$

$$- \int_{a^{*2}}^{V^2} \frac{\dfrac{a_0{}^2}{2V^2} d(V^2)}{\sqrt{\left(\dfrac{1 - \gamma^2}{4}\right) V^4 + \gamma a_0{}^2 V^2 - a_0{}^4}} \tag{15}$$

Both integrals in Eq. 15 are in standard form.† The equation becomes ‡

† See Peirce, *Short Table of Integrals*, Integrals numbers 161 and 183, Ginn and Company, Boston, 1929.

‡ The relation between speed and direction as given by Eq. 16 is valid for isentropic compressive deflections as well as for expansive deflections. From Eq. 16 a polar of the velocity magnitude and direction may be plotted. The resulting *epicycloid diagram* is used in the *method of characteristics* for analyzing two- and three-dimensional flow problems. Details of this method may be found in *Elements of Aerodynamics of Supersonic Flows*, by Antonio Ferri, Macmillan, New York, 1949.

$$\theta = -\frac{1}{2}\sqrt{\frac{\gamma+1}{\gamma-1}}\left\{\sin^{-1}\left[\left(\frac{1-\gamma^2}{2}\right)\frac{V^2}{a_0^2}+\gamma\right]\right.$$

$$-\sin^{-1}\left[\left(\frac{1-\gamma^2}{2}\right)\frac{a^{*2}}{a_0^2}+\gamma\right]\Bigg\}$$

$$-\frac{1}{2}\left\{\sin^{-1}\left(\gamma-2\frac{a_0^2}{V^2}\right)-\sin^{-1}\left(\gamma-2\frac{a_0^2}{a^{*2}}\right)\right\} \quad (16)$$

a^*/a_0 and V/a_0 are easily found in terms of Mach number. For $V = a = a^*$, Eq. 13 becomes

$$\left(\frac{a^*}{a_0}\right)^2 = \frac{2}{\gamma+1} \tag{17}$$

Also from Eq. 13

$$\left(\frac{V}{a_0}\right)^2 = \frac{2}{\gamma-1}\left[1-\left(\frac{a}{a_0}\right)^2\right] \tag{18}$$

$(a_0/a)^2$ has been given by Eq. 17 of Chapter 9. Substituting this value in Eq. 18 yields

$$\left(\frac{V}{a_0}\right)^2 = \frac{M^2}{\dfrac{\gamma-1}{2}M^2+1} \tag{19}$$

It is convenient to replace $(a^*/a_0)^2$ and $(a_0/V)^2$ in Eq. 16 by their equivalents from Eqs. 17 and 19. The flow deflection may then be expressed in terms of Mach number

$$\theta = -\frac{1}{2}\sqrt{\frac{\gamma+1}{\gamma-1}}\left\{\sin^{-1}\left[\left(\frac{1-\gamma^2}{2}\right)\left(\frac{M^2}{1+\dfrac{\gamma-1}{2}M^2}\right)+\gamma\right]-\frac{\pi}{2}\right\}$$

$$-\frac{1}{2}\left\{\sin^{-1}\left[\gamma-2\left(\frac{1+\dfrac{\gamma-1}{2}M^2}{M^2}\right)\right]+\frac{\pi}{2}\right\} \tag{20}$$

For $M = 1$, $\theta = 0$ as it should because θ is measured from the flow direction corresponding to $M = 1$. As M increases, θ increases. Finally, when M becomes infinite, θ reaches the value 130.5°. A plot of θ versus M appears in Fig. 8 and is tabulated in Table 3 at the end of the book. The change in Mach number associated with a given flow deflection may be computed from this curve in the following manner: Read the flow deflection θ_i corresponding to the initial Mach number.

This represents the amount that the stream has been deflected from the $M = 1$ direction. Add to θ_i the desired deflection $\Delta\theta$. The sum $\theta_f = \theta_i + \Delta\theta$ is the amount that the stream must be turned to bring it from the $M = 1$ direction to the direction corresponding to the Mach number after the deflection $\Delta\theta$. This final Mach number is the abscissa of the point on the curve for which θ_f is the ordinate. For example, if a stream with a Mach number of 2 is deflected through 20°, the Mach number

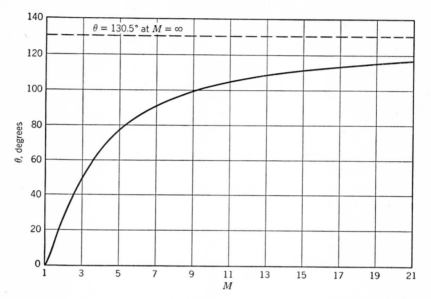

Fig. 8.   Expansive flow deflection versus Mach number.

after deflection will be 2.83. It should be remembered that expansive flow is isentropic. Therefore, the Mach number at any point during the turning determines all the other properties of the flow. The *static-stagnation* ratios versus Mach number are given by Eqs. 16, 18, and 19 of Chapter 9.

10.5   FINITE COMPRESSION WAVES

The flow deflection at point A' in Fig. 7 is in a direction that results in a compression of the fluid. The line A_1A' is the line of disturbance fronts. Because the disturbances created at the nose of the body are finite compressive disturbances, they will steepen as they are propagated outward, and, as explained in Section 10.3, in a very short period of time a discontinuity or *shock wave* develops. Unlike an expansion wave, the change in flow properties across a shock wave is abrupt. The device of integrating infinitesimal changes is therefore not available.

In order to find the changes in flow properties when the fluid passes through a shock wave, it is necessary to consider continuity, equilibrium, and the conservation of energy across the shock. These conditions will show that the speed of propagation of the finite disturbance is greater than the speed of sound. They also show that the compression of the fluid in passing through a shock is not an isentropic process.

Figure 9 is an enlarged view of the leading edge of the body shown in Fig. 7. The axis of reference is now attached to the body so that it appears that the body is stationary in a moving fluid. The flow parameters upstream p_1, ρ_1, and V_1 are known. Let it be required to find the flow parameters downstream, p_2, ρ_2, and V_2.* Two more parameters enter the problem: the deflection angle θ and the wave angle β. It will be shown presently that four equations are available for the solution of the problem and therefore

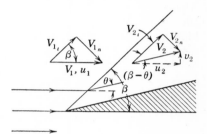

FIG. 9.   Flow through a shock wave.

four unknowns may be determined. In addition to p_2, ρ_2, and V_2, either β or θ can be taken as an unknown. In the following, it is assumed that the wave angle β is known and the deflection angle that corresponds to this wave angle and the upstream conditions will be determined.

The four equations available for the solution of the unknowns follow. Reference should be made to Fig. 9 for the notation used.

1. EQUATION OF CONTINUITY. Conservation of mass requires that, for any unit area of the wave, the mass flux entering must equal the mass flux leaving.

$$\rho_1 V_{1n} = \rho_2 V_{2n} \tag{21}$$

2. EQUATIONS OF EQUILIBRIUM. The pressure and velocity changes across the wave are related by the momentum theorem, which is given by Eq. 13 of Chapter 3. Consider the region $\hat{R}$ shown in Fig. 10. Let

* Equally important applications occur where the downstream parameters are known and the upstream parameters are the unknowns. For example, in wind-tunnel work the downstream parameters are frequently measured and the upstream values are computed.

the faces parallel to the wave be of unit area. According to the momentum theorem, equilibrium normal to the wave is expressed by

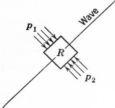

$$p_1 - p_2 = \rho_2 V_{2n}{}^2 - \rho_1 V_{1n}{}^2 \qquad (22)$$

Parallel to the wave, there is no change in pressure, and equilibrium is expressed by

$$0 = \rho_2 V_{2n} V_{2t} - \rho_1 V_{1n} V_{1t} \qquad (23)$$

Fig. 10. Equilibrium in shock flow.

3. ENERGY EQUATION. The energy equation for a gas in motion as given by Eq. 12 of Chapter 9 is applicable to any adiabatic flow whether it is reversible or not, and therefore the value of a^* is constant throughout the flow. Then the following energy equations are applicable where a^* has the same value in both equations.

$$\frac{V_{1n}{}^2 + V_{1t}{}^2}{2} + \frac{\gamma}{\gamma - 1} \frac{p_1}{\rho_1} = \frac{\gamma + 1}{2(\gamma - 1)} a^{*2}$$
$$\frac{V_{2n}{}^2 + V_{2t}{}^2}{2} + \frac{\gamma}{\gamma - 1} \frac{p_2}{\rho_2} = \frac{\gamma + 1}{2(\gamma - 1)} a^{*2} \qquad (24)$$

From Eqs. 21 and 23 it follows that

$$V_{1t} = V_{2t} \qquad (25)$$

The tangential component of velocity is the same on both sides of a shock. This fact was utilized in the treatment of infinitesimal waves in Section 10.2.

Since the tangential components of the velocity do not change when the fluid passes through the wave, the velocity downstream is established once V_{2n} is determined. From Eqs. 21 and 22

$$p_2 - p_1 = \rho_1 V_{1n}(V_{1n} - V_{2n}) \qquad (26)$$

Again using continuity,

$$\frac{p_2}{\rho_2 V_{2n}} - \frac{p_1}{\rho_1 V_{1n}} = V_{1n} - V_{2n}$$

p_2/ρ_2 and p_1/ρ_1 may be eliminated by employing the energy relations Eqs. 24. The station subscript is dropped from V_t because $V_{1t} = V_{2t}$.

$$\frac{\gamma + 1}{2\gamma} a^{*2} \left(\frac{1}{V_{2n}} - \frac{1}{V_{1n}} \right) + \frac{\gamma - 1}{2\gamma} \left[\left(V_{1n} + \frac{V_t{}^2}{V_{1n}} \right) - \left(V_{2n} + \frac{V_t{}^2}{V_{2n}} \right) \right]$$
$$= V_{1n} - V_{2n}$$

which rearranges to the form

$$\left[\frac{\gamma+1}{2\gamma} \frac{a^{*2}}{V_{2n}V_{1n}} - \frac{\gamma-1}{2\gamma} \frac{V_t^2}{V_{2n}V_{1n}} - \frac{\gamma+1}{2\gamma} \right] (V_{1n} - V_{2n}) = 0$$

The above equation is satisfied when either factor is zero. The solution for which $V_{1n} - V_{2n} = 0$ corresponds to a shock wave of zero intensity or a Mach wave. The first factor set equal to zero gives the expression

$$V_{1n}V_{2n} = a^{*2} - \frac{\gamma-1}{\gamma+1} V_t^2 \tag{27}$$

From Fig. 9, $V_{1n} = V_1 \sin \beta$ and $V_t = V_1 \cos \beta$. These expressions are substituted into Eq. 27 with the result

$$V_{2n} = \frac{a^{*2}}{V_1 \sin \beta} - \frac{\gamma-1}{\gamma+1} V_1 \frac{\cos^2 \beta}{\sin \beta}$$

which may be written

$$V_{2n} = \frac{V_1}{\sin \beta} \left[\left(\frac{a^*}{a_0} \frac{a_0}{V_1} \right)^2 - \frac{\gamma-1}{\gamma+1} \cos^2 \beta \right]$$

or, after replacing a^*/a_0 and a_0/V_1 with their equivalents from Eqs. 17 and 19

$$V_{2n} = \frac{V_1}{\sin \beta} \left(\frac{\gamma-1}{\gamma+1} \sin^2 \beta + \frac{2}{\gamma+1} \frac{1}{M_1^2} \right) \tag{28}$$

From Fig. 9, V_{2n} is related to the wave angle β and deflection angle θ by

$$V_{2n} = V_t \tan (\beta - \theta) = V_1 \cos \beta \tan (\beta - \theta)$$

which may be equated to the value of V_{2n} given by Eq. 28 with the result

$$\tan (\beta - \theta) = \frac{1}{\sin \beta \cos \beta} \left\{ \frac{\gamma-1}{\gamma+1} \sin^2 \beta + \frac{2}{\gamma+1} \frac{1}{M_1^2} \right\}$$

From the above it can be seen that only two of the three variables β, θ, and M_1 are independent. An explicit solution for the deflection angle in terms of the upstream Mach number and wave angle is

$$\theta = \beta - \tan^{-1} \left[\frac{1}{\sin \beta \cos \beta} \left(\frac{\gamma-1}{\gamma+1} \sin^2 \beta + \frac{2}{\gamma+1} \frac{1}{M_1^2} \right) \right] \tag{29}$$

From Eq. 29 it may be readily verified that when the wave angle is equal to the Mach angle

$$\beta = \mu = \sin^{-1} \frac{1}{M}$$

the deflection goes to zero as is to be expected, because under these conditions the wave is of infinitesimal strength. When $\beta = \pi/2$ in Eq. 29, corresponding to a shock wave normal to the flow, the deflection again goes to zero.

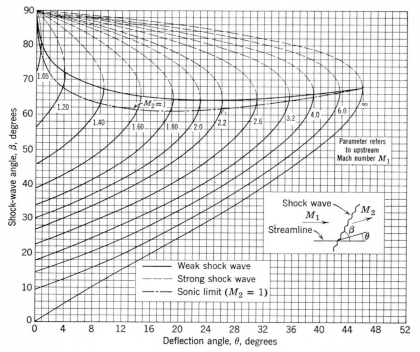

Fig. 11. Variation of shock angle β with flow deflection angle θ. Perfect gas, $\gamma = 1.4$. (Courtesy of the National Advisory Committee for Aeronautics.) A working version of this chart is included with the Tables at the end of the book.

A plot of Eq. 29 for the complete range of Mach numbers is shown in Fig. 11.* Two points should be observed.

(1) For any value of M_1, there are two wave angles that produce the same deflection θ. The wave represented by the larger value of β (dashed curve) is termed a *strong shock*. The smaller value of β (solid curve) corresponds to the *weak shock*. The waves are so named because the strong shock produces the greater entropy rise.

(2) For any value of M_1, there is a maximum deflection angle. The maximum occurs along the solid curve that separates the strong and

* Taken from NACA Report 1135, *Equations, Tables, and Charts for Compressible Flow*, 1953.

weak shocks. Flow deflections in excess of the maximum are not consistent with the basic relations, Eqs. 21 through 24, used in the derivation of Eq. 29.

A working version of Fig. 11 has been included with the tables at the end of the book.

Equation 29 is applicable to conical shocks as well as plane shocks. In the case of the plane shock illustrated in Fig. 9 the deflection angle θ is the same as the angle of the wedge that produces the shock. In the three-dimensional case, the deflection angle θ is *not* the same as the cone angle that generates the conical shock. This point will be discussed in greater detail in Section 10.9.

10.6 THE CHARACTERISTIC RATIOS AS FUNCTIONS OF MACH NUMBER

In this section it is shown that the pressure, density, temperature, and stagnation pressure ratios across a shock wave are functions of the normal component of the upstream Mach number only. From Fig. 9 it can be seen that the normal component of the upstream Mach number is given by

$$M_{1n} = M_1 \sin \beta \tag{30}$$

M_{1n} in the following is referred to as the *normal Mach number*.

The pressure ratio can be derived from Eq. 26, which after substitution from Eq. 27 for $V_{1n}V_{2n}$ becomes

$$\frac{p_2}{p_1} = 1 + \frac{\rho_1}{p_1}\left(V_{1n}{}^2 - a^{*2} + \frac{\gamma - 1}{\gamma + 1}V_t{}^2\right) \tag{31}$$

ρ_1/p_1 is replaced by its equivalent $\gamma/a_1{}^2$ and $V_t{}^2$ by $V_1{}^2 - V_{1n}{}^2$. Then Eq. 31 becomes

$$\frac{p_2}{p_1} = 1 + \frac{2\gamma}{\gamma + 1}\left(\frac{V_{1n}}{a_1}\right)^2 - \gamma\left(\frac{a^*}{a_1}\right)^2 + \frac{\gamma(\gamma - 1)}{\gamma + 1}M_1{}^2 \tag{32}$$

$(a^*/a_1)^2$ can be obtained from Eq. 24. Then, with $(V_{1n}/V_1) = \sin \beta$, Eq. 32 becomes

$$\frac{p_2}{p_1} = \frac{2\gamma}{\gamma + 1}M_{1n}{}^2 - \frac{\gamma - 1}{\gamma + 1} \tag{33}$$

The density ratio across the shock may be found by multiplying the right-hand side of Eq. 26 by $(V_{1n} + V_{2n})$. Equation 26 becomes

$$p_2 - p_1 = (V_{1n}{}^2 - V_{2n}{}^2)\frac{\rho_1 V_{1n}}{V_{1n} + V_{2n}} \tag{34}$$

By using the equation of continuity, Eq. 34 becomes

$$V_{1n}^2 - V_{2n}^2 = (p_2 - p_1)\left(\frac{1}{\rho_1} + \frac{1}{\rho_2}\right) \tag{35}$$

But, from Eq. 24,

$$V_{1n}^2 - V_{2n}^2 = \frac{2\gamma}{\gamma - 1}\left(\frac{p_2}{\rho_2} - \frac{p_1}{\rho_1}\right) \tag{36}$$

Equations 35 and 36 are equated and after some rearrangement we have

$$\frac{\rho_2}{\rho_1} = \frac{(\gamma + 1)/(\gamma - 1) + (p_1/p_2)}{1 + [(\gamma + 1)/(\gamma - 1)](p_1/p_2)} \tag{37}$$

Equation 37 is known as the Rankine-Hugoniot relation. From Eqs. 37 and 33, it can be seen that ρ_2/ρ_1 is a function only of M_{1n}. The expression for temperature ratio follows directly from the equation of state.

$$\frac{T_2}{T_1} = \frac{p_2}{p_1}\frac{\rho_1}{\rho_2} \tag{38}$$

Pressure, density, and temperature ratios across a shock wave in air ($\gamma = 1.4$) are plotted against the normal Mach number in Fig. 12. The numerical data is included in Table 4 at the end of the book. From Eqs. 33, 37, and 38, it can be seen that the pressure and temperature ratios become infinite and that the density ratio approaches 6 as M_{1n} becomes infinite.

The change in entropy between thermodynamic states 1 and 2 of a gas is given by Eq. 35 of Chapter 8.

$$\Delta S = \log\left(\frac{T_2}{T_1}\right)^{c_v}\left(\frac{\rho_1}{\rho_2}\right)^R \tag{39}$$

The change in entropy across a shock wave is then given by

$$S_2 - S_1 = c_v \log\frac{T_2}{T_1}\left(\frac{\rho_1}{\rho_2}\right)^{\gamma-1} \tag{40}$$

With the aid of Eqs. 33, 37, and 38, Eq. 40 may be expressed in terms of the normal Mach number. It can be readily verified that for normal Mach numbers less than unity, Eq. 40 indicates an entropy loss and Eq. 33 indicates a pressure decrease in passing through the shock. An entropy loss is ruled out by the second law of thermodynamics, and a pressure decrease means that the wave is an expansion discontinuity. Equations 33 and 40, therefore, prove that expansion discontinuities

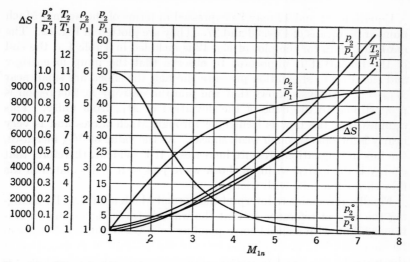

FIG. 12.   Characteristic ratios across a shock wave versus normal Mach number.

cannot exist.   This is the same conclusion reached in the discussion of Section 10.3.

When dealing with the upstream side of the shock only, the entropy is constant for all values of the flow parameters including the stagnation values.   Then, by using the equation of state, we may write the expression for the entropy as

$$S_1 = c_v \log \frac{(T_1{}^0)^\gamma}{(p_1{}^0)^{\gamma-1}} + c_v \log R^{\gamma-1} + S_0$$

A similar expression can be written for the flow downstream of the shock.   Then, because the stagnation temperature has the same value on both sides of the shock, the difference in entropy may be written

$$S_2 - S_1 = c_v \log \left(\frac{p_1{}^0}{p_2{}^0}\right)^{\gamma-1} \tag{41}$$

The ratio of the stagnation pressures across the shock follows immediately from a comparison of Eqs. 40 and 41:

$$\frac{p_2{}^0}{p_1{}^0} = \left(\frac{T_2}{T_1}\right)^{1/(1-\gamma)} \left(\frac{\rho_2}{\rho_1}\right)$$

or, in terms of density and pressure ratios,

$$\frac{p_2{}^0}{p_1{}^0} = \left(\frac{p_1}{p_2}\right)^{1/(\gamma-1)} \left(\frac{\rho_2}{\rho_1}\right)^{\gamma/(\gamma-1)} \tag{42}$$

Equations 41 and 42 may be expressed in terms of the normal Mach number by means of Eqs. 33 and 37. They are plotted in Fig. 12. The numerical data for the plot of Eq. 42 is included in Table 4 at the end of the book. It is important to observe that the jump in entropy and the drop in stagnation pressure through the shock are small near $M_{1n} = 1$. Analysis shows that the jump in entropy in this region is proportional to the cube of the deviation of M_{1n} from unity. This signifies that the flow is isentropic through Mach waves and is very nearly isentropic through weak shocks. As the value of M_{1n} increases, the loss in stagnation pressure increases. It is evident, therefore, that energy is dissipated within a shock wave just as it is dissipated in the flow through a tube with friction.

Finally, it remains to interpret the normal Mach number. By changing the axes of reference so that the wave is traveling through a stationary fluid with a speed corresponding to a Mach number M_1, it can be seen that M_{1n} is simply the ratio of the velocity of propagation of the wave to the speed of sound. When the normal Mach number is unity, the shock is a Mach wave and there are no discontinuities in the flow parameters across it. As the speed of propagation becomes greater, the discontinuity in the flow parameters becomes greater. Thus, the intensity of the discontinuity or shock is a function of the speed of propagation of the wave.

10.7 NORMAL SHOCK WAVE

If the shock is normal to the flow, $\beta = \pi/2$, and because $V_t = 0$, Eq. 27 becomes

$$V_1 V_2 = a^{*2} \tag{43}$$

Equation 43 indicates that if V_1 is greater than a^*, V_2 must be less than a^*. Entropy considerations have shown that the Mach number upstream of a shock must be supersonic. Therefore, for *normal* shock waves, the flow downstream of the shock is subsonic.

Equation 43 may be written

$$\frac{V_1}{a_1} \frac{a_1}{a_0} \frac{V_2}{a_2} \frac{a_2}{a_0} = \left(\frac{a^*}{a_0}\right)^2 \tag{44}$$

From Eq. 12 of Chapter 9, $(a^*/a_0)^2 = 2/(\gamma + 1)$. From Eq. 17 of the same chapter,

$$\frac{a}{a_0} = \left(\frac{\gamma - 1}{2} M^2 + 1\right)^{-\frac{1}{2}}$$

These values are substituted in Eq. 44. Then

$$\frac{M_2}{\sqrt{[(\gamma - 1)/2]M_2{}^2 + 1}} = \frac{2}{\gamma + 1} \frac{\sqrt{[(\gamma - 1)/2]M_1{}^2 + 1}}{M_1}$$

This is readily solved for $M_2{}^2$.

$$M_2{}^2 = \frac{(\gamma - 1)M_1{}^2 + 2}{2\gamma M_1{}^2 - (\gamma - 1)} \tag{45}$$

As $M_1{}^2$ increases, $M_2{}^2$ decreases, finally approaching the value $(\gamma - 1)/2\gamma = \frac{1}{7}$ (for air) as M_1 approaches infinity. A tabulation of M_2 for a range of values of M_1 is included in Table 4 at the end of the book.

10.8 PLANE OBLIQUE SHOCK WAVES

The wedge in Fig. 13 forces the stream to turn through an angle w. Providing w is not too great for the upstream Mach number M_1 considered, the turning can be accomplished by a plane shock wave as

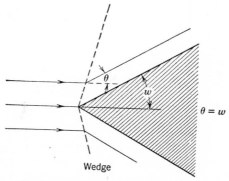

FIG. 13.   Wedge with attached shock.

shown by the dotted line. In this circumstance, w corresponds to the angle θ of Section 10.5. With the value of M_1 and θ known, the wave angle β can be read from Fig. 11. Of the two choices for β, it is an experimental fact that the one corresponding to the *weak* shock usually occurs.

β and M_1 fix the value of the normal Mach number M_{1n}, which in turn determines the change in flow properties across the shock. For the two-dimensional case, the oblique shock wave divides the flow field into two uniform regions of different entropy. For example, if the upstream Mach number is 2 and the wedge angle is 14°, the wave angle is 44° from Fig. 11. Then the normal Mach number from Eq. 30 is 1.39. Opposite $M_{1n} = 1.39$ in Table 4 may be read the ratios of pressure, density, etc., across the shock. To deduce the downstream Mach number, remember that even though there is an entropy rise across the shock the flow is adiabatic and there is no change in stagnation temperature; that is, $T_1{}^0 = T_2{}^0$. We can write

$$\frac{T_2}{T_2{}^0} = \frac{T_2}{T_1} \frac{T_1}{T_1{}^0} \frac{T_1{}^0}{T_2{}^0} = (1.248)(0.5556)(1) = 0.694$$

$T_1/T_1{}^0$ corresponds to $M_1 = 2$ and was read from Table 3 at the end of the book. From the same table, corresponding to $T_2/T_2{}^0 = 0.694$, the value of M_2 is found to be 1.48.

The Mach number downstream of a *weak* oblique shock is supersonic for all turning angles up to a degree of the maximum turning angle. In the example above, for $M_1 = 2$ the maximum turning angle is 23°, and M_2 is sonic for $\theta \simeq 22.7°$ and supersonic for θ less than this value. The boundary between subsonic and supersonic downstream Mach numbers is indicated by the dashed line marked $M_2 = 1$ in Fig. 11. The Mach number downstream of *strong* oblique shocks is subsonic.

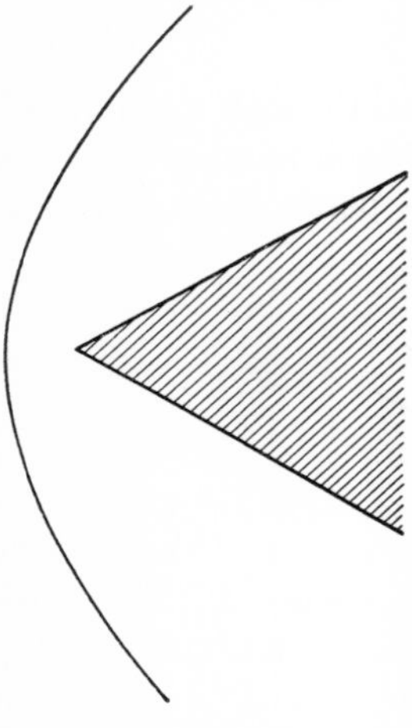

The above discussion assumes the wedge angle does not exceed the maximum turning angle for the M_1 considered. If the wedge angle exceeds the maximum, then a *detached* curved shock appears ahead of the wedge as shown in Fig. 14. At the center of the wave $\beta = \pi/2$, which is the limiting value for the

FIG. 14. Wedge with detached shock.

strong shock. Proceeding away from the center along the shock, the wave angle decreases. This corresponds to a movement downward and towards the right on a strong shock line of Fig. 11. Until a wave angle corresponding to the $M_2 = 1$ line is reached, the flow immediately downstream of the shock will be subsonic. Thus, pressure pulses from the wedge can be communicated to the fluid behind the central portion of the shock and, as a consequence, the flow curves about the wedge in typical subsonic fashion.

The entropy rise across the detached shock depends on the wave angle, which is changing continuously. Therefore, the flow behind the curved shock is not isentropic.

10.9 CONICAL OBLIQUE SHOCK WAVES

As pointed out in Section 10.5, the relation between upstream Mach number M_1, wave angle β, and deflection angle θ is independent of the geometry of the shock. Therefore, if M_1 and θ are given, the change in flow properties across a shock of any configuration may be computed by the methods of the last section.

There is, however, an essential difference between the flow behind a plane shock and that behind an axially symmetric shock as is formed, for instance, in front of a body with a conical nose. The flow behind a conical shock is shown diagrammatically in Fig. 15. Only part of the

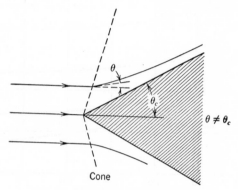

FIG. 15.   Cone with attached shock.

turning takes place at the shock; the increasing radius of the conical cross section with distance downstream makes it necessary, from continuity considerations, that the streamlines have qualitatively the configuration shown. In Fig. 15, therefore, the cone angle θ_c is *greater* than the flow deflection θ through the shock. The flow field downstream of the shock, though isentropic, is not uniform, and therefore the flow parameters immediately downstream of the shock are not the same as they are at the surface of the cone.

Taylor and Maccoll [*] gave an exact solution for the supersonic flow past a cone with an attached shock wave. They were able to patch an isentropic flow about a cone with a shock flow such that the flow parameters immediately downstream of the shock had the same values from the two solutions. The results of their work are summarized in Figs. 16 and 17, which give the shock wave angle and the pressure coef-

[*] G. I. Taylor and J. W. Maccoll, "The Air Pressure on a Cone Moving at High Speeds," *Proc. Roy. Soc. London*, Series A, Vol. 139, pp. 279–311, 1933; J. W. Maccoll, "The Conical Shock Wave Formed by a Cone Moving at High Speed," *Proc. Roy. Soc. London*, Series A, Vol. 150, pp. 459–472, 1937.

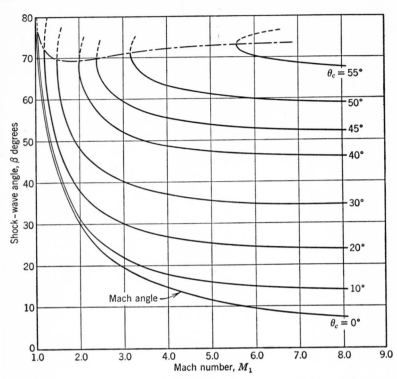

Fig. 16. Shock angle versus Mach number for various cone angles. (Courtesy of J. W. Maccoll, "The Conical Shock Wave Formed by a Cone Moving at High Speed," *Proc. Roy. Soc. London*, April 1937.)

ficient at the surface of the cone as functions of Mach number and cone angle. As for the wedge, there is a maximum cone angle, which is a function of Mach number, beyond which a conical shock will not form. Here again, a detached shock will exist. In keeping with previous remarks, it can be seen that, for a given M_1, the maximum cone angle is greater than the maximum wedge angle. Figure 18 shows an attached and a detached shock on a body with a conical nose at a Mach number of 1.9.*

---

* Interferometer, schlieren, and shadowgraph are three devices for detecting shock waves optically. They detect density, density gradient, and rate of change of density gradient, respectively. The photographs of Fig. 18 were taken with a schlieren system. For a description of the schlieren technique, see, for example, *Physical Measurements in Gas Dynamics and Combustion*, edited by R. W. Ladenburg, B. Lewis, R. N. Pease, and H. S. Taylor, Volume IX in the series High Speed Aerodynamics and Jet Propulsion, Princeton University Press, Princeton, New Jersey, 1957.

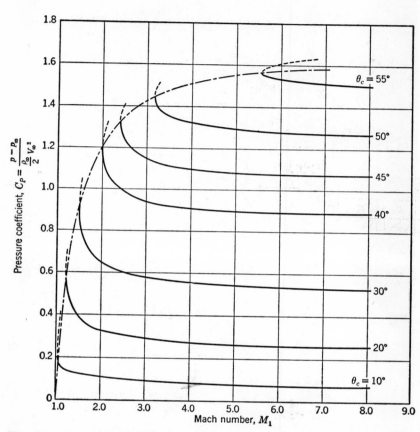

Fig. 17. Pressure coefficient versus Mach number for various cone angles. (Courtesy of J. W. Maccoll, "The Conical Shock Wave Formed by a Cone Moving at High Speed," *Proc. Roy. Soc. London*, April 1937.)

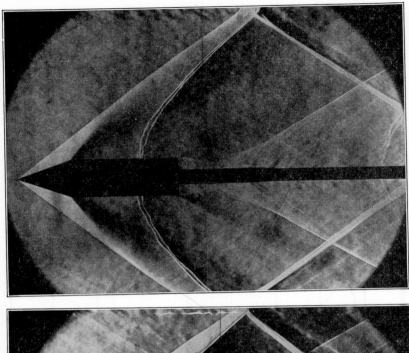

Fig. 18. Schlieren photographs of attached and detached shock waves for flow past cones of different vertex angles. $M = 1.90$. (Courtesy University of Michigan Aeronautical Research Center.)

10.10 SHOCKS IN TUBES

In Section 9.6, the one-dimensional isentropic flow in channels is treated. Referring to Fig. 8 of Chapter 9, if the end pressure is below point 2, only one isentropic flow is possible, namely, point 3. This indicates that only by a change of entropy is it possible to reach end pressures between points 2 and 3. We can fill in this space by plotting isentropic curves for different values of p_0 according to Eq. 26 of Chapter 9. First, it must be shown that the throat area for sonic flow varies with p_0, that is, with the entropy. Consider successive throats in a tube, and let $M = 1$ at each throat. Then

$$\rho_1^* a_1^* A_1^* = \rho_2^* a_2^* A_2^*$$

where the subscripts refer to the separate throats. Because $a_1^* = a_2^*$ as long as the flow is adiabatic, regardless of changes in entropy, and because ρ_1^* and ρ_2^* are constant multiples of their respective stagnation values, the above equation becomes

$$\rho_1^0 A_1^* = \rho_2^0 A_2^*$$

Because $T_1^0 = T_2^0$, the equation of state enables us to write

$$p_1^0 A_1^* = p_2^0 A_2^*$$

or

$$\frac{p_1^0}{p_2^0} = \frac{A_2^*}{A_1^*} \tag{46}$$

Then, for flow through a tube, if a shock occurs, Eq. 26 of Chapter 9 also represents the flow downstream of a shock in which the new p_0

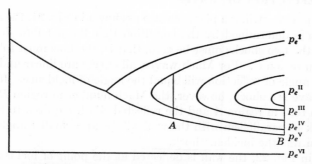

FIG. 19.   Nonisentropic flow through a channel.

and A^* are related to the old values through Eq. 46. The result is a series of isentropic curves as shown in Fig. 19. The vertex of each curve occurs at that point in the channel where $A = A_2^*$; the upper portion represents a subsonic, the lower represents a supersonic flow.

Since the flow changes from supersonic to subsonic through a normal shock, an end pressure p_e^I can be reached if a shock occurs at A and the flow downstream of the shock is isentropic. As p_e decreases, the shock will move downstream until for $p_e = p_e^{II}$ it is at the exit. The adjustment to still lower exit pressures may take place outside the channel, as shown in Fig. 20. As long as $p_e > p_e^V$, oblique shocks can provide

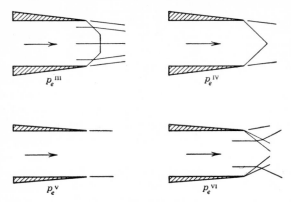

FIG. 20.   Pressure adjustments outside of the channel.

the necessary increase in pressure from the exit to the surroundings. For $p_e = p_e^V$ the isentropic flow without shocks will exist. For $p_e < p_e^V$ the adjustment takes place through expansion waves emanating from the lip.

10.11   REFLECTION OF WAVES

When a wave strikes a plane surface as shown in Fig. 21, the angle of reflection is determined by the condition that the net flow deflection through the two shocks must be zero, that is, the flow must follow the surface in region C. For Mach waves, all effects are linear and, therefore, the angle of reflection will equal the angle of incidence. If the incident wave is a shock, however, the Mach number in region B will be less than that in region A and the reflected shock required to turn the flow back to parallelism with the wall will be at a smaller angle to the wall than was the incident shock.

If, as in Fig. 22, the wall is deflected at the point of incidence to a direction parallel to the streamlines downstream of the incident shock, no reflected shock occurs. This principle of *absorption* of waves is employed in the design of nozzles to achieve *supersonic* shock-free flow.*

* A. E. Puckett, "Supersonic Nozzle Design," *J. Applied Mechanics*, December 1946, p. 265.

If the Mach number in region B is so low that the turning required is greater than the maximum deflection angle θ_m for that Mach number,

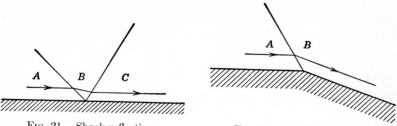

FIG. 21.   Shock reflection.   FIG. 22.   Shock absorption.

a so-called *Mach reflection* as shown in Fig. 23 may be formed.   In this event, the reflected shock as well as that which connects the intersection with the wall may be curved; however, at the point where the shock strikes the wall it must be normal so that no turning will result. The flow in at least a portion of region C is subsonic and the streamlines are not parallel to each other.

When a shock wave reflects from a free surface such as that at the boundary of a jet (see Fig. 20), the boundary condition requires that

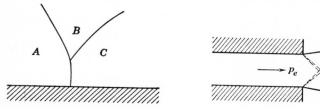

FIG. 23.   Mach reflection.   FIG. 24.   Shock reflection from a free surface.

the pressure be constant and equal to that in the surrounding space. Figure 24 shows the wave configuration for the case of the surrounding pressure less than that in the jet.   Expansion waves originate at the lip, and the jet expands.   When these waves reach the opposite boundary of the jet, they must reflect as compression waves if the pressure at the boundary is to be constant.   As a result, the stream expands and contracts along the flow with a wave length dependent on the Mach number of the issuing flow.

The above phenomena are sometimes considerably altered by the presence of the boundary layer and of the mixing region at the boundary of the jet.   The alternation due to the boundary layer is discussed in Section 14.9.

Wings in Compressible Flow

CHAPTER 11

11.1 INTRODUCTION

The analyses in preceding sections have shown the essential difference between subsonic and supersonic flows. As to be expected, the aerodynamic characteristics of wings show a marked difference in the two regimes. This is evident when we remember that disturbances generated at any point on a wing in subsonic flow are propagated throughout the field, and therefore a tip modification or flap deflection influences the pressure distribution over the entire wing. In contrast, disturbances in a supersonic flow have a limited *zone of action*. As a consequence, the pressure distribution over certain areas of the wing may be entirely unaffected by geometry changes at other areas.

Under certain conditions, pressure distributions over two-dimensional wings in supersonic flow may be computed by applying directly the shock and Prandtl-Meyer flow theory of Chapter 10. In most cases of interest, however, exact solutions of the wing problem are not feasible and recourse is made to approximations. By assuming a wing geometry that disturbs the flow only slightly, it is possible to approximate the flow field by the solution of a linear differential equation over much of the Mach number range.

In this chapter the equation governing the steady flow of a nonviscous compressible fluid is derived and then linearized in accordance with small perturbation theory. Solution of the equation in the subsonic range is made by a transformation of variables that converts the problem to an equivalent one in incompressible flow. In the supersonic range, the solution is found by superimposing elementary solutions in a manner that will satisfy the boundary conditions of the

192

problem. The procedures used follow closely those introduced earlier in the text in connection with incompressible wing theory.

The material presented in the following sections is meant as an introduction to some of the methods of wing theory. An attempt is made to explain the underlying principles and to show their relation to material presented in previous chapters. For complete mathematical developments and summaries of results, the reader is referred to original papers and to texts on wing theory.*

11.2 THE FLOW EQUATION

For an incompressible potential flow, the velocity pattern is given by a solution of Laplace's equation $\nabla^2\varphi = 0$, where φ is the velocity potential satisfying the boundary conditions of the problem considered. In high-speed flight, the fluid density may not be considered constant and the flow equation is much more complicated. In this section the equation governing the steady flow of a nonviscous compressible fluid is derived by combining the equations of continuity, motion, and energy. Isentropy and irrotationality are assumed. For simplicity, the derivation is carried out in two dimensions. The three-dimensional equation may be derived by following an identical procedure with the z component of velocity considered.

The equations of motion and continuity may be written

$$u\frac{\partial u}{\partial x} + v\frac{\partial u}{\partial y} = -\frac{1}{\rho}\frac{\partial p}{\partial x}$$

$$u\frac{\partial v}{\partial x} + v\frac{\partial v}{\partial y} = -\frac{1}{\rho}\frac{\partial p}{\partial y} \tag{1}$$

$$\frac{\partial \rho u}{\partial x} + \frac{\partial \rho v}{\partial y} = 0$$

Using the relation $a^2 = dp/d\rho$, the first two equations may be written

$$u\frac{\partial u}{\partial x} + v\frac{\partial u}{\partial y} = -\frac{a^2}{\rho}\frac{\partial \rho}{\partial x}$$

$$u\frac{\partial v}{\partial x} + v\frac{\partial v}{\partial y} = -\frac{a^2}{\rho}\frac{\partial \rho}{\partial y}$$

* One excellent volume that contains a comprehensive treatment of the theory and an extensive bibliography of original papers is: *General Theory of High Speed Aerodynamics*, edited by W. R. Sears, Volume VI in the series High Speed Aerodynamics and Jet Propulsion, Princeton University Press, Princeton, New Jersey, 1954.

The first of these equations is multiplied by u and the second by v, and the two are added, giving

$$u^2 \frac{\partial u}{\partial x} + uv \frac{\partial u}{\partial y} + uv \frac{\partial v}{\partial x} + v^2 \frac{\partial v}{\partial y} = -\frac{a^2}{\rho} \left(u \frac{\partial \rho}{\partial x} + v \frac{\partial \rho}{\partial y} \right) \qquad (2)$$

The third of Eqs. 1 may be expanded and becomes

$$\frac{\partial u}{\partial x} + \frac{\partial v}{\partial y} = -\frac{1}{\rho} \left\{ u \frac{\partial \rho}{\partial x} + v \frac{\partial \rho}{\partial y} \right\} \qquad (3)$$

Substituting Eq. 3 in the right side of Eq. 2 gives

$$\left(\frac{u^2}{a^2} - 1 \right) \frac{\partial u}{\partial x} + \frac{uv}{a^2} \left(\frac{\partial u}{\partial y} + \frac{\partial v}{\partial x} \right) + \left(\frac{v^2}{a^2} - 1 \right) \frac{\partial v}{\partial y} = 0 \qquad (4)$$

Introducing the irrotationality condition $(\partial v/\partial x - \partial u/\partial y) = 0$ and the velocity potential, Eq. 4 becomes

$$\left(\frac{u^2}{a^2} - 1 \right) \frac{\partial^2 \varphi}{\partial x^2} + \left(\frac{2uv}{a^2} \right) \frac{\partial^2 \varphi}{\partial x \partial y} + \left(\frac{v^2}{a^2} - 1 \right) \frac{\partial^2 \varphi}{\partial y^2} = 0 \qquad (5)$$

Equation 5 is the steady flow equation for a nonviscous compressible fluid. Its three-dimensional counterpart is:

$$\left(\frac{u^2}{a^2} - 1 \right) \frac{\partial^2 \varphi}{\partial x^2} + \left(\frac{v^2}{a^2} - 1 \right) \frac{\partial^2 \varphi}{\partial y^2} + \left(\frac{w^2}{a^2} - 1 \right) \frac{\partial^2 \varphi}{\partial z^2} + \frac{2}{a^2} \left\{ uv \frac{\partial^2 \varphi}{\partial x \partial y} + \right.$$
$$\left. vw \frac{\partial^2 \varphi}{\partial y \partial z} + wu \frac{\partial^2 \varphi}{\partial z \partial x} \right\} = 0 \qquad (6)$$

The sonic speed a is a variable. It may be put in terms of the flow speed by using the energy relation, Eq. 9 of Chapter 9, in the form

$$a^2 + \frac{\gamma - 1}{2} V^2 = a_\infty{}^2 + \frac{\gamma - 1}{2} V_\infty{}^2 \qquad (7)$$

All velocities may, of course, be written in terms of the velocity potential. Equations 5 and 6 may therefore be written with φ as the only dependent variable. Because of the great complexity of the resulting potential equation, an analytical solution for boundary conditions corresponding to shapes of interest in aerodynamics is not possible. Fortunately, many practical flow problems can be approximately represented by a linearized form of the flow equation. This form is developed in the next section.

It should be observed that for an incompressible fluid, a is infinite and Eqs. 5 and 6 reduce to Laplace's equation, solutions of which are treated in earlier chapters.

11.3 FLOW EQUATION FOR SMALL PERTURBATIONS

A thin body at a small angle of attack in motion through a fluid, in general, disturbs the fluid only slightly. That is, the perturbation caused by the body is small compared to the velocity of the body.

Consider a thin body moving with speed $-V_\infty$ through a fluid. An observer stationed on the body will see a uniform stream V_∞ on which are superimposed perturbation components u', v', and w'. The perturbation components, except at stagnation points, will be small compared to V_∞. Assuming V_∞ to be in the direction of the x-axis, the total velocity at any point will be given by the three components.

$$V_\infty + u' \tag{8}$$
$$v'$$
$$w'$$

Expressions 8 are substituted into Eq. 5, giving the result

$$\left(\frac{V_\infty{}^2 + 2u'V_\infty + u'^2}{a^2} - 1\right)\frac{\partial^2\varphi}{\partial x^2} + 2\left(\frac{V_\infty v' + u'v'}{a^2}\right)\frac{\partial^2\varphi}{\partial x\partial y} +$$

$$\left(\frac{v'^2}{a^2} - 1\right)\frac{\partial^2\varphi}{\partial y^2} = 0 \tag{9}$$

Since V_∞ is a constant, the second derivative of its potential is zero, and therefore φ in Eq. 9 may be regarded as either the perturbation potential or the total potential of the flow. In this chapter, φ is taken as the perturbation potential. It will be shown that under certain conditions the bracketed coefficients are constants and Eq. 9 becomes a linear equation in the perturbation potential.

If the velocity is written as the sum of free-stream and perturbation parts in Eq. 7, the sonic ratio becomes

$$\left(\frac{a}{a_\infty}\right)^2 = 1 - \frac{\gamma - 1}{2}M_\infty{}^2\left(2\frac{u'}{V_\infty} + \frac{u'^2}{V_\infty{}^2} + \frac{v'^2}{V_\infty{}^2}\right)$$

or neglecting higher order terms in the perturbation to free stream ratio

$$\left(\frac{a}{a_\infty}\right)^2 \simeq 1 - (\gamma - 1)M_\infty{}^2\frac{u'}{V_\infty} \tag{10}$$

From Eq. 10, it can be seen that a may be replaced with a_∞ providing

$$M_\infty^2 \frac{u'}{V_\infty} \ll 1$$

Because the condition $u'/V_\infty \ll 1$ has already been assumed, it follows from Eq. 10 that a may be replaced with a_∞ except when M_∞ is very large, that is, except in the hypersonic range. With this restriction in mind, Eq. 9 may be written

$$\left\{ M_\infty^2 - 1 + M_\infty^2\left(2\frac{u'}{V_\infty} + \frac{u'^2}{V_\infty^2}\right)\right\} \frac{\partial^2 \varphi}{\partial x^2} + 2M_\infty^2 \left\{\frac{v'}{V_\infty} + \frac{u'v'}{V_\infty^2}\right\} \frac{\partial^2 \varphi}{\partial x \partial y} +$$

$$\left\{ M_\infty^2\left(\frac{v'}{V_\infty}\right)^2 - 1\right\} \frac{\partial^2 \varphi}{\partial y^2} = 0 \quad (11)$$

Assuming the second order derivatives in Eq. 11 to be of the same order of magnitude, a further simplification is achieved by discarding all terms in the coefficients that are small compared to unity. The coefficient of the first term may be written

$$\left(M_\infty^2 - 1\right)\left\{ 1 + \frac{M_\infty^2}{M_\infty^2 - 1}\left(2\frac{u'}{V_\infty} + \frac{u'^2}{V_\infty^2}\right)\right\}$$

which simplifies to $(M_\infty^2 - 1)(1)$ provided that

$$\frac{M_\infty^2}{M_\infty^2 - 1}\frac{u'}{V_\infty} \ll 1$$

The above condition is fulfilled if the additional requirement is imposed that the flow not be transonic, that is, that M_∞ not be close to unity.

The coefficient of the second term of Eq. 11 is small compared to unity provided that

$$M_\infty^2 \frac{v'}{V_\infty} \ll 1$$

which is satisfied if the perturbations are small and the hypersonic range is avoided. The same restrictions reduce the coefficient of the third term to -1.

Equation 11 becomes finally

$$(1 - M_\infty^2)\frac{\partial^2 \varphi}{\partial x^2} + \frac{\partial^2 \varphi}{\partial y^2} = 0 \quad (12)$$

A similar analysis applied to the three-dimensional flow equation gives the result

$$(1 - M_\infty^2) \frac{\partial^2 \varphi}{\partial x^2} + \frac{\partial^2 \varphi}{\partial y^2} + \frac{\partial^2 \varphi}{\partial z^2} = 0 \tag{13}$$

The specific restrictions that make Eqs. 12 and 13 valid approximations to Eqs. 5 and 6 respectively are

$$M_\infty^2 \frac{u'}{V_\infty} \ll 1 \qquad M_\infty^2 \frac{v'}{V_\infty} \ll 1 \qquad M_\infty^2 \frac{w'}{V_\infty} \ll 1$$

$$\frac{M_\infty^2}{M_\infty^2 - 1} \frac{u'}{V_\infty} \ll 1 \tag{14}$$

The conditions expressed by the inequalities above are satisfied away from stagnation points of thin bodies moving through a fluid at other than transonic or hypersonic speeds.

Equation 13 is a linear differential equation that may be solved for a given set of boundary conditions by superimposing elementary solutions. This technique, which is analogous to the procedure used in Chapters 4, 5, and 6 for incompressible flows is employed in the supersonic range $(M_\infty > 1)$. In the subsonic range $(M_\infty < 1)$, Eq. 13 is readily reduced to Laplace's equation by a transformation of variables, thereby reducing the subsonic compressible flow problem to an equivalent incompressible flow problem.

11.4 THE PRESSURE COEFFICIENT FOR SMALL PERTURBATIONS

For small perturbations the difference between the pressure p at any point in the flow and the free stream pressure p_∞ is given to first order of approximation by Eq. 11 of Chapter 7 (gravity neglected)

$$p - p_\infty = dp = -\rho \, d \frac{V^2}{2} \tag{15}$$

ρ may be expressed as the sum of a free-stream part ρ_∞ and a perturbation part ρ'. Also, $d(V^2/2)$ is interpreted as the difference $(V^2 - V_\infty^2)/2$.

$$\frac{V^2 - V_\infty^2}{2} = V_\infty u' + \frac{u'^2 + v'^2 + w'^2}{2}$$

Making these substitutions in Eq. 15 leads to

$$p - p_\infty = -(\rho_\infty + \rho') \left\{ V_\infty u' + \frac{u'^2 + v'^2 + w'^2}{2} \right\}$$

After neglecting all terms greater than first degree in the perturbations, the above equation becomes

$$p - p_\infty = -\rho_\infty V_\infty u'$$

which leads to the pressure coefficient

$$C_p \equiv \frac{p - p_\infty}{\frac{1}{2}\rho V_\infty{}^2} = -\frac{2u'}{V_\infty} \tag{16}$$

11.5 LIFTING AND NONLIFTING COMPONENTS— BOUNDARY CONDITIONS

As explained in previous chapters on airfoil theory, the wing is a barrier to the flow in the sense that there can be no resultant velocity component normal to the surface. In other words, the sum of the components of the free-stream and perturbation velocities normal to the

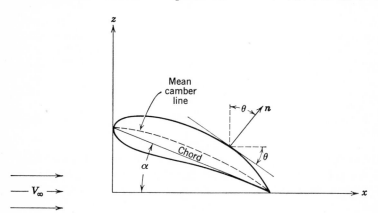

Fig. 1.   Section geometry.

surface must be zero. With reference to Fig. 1, which represents an airfoil section with exaggerated thickness, camber, and angle of attack, the condition of vanishing normal component at the boundary is expressed by

$$V_{\infty n} + \frac{\partial \varphi}{\partial n} = 0 \tag{17}$$

θ is the angle between the tangent to the surface and the free-stream direction. Then

$$V_{\infty n} = -V_\infty \sin \theta \simeq -V_\infty \theta \tag{18}$$

For situations in which small perturbation theory is applicable, θ is small and to close approximation it may be taken as the sum of the following three parts (Fig. 2): (a) angle between the free stream and the chord line, that is, the angle of attack, α; (b) angle between the chord line and the tangent to the mean camber line; (c) angle between the tangent to the mean camber line and the tangent to the surface.

As a consequence of the additive character of the three contributions, the flow field may be treated as the superposition of a flat plate at an angle of attack, the mean camber line at *zero* angle of attack, and a symmetrical thickness envelope at *zero* angle of attack.*

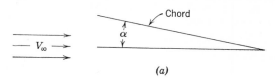

(a)

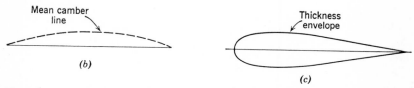

(b)

(c)

FIG. 2. Resolution of slope θ into parts due to angle of attack, camber, and thickness.

Items (a) and (b) contribute to the lift. Item (c) is nonlifting. To find the flow pattern or pressure distribution for the airfoil of Fig. 1 the lifting and nonlifting problems are solved separately and the results added.

Finally, following the procedure of Chapter 5, the *planar wing* approximation is made and the boundary condition expressed by Eq. 17 is satisfied in the $z = 0$ plane. Equation 17 becomes:

$$\left(\frac{\partial \varphi}{\partial z}\right)_{z=0} = V_\infty \theta \tag{19}$$

For the lifting problem, θ has the same sign on the upper and lower surfaces of the wing, and therefore $\partial \varphi / \partial z$ has the same sign at $z = 0+$ and $z = 0-$. For the nonlifting problem $\partial \varphi / \partial z$ has opposite signs at $z = 0+$ and $z = 0-$.

This important idea has a bearing on the solution of the flow problems and is used later in Sections 11.9 and 11.10.

* The mean camber line and thickness envelope have been defined in Chapter 5.

11.6 PLANAR WINGS IN SUBSONIC FLOW—PRANDTL-GLAUERT TRANSFORMATION

By a suitable transformation of variables, Eq. 13 can be reduced to Laplace's equation when $M_\infty < 1$. This suggests that the subsonic compressible flow problem can be reduced to an equivalent incompressible flow problem. In this section, the Prandtl-Glauert rule which gives the details of the transformation is developed.

The applicable equations are 13 and 19, which are written in the form

$$(1 - M_\infty{}^2)\varphi_{xx} + \varphi_{yy} + \varphi_{zz} = 0 \tag{20}$$

$$\theta = \frac{1}{V_\infty}\,\varphi_z \tag{21}$$

If x in Eq. 20 is replaced with

$$x = x_0 \sqrt{1 - M_\infty{}^2} \tag{22}$$

and all other variables are left the same, the equation reduces to

$$\varphi_{x_0 x_0} + \varphi_{yy} + \varphi_{zz} = 0 \tag{23}$$

which is Laplace's equation in the variable x_0, y, z. The transformation has stretched the x-coordinate by the factor $1/\sqrt{1 - M_\infty{}^2}$. *Corresponding* points in the two fields shown in Fig. 3 have the same y- and z-

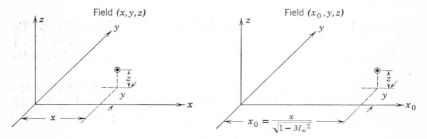

FIG. 3.   Prandtl-Glauert transformation.

coordinates and the x-coordinates are related by Eq. 22. The values of φ at *corresponding points are identical.* Because the z-coordinate in the two fields is the same, it must also be true that the values of φ_z *at corresponding points are identical.*

To apply this information, consider a wing in field (x, y, z) that is in the presence of a stream for which $0 < M_\infty < 1$. This case will be referred to in the following as the subsonic wing. In accordance with the boundary condition, Eq. 21, specific values of φ_z will be forced at a group of points in the $z = 0$ plane as represented by the shaded area in Fig. 4a. The corresponding points in the $z = 0$ plane of field (x_0, y, z), drawn shaded in Fig. 4b, must have the same value of φ_z. Consequently, according to Eq. 21, the Mach zero wing of Fig. 4b must have the same slope at corresponding points as the subsonic wing of Fig. 4a. If the two wings have the same slopes at corresponding points, then the wing cross sections have the same shape.

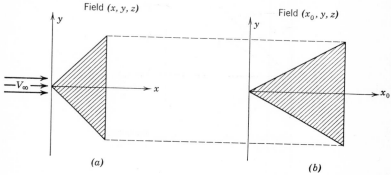

Field (x, y, z)

Field (x_0, y, z)

$-V_\infty$

x

x_0

(a)

(b)

FIG. 4. Application of the Prandtl-Glauert transformation to the finite wing.

Because the flow about the Mach zero wing is governed by Eq. 23, the following conclusion can be drawn:

Equations 20 and 21 may be solved by finding the solution to Eq. 23 for a wing of greater sweep, smaller aspect ratio, and the same section shape.

The manner of defining aspect ratio and sweep will determine the way these quantities are related for the two wings. For the triangular wing in Fig. 4, the leading edge sweep angle σ_0 of the Mach zero wing is related to the leading edge sweep angle σ of the subsonic wing by the formula

$$\frac{\tan \sigma_0}{\tan \sigma} = \frac{\dfrac{n}{b/2}}{\dfrac{m}{b/2}} = \frac{n}{m} = \frac{1}{\sqrt{1 - M_\infty^2}}$$

$$\sigma_0 = \tan^{-1}\left\{\frac{\tan \sigma}{\sqrt{1 - M_\infty^2}}\right\} \tag{24}$$

The geometry is shown in Fig. 5. The aspect ratio $\mathcal{R}_0$ of the Mach zero wing is related to the aspect ratio $\mathcal{R}$ of the subsonic wing by the formula

$$\frac{\mathcal{R}_0}{\mathcal{R}} = \frac{b^2/S_0}{b^2/S} = \frac{S}{S_0} = \frac{c}{c_0} = \sqrt{1 - M_\infty^2}$$

$$\mathcal{R}_0 = \sqrt{1 - M_\infty^2}\,\mathcal{R} \qquad\qquad (25)$$

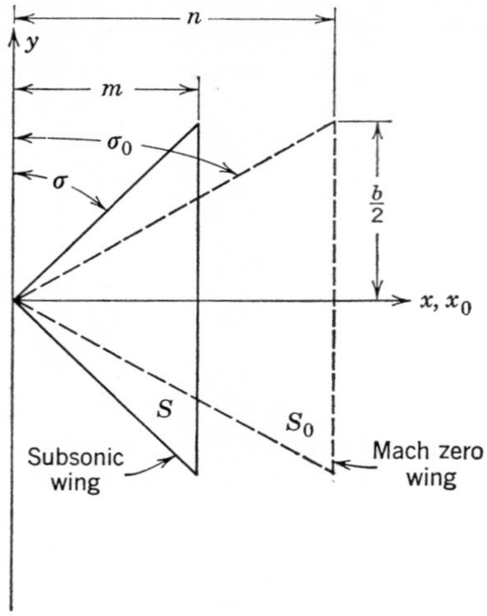

Fig. 5.   Geometric relations for the Mach zero and subsonic wings.

The pressure coefficient Eq. 16, may be written for the subsonic and Mach zero wings as

$$C_p = \frac{-2\varphi_x}{V_\infty} \qquad\qquad (26)$$

$$C_{p_0} = \frac{-2\varphi_{x_0}}{V_\infty}$$

Using Eq. 22, we can write at corresponding points

$$\varphi_x = \frac{1}{\sqrt{1 - M_\infty^2}}\,\varphi_{x_0} \qquad\qquad (27)$$

Therefore, at corresponding points we have the Prandtl-Glauert rule,

$$C_p = \frac{C_{p_0}}{\sqrt{1 - M_\infty^2}} \qquad\qquad (28)$$

The pressure coefficient on the subsonic wing is greater than it is at a corresponding point on the Mach zero wing by the factor $1/\sqrt{1 - M_\infty^2}$.

It must be kept in mind that the Mach zero wing to which C_{p_0} refers has a different planform for each value of M_∞.

It is interesting to notice that the sectional lift of the subsonic wing is exactly equal to the sectional lift of the corresponding Mach zero wing. Using the notation C_{p_L} and C_{p_U} to represent the pressure coefficients on the lower and upper surfaces respectively, the sectional lift may be written

$$L' = \int_{L.E.}^{T.E.} (C_{p_L} - C_{p_U}) q \, dx$$

$$= \int_{L.E.}^{T.E.} \frac{(C_{p_L} - C_{p_U})_0}{\sqrt{1 - M_\infty^2}} \, q \, d(\sqrt{1 - M_\infty^2} \, x_0) = L_0' \quad (29)$$

Because there is no difference in span between the subsonic and Mach zero wings, it follows that the total lift is also the same for the two.

For the special case of two-dimensional wings, Eq. 28 has a simple interpretation. No planform distortions are involved. The subsonic and Mach zero wings differ only in chord length. This distinction in size cannot influence the nondimensional pressure coefficient and, therefore, C_{p_0} may be viewed as the pressure coefficient of the subsonic wing operating at Mach zero. C_{p_0}, being free of planform influences, is independent of M_∞.

By the same argument, the lift curve slope for a section of a two-dimensional wing may be written

$$\frac{dc_l}{d\alpha} = \frac{(dc_l/d\alpha)_0}{\sqrt{1 - M_\infty^2}}$$

where $(dc_l/d\alpha)_0$ is the lift curve slope of the subsonic wing operating at zero Mach number. A comparison of the above formula with experiment is shown in Fig. 10 of Appendix C. The experimental curve reaches a peak and then drops off rapidly as a Mach number of unity is approached. This is a transonic effect and is discussed in the next section.

11.7 THE CRITICAL MACH NUMBER OF AN AIRFOIL

The Prandtl-Glauert rule treated in the last section shows the influence of compressibility on the pressure coefficient in the subsonic range. It is understood that Eq. 28 is limited in application to those flow fields that satisfy the conditions of small perturbation theory. It is valid only for values of M_∞ for which the flow is irrotational outside the boundary layer. In other words, any shock waves in the flow must be of negligible intensity.

Experiments show * that, at a certain value of the free-stream Mach number less than unity, a shock wave forms on the upper surface of the airfoil. The shock first appears at a point on the airfoil where the local velocity just exceeds the local velocity of sound, that is, where the local Mach number just exceeds unity. At a certain value of the free-stream Mach number, the local Mach number at the point of minimum pressure on the airfoil will reach unity; this value of the free-stream Mach number is called the critical Mach number of the airfoil in the following paragraphs. Shock wave configurations on the upper surface of an airfoil at a free-stream Mach number greater than critical are shown in Fig. 9 of Chapter 14.

Above the critical Mach number the flow is partly subsonic and partly supersonic, and the theoretical considerations of the last section do not apply. It is to be expected that no drastic change in the pressure distribution occurs when the critical Mach number is reached, for if a shock occurs at the point of local sonic velocity it will be of infinitesimal strength, and the losses through it will be of no consequence. As the free-stream Mach number is increased above critical, a shock wave of increasing intensity becomes observable. A rising drag coefficient attends the increasing shock intensity. The high pressure behind the shock is communicated upstream through the subsonic portion of the boundary layer and the pressure discontinuity at the shock in the main flow appears as a steep gradient in the boundary layer. For some value of the free-stream Mach number above critical the adverse pressure gradient causes separation of the flow from the body, and a large rise in drag and decrease in lift occurs. The Mach number at which the lift drops off has been called the *Mach number of divergence*. Experimental results that show the behavior of the lift curve slope and drag coefficient in the neighborhood of the divergence Mach number are shown in Figs. 10 and 12 respectively of Appendix C.

The Mach number of divergence is greater than the critical Mach number and defines the upper limit of usefulness of high speed subsonic airfoils. Because the flow is partly subsonic and partly supersonic above the critical Mach number, the Mach number of divergence cannot be predicted theoretically.

The critical Mach number that defines the upper limit of applicability of subsonic theory can be predicted approximately from the Prandtl-Glauert formula, Eq. 28 of the last section. For two-dimensional wings, Eq. 28 is particularly simple in that C_{p_0} is the zero Mach number pres-

* For example, see J. Stack, W. F. Lindsey, and R. E. Littell, *The Compressibility Burble and the Effect of Compressibility on the Pressures and Forces Acting on an Airfoil*, NACA Report 646, 1938.

sure coefficient for the wing being considered; that is, planform distortion does not enter the problem. Then, if low-speed pressure distribution data is known for a two-dimensional wing, the critical Mach number can be computed as outlined below.

In Eq. 16 of Chapter 9, the static-stagnation ratio of the pressure is given by

$$\frac{p}{p_0} = \left(1 + \frac{\gamma - 1}{2} M^2\right)^{\gamma/(1-\gamma)}$$

Let p and M be the pressure and Mach number at the point of minimum pressure on the airfoil. Let p_∞ and M_∞ be the pressure and Mach number of the free stream. Then,

$$\frac{p}{p_\infty} = \left\{\frac{1 + [(\gamma - 1)/2]M^2}{1 + [(\gamma - 1)/2]M_\infty^2}\right\}^{\gamma/(1-\gamma)} \tag{30}$$

The pressure coefficient at the point of minimum pressure is

$$\frac{p - p_\infty}{(\rho_\infty/2)V_\infty^2} = C_p = \frac{2}{\gamma M_\infty^2}\left\{\frac{p}{p_\infty} - 1\right\} \tag{31}$$

Substituting Eq. 30 in Eq. 31, the pressure coefficient becomes

$$C_p = \frac{2}{\gamma M_\infty^2}\left[\left\{\frac{1 + [(\gamma - 1)/2]M^2}{1 + [(\gamma - 1)/2]M_\infty^2}\right\}^{\gamma/(1-\gamma)} - 1\right]$$

If $M = 1$, then by definition $M_\infty = M_{cr}$ and $C_p = C_{p_{cr}}$.

$$C_{p_{cr}} = \frac{2}{\gamma M_{cr}^2}\left[\left\{\frac{(\gamma + 1)/2}{1 + [(\gamma - 1)/2]M_{cr}^2}\right\}^{\gamma/(1-\gamma)} - 1\right] \tag{32}$$

From Eq. 32 may be found the critical Mach number of the airfoil when the pressure coefficient at the point of minimum pressure is known. A plot of $C_{p_{cr}}$ versus M_{cr} is represented by the solid line in Fig. 6.

From the test data at low speeds, the pressure coefficient at the point of minimum pressure may be found. Then, by applying the Prandtl-Glauert rule,

$$C_p = \frac{C_{p_0}}{\sqrt{1 - M_\infty^2}} \tag{28}$$

The pressure coefficient at the point of minimum pressure for several values of the free-stream Mach number may be computed. The dotted line in Fig. 6 represents the plot of such a computation for the 4412 airfoil at an angle of attack of 1°52.5′. At the intersection, Eqs. 32 and 28 are both satisfied, and therefore the Mach number at the point of intersection represents the critical Mach number of the airfoil.

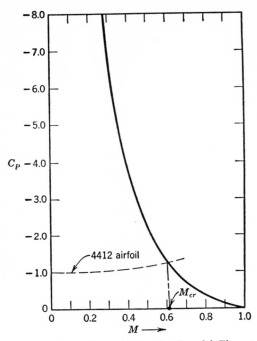

FIG. 6.   Critical Mach number by the Prandtl-Glauert rule.

The critical Mach number decreases with increases in thickness and camber, and it is generally the maximum for angles of attack for which the negative pressure peaks are small, that is, at a low angle of attack. A plot of critical Mach number versus lift coefficient for several airfoils is shown in Fig. 9 of Appendix C.

11.8   THE THIN WING IN SUPERSONIC FLOW

The shock expansion method of calculating the pressure distribution on a two-dimensional wing utilizes oblique shock theory and the Prandtl-Meyer flow discussed in Chapter 10. At the nose of the airfoil, the flow must be turned from the free-stream direction to a direction tangent to the airfoil surface. If the amount of turning required does not exceed the maximum deflection angle for the free-stream Mach number considered, then the flow configuration will appear as shown in Fig. 7. The oblique shock at the nose turns the flow and compresses the fluid. The pressure just downstream of the shock may be calculated by oblique shock theory. As the fluid proceeds along the surface it is expanded and the pressure at any point may be computed from Prandtl-Meyer theory.

The shock expansion method is exact and is applicable as long as the initial turning can be accomplished by an oblique shock. If the turning cannot be accomplished by an oblique shock, a detached shock appears ahead of the airfoil, as shown in Fig. 14 of Chapter 10.

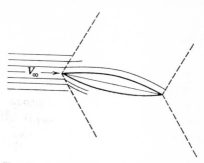

FIG. 7. Flow configuration in the shock-expansion method of calculating pressure distributions.

The role of two-dimensional section properties in finite-wing theory is not the same in subsonic and supersonic flow. In subsonic flow, every section of the finite wing feels the effect of the wing tips. In contrast, finite wings in supersonic flow may have completely two-dimensional sections. This can be illustrated by the finite wing of Fig. 8. According to the rule of forbidden signals, any point on the

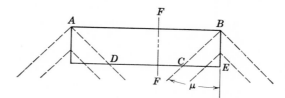

FIG. 8.   Finite wing in supersonic flow.

wing influences only that part of the wing lying within the downstream Mach cone of the point. Therefore, the side edge BE influences only the triangular area BCE. Any section of the wing, for example, FF, lying within the trapezoidal area $ABCD$ is completely two-dimensional.

At first glance, this fact would appear to be a strong case for emphasizing two-dimensional section characteristics in supersonic wing theory. In practice, however, the supersonic wing tends to have large sweep or low-aspect ratio or both, so that little if any of its area is two-dimensional.

To deal exactly with the supersonic finite wing would involve shock waves and rotational flow. However, even ignoring shocks and assuming isentropy, the equation governing the flow, Eq. 6, is too complicated to solve. The assumption of small perturbations is made at the outset, which reduces the problem to the linear equation

$$(1 - M_\infty{}^2)\varphi_{xx} + \varphi_{yy} + \varphi_{zz} = 0 \qquad (13)$$

which is solved for the planar wing boundary condition

$$\{\varphi_z\}_{z=0} = V_\infty\theta \qquad (19)$$

The approach used in the remainder of this chapter follows that introduced in the incompressible flow theory of Chapters 4, 5, and 6. The *supersonic source*, an elementary solution of Eq. 13, is used to generate particular solutions that satisfy the boundary condition, Eq. 19.* A trailing edge consideration corresponding to the Kutta condition must also be applied in some cases.

The purpose here is to introduce the reader to some of the concepts involved in the solution of the finite-wing problem by the method of sources. The two-dimensional wing is treated because it represents a simple application of the method and because section properties at supersonic speed contrast interestingly with the incompressible flow properties developed in Chapter 5.

The aerodynamic behavior of supersonic wings as determined by experiment is discussed in Section 4 of Appendix C. Figures are given there which compare experimental results with the linearized theory of this chapter.

For a bibliography of the vast literature on supersonic wing theory and a comprehensive treatment of the various methods of solving Eq. 13, the reader is referred to the work of Heaslet and Lomax.†

11.9 THE SUPERSONIC SOURCE

For a thin body in a supersonic stream, the perturbation potential must satisfy Eq. 13. Using the notation

$$B^2 = M_\infty{}^2 - 1 \qquad (33)$$

Eq. 13 may be written

$$-B^2\varphi_{xx} + \varphi_{yy} + \varphi_{zz} = 0 \qquad (34)$$

---

* Two references in which supersonic finite-wing theory has been developed, using the method of sources are Allen E. Puckett, "Supersonic Wave Drag of Thin Airfoils," *J. Aero. Sci.*, September 1946; and John E. Evvard, *Use of Source Distributions for Evaluating Theoretical Aerodynamics of Thin Finite Wings at Supersonic Speeds*, NACA Report 951, 1950.

† *General Theory of High Speed Aerodynamics*, edited by W. R. Sears, Vol. VI, Section D, in the series High Speed Aerodynamics and Jet Propulsion, Princeton University Press, Princeton, N. J., 1954.

An elementary solution from which particular solutions may be found by superposition is of the form

$$\varphi = \frac{-C}{h} \tag{35}$$

where the hyperbolic radius h is given by

$$h = \sqrt{x^2 - B^2(y^2 + z^2)} \tag{36}$$

and C is a constant. The reader may verify by direct substitution that expression 35 is a solution of Eq. 34.

For the incompressible flow case, $M_\infty = 0$, Eq. 34 reduces to Laplace's equation, the hyperbolic radius h reduces to the geometric radius r, and the elementary solution, Eq. 35, is that of a source at the origin in three-dimensional flow.* The name *source* is carried over to the supersonic case though the physical interpretation of fluid issuing from a point is no longer applicable.

To interpret the hyperbolic radius, consider a cone with apex at the source, as shown in Fig. 9. The axis of the cone is in the free-stream

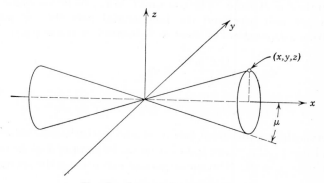

Fig. 9.   Supersonic point source.

direction and the semiapex angle is the Mach angle μ. From Eq. 1 of Chapter 10

$$\sin \mu = \frac{1}{M_\infty}$$

and, therefore,

$$\cot \mu = \sqrt{M_\infty^2 - 1} = B \tag{37}$$

From Fig. 9 it can be seen that field points (x, y, z) lying on the surface

* See Section 4.3.

of the cone satisfy the relation

$$\frac{x}{\sqrt{y^2 + z^2}} = \cot \mu = B \tag{38}$$

By using Eqs. 37 and 38 in Eq. 36 it can be seen that h vanishes for field points lying on the Mach cone. h is real for field points within the Mach cone and imaginary outside the Mach cone.

The source potential as given by Eq. 35 is defined as zero for all field points lying outside the downstream Mach cone extending from the source. Physically, field points inside the downstream Mach cone correspond to the zone of action of the source, while all other points are in the zone of silence.

The position of a source within the field will be denoted by the *source coordinates* (ξ, η, ζ). The hyperbolic radius connecting an arbitrarily located source with the field point x, y, z is given by

$$h = \sqrt{(x - \xi)^2 - B^2[(y - \eta)^2 + (z - \zeta)^2]}$$

In planar wing theory a sheet of continuously distributed sources is placed in the $\zeta = 0$ plane. The constant C in Eq. 35 becomes the source strength per unit area and the incremental perturbation potential arising from an increment of sheet $d\xi\, d\eta$ located at source point $(\xi, \eta, 0)$ is

$$d\varphi = \frac{-C(\xi, \eta, 0)}{h} \, d\xi \, d\eta \tag{39}$$

$$h = \sqrt{(x - \xi)^2 - B^2\{(y - \eta)^2 + z^2\}} \tag{40}$$

In general, the perturbation potential and perturbation velocities at any field point (x, y, z) are found from an integral of Eq. 39 over the source points $(\xi, \eta, 0)$. The one important exception is the perturbation velocity,

$$w = \varphi_z$$

at field points lying in the z equals zero plane.

The perturbation velocity dw arising from an incremental source at $(\xi, \eta, 0)$ is given by the z-derivative of Eq. 39.

$$dw = -B^2 C(\xi, \eta) \frac{z}{h^3} \, d\xi \, d\eta \tag{41}$$

For field points in the $z = 0$ plane, dw vanishes everywhere except at the source itself. At the source point both numerator and denominator of the right-hand side of Eq. 41 vanish and no information on

dw can be gained. w has been evaluated at the source point * with the result,

$$w = \pm \pi C \tag{42}$$

That is, w at any point on the source sheet arises only from the source at that point. w is a point property rather than an integrated property of the source sheet. The positive sign refers to the upper surface of the sheet $z = 0+$ and the negative sign to the lower surface $z = 0-$.

11.10   THE NONLIFTING PROBLEM

The nonlifting part of any wing is a symmetrical thickness envelope, as explained in Section 11.5. At any point along the chord of the

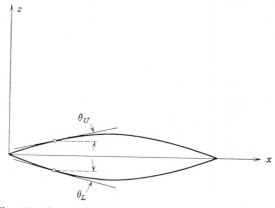

FIG. 10.   Boundary condition for the nonlifting problem.

typical cross section shown in Fig. 10, the slopes θ of the upper and lower surfaces have equal magnitudes and opposite signs.

$$\theta_L = -\theta_U \tag{43}$$

From Eq. 19, the planar wing boundary condition is

$$\left\{ \frac{\partial \varphi}{\partial z} \right\}_{z=0\pm} = \pm V_\infty \theta_U \tag{44}$$

The source of strength C in the $\zeta = 0$ plane provides a w perturbation equal to $+\pi C$ at $z = 0+$ and $-\pi C$ at $z = 0-$. Therefore, from Eqs. 42 and 44, the source distribution that will satisfy the boundary condition at $z = 0+$ and $z = 0-$ is

$$C(\xi, \eta) = \frac{V_\infty}{\pi} \theta_U \tag{45}$$

* Allen E. Puckett, "Supersonic Wave Drag of Thin Airfoils."

The velocity potential at any field point (x, y, z) is given by the integral of Eq. 39. Using Eq. 45 for the source strength,

$$\varphi = \iint_{\text{wing}} - \frac{V_\infty}{\pi} \theta_U \frac{d\xi \, d\eta}{h} \tag{46}$$

The pressure coefficient is obtained from the x-derivative of the potential as shown by Eq. 16. Therefore,

$$C_p(x, y, 0\pm) = + \frac{2}{\pi} \frac{\partial}{\partial x} \iint_{\text{forecone}} \frac{\theta_U}{h} \, d\xi \, d\eta \tag{47}$$

The pressure coefficient at any point on a nonlifting wing can be obtained from Eq. 47. It remains only to discuss the region of integration indicated by the word *forecone* appended to the integral sign. To find the pressure coefficient at point A on the wing of Fig. 11, the

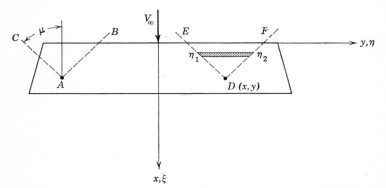

FIG. 11.   Region of integration for calculating the pressure coefficient.

integration indicated in Eq. 47 must include all source points that can affect A. A study of the figure will reveal that any source lying within the Mach cone extending forward from A will contain A in its zone of action. Therefore, the forecone ABC is the appropriate region of integration for the point A. Because the forecone from A intersects the tip, A experiences a tip effect.

In contrast, the forecone from D does not intersect the tip and if θ is independent of η, the pressure coefficient at point D will be that of a two-dimensional wing. As a simple application of Eq. 47, the two-dimensional pressure coefficient is determined by calculating C_p at field point $(x, y, 0\pm)$ represented by the point D.

$$C_p(x, y, 0\pm) = \frac{2}{\pi} \frac{\partial}{\partial x} \int_0^x \theta_U \int_{\eta_1}^{\eta_2} \frac{d\eta}{h} \, d\xi \tag{48}$$

The limit η_1 is expressed in terms of ξ by noting that the line DE has a slope $\tan \mu = 1/B$ and passes through the point $(x, y, 0)$. Therefore, the equation connecting ξ and η along DE is

$$\eta - y = \frac{1}{B}(\xi - x)$$

and η_1 is

$$\eta_1 = \frac{\xi - x}{B} + y$$

Similarly,

$$\eta_2 = \frac{\xi - x}{-B} + y \tag{49}$$

The inner integral of Eq. 40 is expanded to read *

$$\int_{\eta_1}^{\eta_2} \frac{d\eta}{h} = \int_{[(\xi - x)/B]+y}^{[(\xi - x)/-B]+y} \frac{d\eta}{\sqrt{(x - \xi)^2 - B^2(y - \eta)^2}} = \frac{\pi}{B} \tag{50}$$

Using the result above in Eq. 48 leads to a value of the two-dimensional pressure coefficient given by

$$C_p(x, y, 0\pm) = \frac{2\theta_U}{B} = \frac{2\theta_U}{\sqrt{M_\infty^2 - 1}} \tag{51}$$

11.11   THE LIFTING PROBLEM—SUPERSONIC EDGES

The lifting component of a wing is the mean camber surface at an angle of attack, as explained in Section 11.5. At any point along the chord, the slopes of the upper and lower surfaces have the same magnitude and sign,

$$\theta_L = \theta_U$$

and therefore the source, which provides oppositely directed z-perturbations at $z = 0+$ and $z = 0-$, cannot be used without further discussion of the physics of the problem.

The upper and lower surfaces of a two-dimensional lifting wing are independent of each other in the sense that disturbances at the upper surface are communicated only to the fluid within the zones of action of points on the upper surface. Consider, for instance, Fig. 12. Because no point on the lower surface is affected by the fluid in the shaded area, it follows that the lower surface cannot be influenced by the upper sur-

---

* The integral of Eq. 50 after slight rearrangement of the denominator is in standard form and may be found, for example, as formula 161 in B. O. Peirce, *A Short Table of Integrals*, third revised edition, Ginn and Co., Boston, Mass., 1929. The integrand is undefined on the Mach cone at η_1 and η_2. Therefore, the definite integral must be evaluated by the usual limiting process.

face. By the same reasoning, the upper surface cannot be influenced
by the lower surface. Some finite wings also have upper and lower sur-

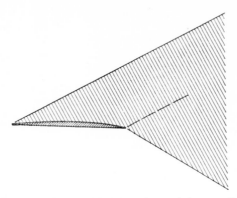

FIG. 12.   Independent upper and lower surfaces of the two-dimensional wing.

faces that are independent. To see this it is convenient to distinguish
between supersonic and subsonic edges in the following manner.

If the component of the free-stream normal to an edge of a finite wing
is supersonic, the edge is called supersonic. In the wing of Fig. 13a, the
leading edge AB and the side edge BC are subsonic, while the trailing
edge CD is supersonic. An edge that is swept inside the downstream

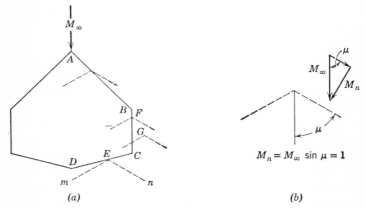

FIG. 13.   Subsonic and supersonic edges.

Mach cone is subsonic. This becomes evident when it is recognized
that the component of the free-stream normal to the Mach cone is
sonic, as shown in Fig. 13b.

A disturbance at point E on the lower surface is propagated within the downstream Mach cone nEm of Fig. 13a. Since no part of the upper surface lies within the zone of action of any point inside the Mach cone, there is no communication between upper and lower surfaces at E or at any other point along the trailing edge.

At point F on the side edge, matters are different. A disturbance on the lower surface at F is felt in the fluid at G, and the fluid at G has part of the upper surface within its zone of action. There is communication between the upper and lower surfaces all along the side edge BC and, by a similar argument, along the leading edge AB.

The wing in Fig. 14 has completely supersonic edges and therefore the upper and lower surfaces are independent. In this circumstance the upper half space prob-

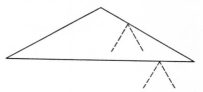

FIG. 14.   Supersonic lifting wing with independent upper and lower surfaces.

lem can be solved separately from the lower half space problem and the source solution is easily adapted to the lifting surface.

To solve the problem, sources are distributed in the $\zeta = 0$ plane that will satisfy the boundary condition at $z = 0+$. The resulting pressure coefficient at any point on the upper surface is given by Eq. 47.

$$C_p(x, y, 0+) = \frac{2}{\pi} \frac{\partial}{\partial x} \iint_{\text{forecone}} \frac{\theta}{h} \, d\xi \, d\eta \qquad (47)$$

Sources of opposite sign are then distributed in the $\zeta = 0$ plane that satisfy the boundary conditions at $z = 0-$. Equation 47 is again applicable, but with a change in sign. The pressure coefficient on the lower surface will be the negative of the pressure coefficient on the upper surface.

$$C_p(x, y, 0-) = -C_p(x, y, 0+) \qquad (52)$$

Equations 47 and 52 give the pressure coefficient for any lifting surface with supersonic edges. The two-dimensional wing is an example of a lifting surface with supersonic edges. Therefore, Eqs. 47 and 52 apply. Equation 47 has been evaluated for the two-dimensional case and is given by Eq. 51. Therefore, for the two-dimensional lifting wing,

$$C_p(x, y, 0\pm) = \pm \frac{2\theta}{\sqrt{M_\infty^2 - 1}} \qquad (53)$$

No subscript has been appended to the slope θ because upper and lower surfaces at any point on the lifting component of the wing have the same slope.

11.12 THE LIFTING PROBLEM—SUBSONIC EDGES

The portion of the $z = 0$ plane not occupied by the wing but lying within the wing's zone of action is termed the *wake*. For example, in Fig. 15 the wake is the portion of the $z = 0$ plane not occupied by the wing that lies between the lines AB and CD. To apply the method of sources to a lifting component having subsonic edges, a portion of the wake must be considered. Specifically, we must consider the part of the wake that affects the wing, for it is through this part that pressure disturbances are communicated between upper and lower surfaces.

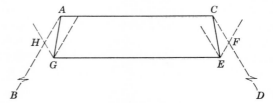

Fig. 15.   Wake of a supersonic wing.

The wake enclosed by the aft cone from C and the forecone from E, that is, the area in the triangle CFE, has the upper surface within its zone of action. But area CFE is the wake of the lower surface, and therefore it serves to connect the upper and lower surfaces. A similar argument applies to the area AHG. Apart from these two segments, no other portion of the wake is of concern.

Now assume the wing is extended into the critical wake areas so that its periphery is given by $AHGEFCA$. A fictitious wing of this type has no subsonic edge and the method of calculating C_p described in the last section applies. Actual evaluation of the integral of Eq. 47 is not possible, however, because the surface slope in the fictitious areas is unknown.

In solving the upper and lower half space problems for the fictitious wing, sources of equal magnitude and opposite sign are placed at each point on the real wing. These generate upper and lower surface values of C_p over all of the $z = 0$ plane lying within the lines AB and CD of Fig. 15. Because of the result,

$$C_p(x, y, 0-) = -C_p(x, y, 0+)$$

there is a discontinuity of pressure in the $z = 0$ plane that cannot be tolerated at points where there is no wing surface to support the discontinuity; that is, the physical requirement of a single valued pressure distribution in the wake is violated. Only that portion of the wake that affects the wing need be remedied, and to do this sources are distributed in the areas CFE and AHG that will cancel out the pressure discontinuity.

In general, the determination of the source distribution required in the fictitious areas involves the solution of an integral equation. This is the central mathematical problem in the pressure computation. Once the proper source strength is known, however, the slope of the fictitious area is established and the pressure coefficient at any point on the real wing may be computed from Eq. 47.

By a suitable change of coordinates, Evvard * has shown that for a large class of lifting surfaces with subsonic edges, the solution of the integral equation may be avoided. This reduces the subsonic edge problem to one of no greater difficulty than the supersonic edge problem.

Finally, it should be remarked that if the subsonic edge is a trailing edge, uniqueness of the solution requires the application of a Kutta condition.

11.13 SECTION CHARACTERISTICS FOR THE INFINITE SUPERSONIC WING

Two-dimensional section properties corresponding to those derived in Chapter 5 for incompressible flow can be obtained from the pressure coefficients for the lifting and nonlifting components. The subscripts U and L are used to denote upper and lower surfaces respectively. For the nonlifting component, the pressure coefficients are given by Eq. 51,

$$C_{p_U} = C_{p_L} = C_p(x, y, 0\pm) = \frac{2\theta_U}{\sqrt{M_\infty{}^2 - 1}} \tag{54}$$

and for the lifting components, by Eq. 53

$$C_{p_U} = C_p(x, y, 0+) = \frac{2\theta}{\sqrt{M_\infty{}^2 - 1}}$$

$$C_p = C_p(x, y, 0-) = \frac{-2\theta}{\sqrt{M_\infty{}^2 - 1}} \tag{55}$$

As is indicated in Fig. 16, the pressure distribution may be obtained as the sum of three parts: (a) a flat plate at an angle of attack, (b) the

* John C. Evvard, *Use of Source Distribution for Evaluating Theoretical Aerodynamic Characteristics of Thin Finite Wings at Supersonic Speeds.*

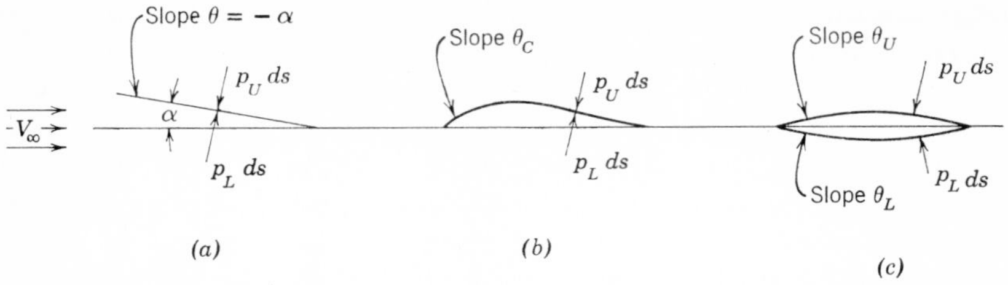

$$\theta = -\alpha$$

$$\theta = \theta_C$$

FIG. 16. Resolution of pressure distribution into parts due to angle of attack, camber, and thickness.

mean camber line at zero angle of attack, and (c) a symmetrical thickness envelope. This division was justified in Section 11.5.

For the lift contribution (a) the slope is the negative of the angle of attack.

$$\theta = -\alpha$$

and for the contribution (b) the notation

$$\theta = \theta_C$$

is used. In keeping with small perturbation theory, the cosines of all angles are set equal to unity and the sines are set equal to the angle. We shall see that the lift is determined by (a), the moment by (a) and (b), and the drag by (a), (b), and (c).

1. LIFT

The lift coefficient is given by

$$c_l = \frac{L'}{qc} = \int_0^c \frac{p_L - p_U}{qc}\,dx = \int_0^1 (C_{p_L} - C_{p_U})d\frac{x}{c} \tag{56}$$

For the flat plate at an angle of attack, using Eq. 55,

$$c_l = \frac{4\alpha}{\sqrt{M_\infty^2 - 1}} \int_0^1 d\frac{x}{c} = \frac{4}{\sqrt{M_\infty^2 - 1}}\alpha \tag{57}$$

From the mean camber line there is no contribution because the integral of the slope is zero. The thickness envelope is nonlifting. Therefore, Eq. 57 represents the entire lift coefficient. Accordingly, the lift curve slope m_0 and angle of zero lift α_{L0} are given by

$$m_0 = \frac{4}{\sqrt{M_\infty^2 - 1}} \tag{58}$$

$$\alpha_{L0} = 0 \tag{59}$$

2. MOMENT

The moment coefficient about the leading edge is approximately

$$c_{m\text{L.E.}} = \frac{M_{\text{L.E.}}}{qc^2} = -\int_0^c \frac{p_L - p_U}{qc^2}\, x\, dx = -\int_0^1 (C_{p_L} - C_{p_U}) \frac{x}{c}\, d\,\frac{x}{c} \tag{60}$$

Both the flat plate at an angle of attack and the mean camber line contribute to $c_{m\text{L.E.}}$. From the flat plate, using Eq. 55,

$$\{c_{m\text{L.E.}}\}_\alpha = \frac{-4\alpha}{\sqrt{M_\infty{}^2 - 1}} \int_0^1 \frac{x}{c}\, d\,\frac{x}{c} = -\frac{2\alpha}{\sqrt{M_\infty{}^2 - 1}} = -\frac{c_l}{2} \tag{61}$$

which indicates that the center of pressure due to angle of attack is at the midchord. From the mean camber line, again using Eq. 55,

$$\{c_{m\text{L.E.}}\}_{\theta C} = +\frac{4}{\sqrt{M_\infty{}^2 - 1}} \int_0^1 \theta_C \frac{x}{c}\, d\,\frac{x}{c} = m_0 K_1 \tag{62}$$

where the integral K_1 depends only on the shape of the airfoil and is zero for symmetrical airfoils. Because the mean camber line contributes no lift, the moment given by Eq. 62 is a couple. The midchord is the point about which the moment coefficient is independent of angle of attack, and therefore is the aerodynamic center. The sectional moment characteristics are

$$\text{a.c. at midchord} \tag{63}$$

$$c_{mac} = m_0 K_1 \tag{64}$$

3. DRAG

All three components shown in Fig. 16 contribute to the drag. The drag due to the flat plate at an angle of attack is the force normal to the plate times $\sin\alpha$. This may be written approximately in coefficient form as *

$$(c_d)_\alpha = c_l \alpha = \frac{c_l{}^2}{m_0} \tag{65}$$

From the mean camber line, using Eq. 55,

$$(c_d)_{\theta C} = -\int_0^c \frac{p_L - p_U}{qc} \theta_C\, dx = \frac{4}{\sqrt{M_\infty{}^2 - 1}} \int_0^1 \theta_C{}^2\, d\,\frac{x}{c} = m_0 K_2 \tag{66}$$

* The infinite wing in incompressible flow does not show a comparable drag because of the presence of leading edge suction.

The thickness envelope, using Eq. 54, contributes to the drag coefficient

$$(c_d)_t = \frac{4}{\sqrt{M_\infty^2 - 1}} \int_0^1 \theta_U^2\, d\frac{x}{c} = m_0 K_3 \tag{67}$$

K_2 and K_3 are integrals that depend only on the shape of the section. The total drag coefficient for the infinite wing neglecting viscous effects is

$$c_d = \frac{c_l^2}{m_0} + m_0(K_2 + K_3) \tag{68}$$

Measurements by Stanton * and Ferri † show that the lift curve slope, Eq. 58, is in fair agreement with experiment though it is definitely high. At Mach numbers near unity the formula is, of course, invalid. The angle of zero lift, Eq. 59, is zero because of the linearization. Second order theory shows a dependence on mean camber line shape. The center of pressure according to Eq. 61 is at the midchord for a symmetrical airfoil. Experiment shows it to be slightly ahead of the midchord and weakly dependent on Mach number.

The so-called *wave drag* as given by Eq. 68 has no counterpart in incompressible flow, where the drag of an infinite wing, viscosity neg-

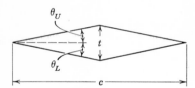

Fig. 17. Section for minimum profile drag.

lected, is zero. To the drag indicated by Eq. 68 must be added the skin friction and form drag generated by the fluid viscosity. The part of the *wave drag* dependent upon *profile shape* can be reduced by proper design. For an airfoil of given thickness it can be shown that the shape having the least profile drag is the symmetrical wedge shown in Fig. 17. The integral K_2 vanishes and K_3 may be evaluated using the approximation $\theta_U \simeq t/c$

$$K_3 = \int_0^1 \left(\frac{t}{c}\right)^2 d\frac{x}{c} = \left(\frac{t}{c}\right)^2$$

from which the wave drag at zero lift becomes

$$c_d = m_0\left(\frac{t}{c}\right)^2$$

* T. E. Stanton, *A High Speed Wind Channel for Test on Airfoils*, British Aeronautical Research Comm., Reports and Memoranda 1130, 1928.
† A. Ferri, *Experimental Results with Airfoils Tested in the High Speed Tunnel at Guidonia*, NACA TM 946, 1939.

The minimum profile drag varies as the square of the thickness to chord ratio.

11.14 INFLUENCE OF SWEEP ON DRAG

It has been shown in the last section that associated with the infinite wing in supersonic flight is a wave drag that is in part dependent upon the form of the airfoil and in part dependent upon the square of the lift coefficient. Only the trivial case of a flat plate operating at zero lift is free of wave drag.

One method of reducing the wave drag of wings is to incorporate sweepback. This may be seen by considering first the motion of an infinite wing parallel to itself through a frictionless fluid. As the wing slips through the fluid in a spanwise direction, its configuration viewed with respect to the surrounding fluid remains unchanged. Therefore, its spanwise motion can have no influence on the velocity and pressure patterns in the fluid.

If the wing is moving obliquely to itself, the spanwise component of its motion cannot influence the pressure distribution. As shown in Fig. 18, only the normal component of its motion $V_\infty \cos \sigma$ influences

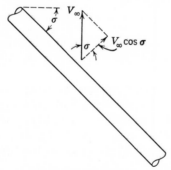

FIG. 18.   Infinite yawed wing.

the velocity and pressure fields. σ is the sweep angle measured between the leading edge and the normal to the direction of motion. If $V_\infty \cos \sigma$ is less than the velocity of sound, the wing, in effect, is moving subsonically and the wave drag associated with supersonic flow is absent. It should be remembered that if $V_\infty \cos \sigma$ is so close to a_∞ that the local normal Mach number at some point on the wing section exceeds unity, then the adverse effects of an unswept wing flying above its critical Mach number are encountered.

If the normal velocity is less than sonic, the leading edge will be swept inside the Mach cone as explained in Section 11.11. With this in mind, the physical reasoning for the influence of sweep is further clarified by Fig. 19. The airfoil at A' cannot notify the fluid at B or C of its presence because the flow is supersonic. However, the effect of the wing at B' is felt in the fluid between A' and B because this region lies behind the Mach cone of B'. Similarly, the influence of C' is felt between A' and C. In this manner the fluid at A' is warned of the

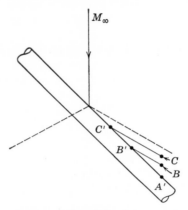

FIG. 19.   Mechanism of flow deflection around a swept wing.

presence of the wing even though the flow is supersonic. As a result, the streamlines curve around the section at A' in typical subsonic fashion.

The preceding argument applies to wings of infinite span. Its obvious extension to a swept wing of finite span is possible only for that portion of the wing that can be considered two-dimensional. It can be expected, therefore, that even though the wing is swept behind the Mach cone, wave drag will be present near the tips and in the region of the plane of symmetry.

The Dynamics of Viscous Fluids

CHAPTER 12

12.1 INTRODUCTION

In Chapters 12 through 16, the aim will be to give the reader an understanding of the role played by viscosity in determining the flow of fluids. The exact equations of conservation of mass, momentum, and energy, which were derived for inviscid flow in Chapters 3 and 8, are derived, including viscosity effects, in Appendix B. The attendant complications are so great that few exact solutions of technical importance exist. However, remarkably good approximate solutions to a large number of important engineering problems have been obtained through simplification of the equations according to the circumstances of the particular application being treated.

Many of the solutions that have been obtained depend on a physical insight for their mathematical formulation. This insight is necessary to the solution of engineering problems, and we shall therefore stress the physical reasoning leading to the simplified equations.

The analyses of the preceding chapters apply to a good approximation to the flow outside the boundary layer and the wake behind the body. Then, as long as the angle of attack is small, we may expect the perfect-fluid analysis to give a good approximation to the pressure distribution and therefore to the lift and moment acting on an airfoil. This reasoning is not completely self-evident because it presumes that the pressure at the outer edge of the boundary layer is the same as that at the solid surface. The presumption is justified in this chapter on intuitive grounds.

As soon as the angle of attack becomes large enough to cause the airfoil to *stall*, the perfect-fluid analysis is no longer of any value and

223

we must rely almost entirely on empirical results. The stall is synonymous with flow separation, which is described in Chapters 13 and 16.

Two types of drag, *form* or *pressure drag* and *skin friction*, are encountered in the flow of a viscous incompressible fluid past a body. Form or pressure drag is due to the separation of the flow from the body, for example, as occurs with a stalled airfoil. As a result of flow separation the configuration of the streamlines and hence the pressure distribution over the body are altered considerably from what they are for perfect-fluid flow. The integration over the surface of the downstream component of the pressure forces on the elements of the surface gives the form drag. This integration neglects the skin friction because the skin friction acts tangentially to the surface. A *streamline body* is defined as a body for which the major contribution to the drag is skin friction; a body for which the major contribution is form drag is defined as a *bluff body*. An airfoil, for instance, is a streamline body at low angles of attack, since skin friction accounts for 80 to 90 per cent of the drag. At angles of attack for which the airfoil is stalled, 80 to 90 per cent of the drag is form drag, and so in this case the airfoil is a bluff body.

In taking up the factors affecting the type of flow and hence the shearing stress, we shall deal constantly with *similarity parameters*, one of which is the Reynolds number, $Re = Vl/\nu$ derived in Appendix A. The Reynolds number is actually a *class* of similarity parameters, depending upon the particular characteristic length l which is used in its definition. The chord of an airfoil, the distance from the leading edge to the point of transition from laminar to turbulent flow in the boundary layer, the thickness of the boundary layer, and the height of roughness elements are some of the characteristic lengths; each is important for a different aspect of the flow. Turbulence in the incident airstream and curvature of the surface introduce other parameters. The reader should constantly keep in mind that in all viscous-flow problems a number of similarity parameters govern the phenomena observed. Much of the work in aerodynamics has for its object the identification and the evaluation of the effects of those parameters which govern the particular aspects of flow being considered.

The two distinct types of flow—laminar and turbulent—will be treated in the following chapters. These flows are distinguished from each other according to the physical mechanism of the stresses. In laminar flow, solutions to problems can be obtained by more or less straightforward simplifications of the conservation equation. In turbulent flow, however, the number of variables outnumbers the equations, so great dependence is placed on dimensional reasoning and on hypotheses suggested by experimental results.

12.2 THE NO-SLIP CONDITION

It was pointed out in Chapter 1 that the distinguishing feature of the flow of a viscous fluid around a body is the fact that at the fluid-solid interface no relative motion exists between the fluid and the body; that is, the *no-slip condition* prevails at a solid surface. The difference between the flow of viscid and inviscid fluids is therefore manifested in the boundary conditions. For inviscid fluids, the boundary condition at a solid surface is the vanishing of the velocity component normal to the surface. For a viscous fluid, however, the boundary condition must be that the *total* velocity vanishes at the surface.*

12.3 THE BOUNDARY LAYER

The boundary layer is defined as the layer adjacent to a body within which the major effects of viscosity are concentrated. Intuitively, we would expect that the alteration to the flow caused by the no-slip condition will decrease as we move out from the surface and hence that the effect will not be detectable beyond a certain distance. In other words, outside of the boundary layer, the flow of a viscous fluid will resemble closely that of an inviscid fluid.

The justification for applying the results of perfect fluid analyses to viscous flows was provided by Ludwig Prandtl in 1904. He postulated that for fluids of small viscosity, the effects of viscosity on the flow around streamline bodies are concentrated in a *thin* boundary layer. The limitation of Prandtl's hypothesis to fluids of small viscosity is broad enough to include gases as well as "watery" fluids.

We must, of course, specify a characteristic dimension *with respect to which* the boundary layer is thin. On an airfoil, for instance, at speeds of significance in aeronautics, the boundary layer will vary from practically zero thickness near the leading edge to a few per cent of the chord at the trailing edge. Then, the characteristic length with respect to which the boundary layer is thin is the distance from the forward stagnation point of the body to the point being considered.

---

* No *direct* experimental check of the no-slip condition exists. Its acceptance rests rather on the excellent agreement between the theory employing this condition and experiment. A discussion of the condition is given in *Modern Developments in Fluid Dynamics*, edited by Sydney Goldstein, Oxford University Press, 1938. In low-density flow such as exists at altitudes above a few hundred thousand feet, the mean free path of molecules is relatively large and the no-slip condition no longer obtains. Flow of air at low densities is described briefly in Appendix D.

The most important deduction from Prandtl's hypothesis of a thin boundary layer is that the *pressure change through the boundary layer is essentially zero*. This deduction is justified here on intuitive grounds. Figure 1a shows schematically the streamlines and velocity distributions in the boundary layer along a flat plate. The boundary layer thickness, designated by δ, is small everywhere, and hence $d\delta/dx$ will

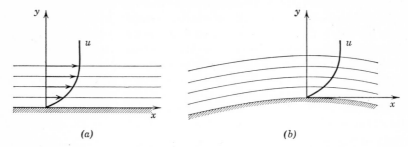

(a)   (b)

Fig. 1.   Coordinate systems for boundary layer equation.

also be small. The streamlines will therefore be only very slightly curved and the radius of curvature will be large. From the equilibrium condition (Section 3.5)

$$\frac{\partial p}{\partial y} = \frac{\rho u^2}{R}$$

and it follows that $\partial p/\partial y$ will be negligible. If the surface is curved, as shown in Fig. 1b, the conclusion is still valid. Experiment and theory indicate that $\partial p/\partial y$ may be neglected even over surfaces of quite small radius of curvature.

Since the pressure is nearly constant through the boundary layer, the *stagnation* pressure, p_0, will, by virtue of Bernoulli's equation $p + \frac{1}{2}\rho V^2 = p_0$ (Section 3.4), vary from p at $y = 0$ to p_0 at $y = \delta$. Then by Section 3.5

$$\frac{\partial H}{\partial n} = \frac{\partial p_0}{\partial y} = (\text{curl}_z \ \mathbf{V})\rho V$$

and since $\partial p_0/\partial y$ is different from zero, $\text{curl}_z \ \mathbf{V}$ has a finite value; that is, the boundary layer is a field of rotational flow. This conclusion also follows from the definition of $\text{curl}_z \ \mathbf{V}$ in two dimensions:

$$\text{curl}_z \ \mathbf{V} = \frac{\partial v}{\partial x} - \frac{\partial u}{\partial y}$$

Since δ is everywhere small, the component of velocity normal to the surface, v, must be small everywhere, and therefore $|\partial v/\partial x| \ll |\partial u/\partial y|$. Hence the flow is rotational throughout the boundary layer.

With δ small and $\partial p/\partial y$ negligible, it follows that the pressure distribution over a streamlined body is very nearly that calculated for an inviscid flow. Therefore, the lift and moment acting on wings and bodies may be calculated, as in previous chapters, by integrating the pressure distribution derived on the basis of inviscid flow.

For instance, in Section 5.6, we found that for a thin airfoil at a small angle of attack in an inviscid flow $\partial c_l/\partial \alpha = 2\pi$ and the aerodynamic center is at the $\frac{1}{4}$ chord point. Actually, for airfoils up to about 15 per cent thickness to chord ratio, $\partial c_l/\partial \alpha = 2\pi\eta$, where η has values between 0.9 and 1.0, depending on the camber and thickness distribution; and the aerodynamic center of most airfoils is 1 to 2 per cent ahead of the $\frac{1}{4}$ chord point. We see, therefore, that the effect of viscosity on these aerodynamic characteristics is not large. Further comparisons between theory and experiment are given in Appendix C.

The inviscid flow analyses cannot, of course, predict the frictional drag of bodies. The following chapters are devoted to the determination of the frictional drag and the factors that affect it.

Deductions based on the hypothesis of a thin boundary layer break down in regions of "flow separation" such as occur at a high angle of attack. These limitations will be described in Section 13.4.

12.4 VISCOUS STRESSES

The analysis of the boundary layer must rest on an understanding of the viscous stress. The approximate derivations of Chapter 1 yielded expressions for the coefficient of viscosity μ and the shearing stress τ in terms of the properties of the fluid and of the flow. These expressions are

$$\mu = \tfrac{1}{3}\rho cL$$

$$\tau = \mu \frac{\partial u}{\partial y} \tag{1}$$

where c is the average velocity of the molecules,* L is a length associated with the mean free path of the molecules between collisions, u is the ordered velocity, and y is the coordinate normal to the flow. It was concluded there that μ is independent of the pressure and proportional to the square root of the absolute temperature.

The concept of a shearing stress which must constantly be kept in mind is that of a rate of transfer of downstream momentum in the

---

* In the more accurate derivation of μ, where l is the mean free path between collisions, $\mu = 0.49\rho cl$.

direction lateral to the flow.   This transfer is accomplished by the random motion of the molecules, effecting a continuous exchange of momentum between faster- and slower-moving layers of the flow. Equation 1 refers to a molecular process, but the process is qualitatively unchanged when the flow becomes turbulent, the only difference being that in a turbulent flow relatively large masses of fluid carry out the momentum transport.   Regardless of the type of flow, we may describe the shearing stress between two layers of fluid as a transfer phenomenon; one is a molecular transfer, the other a turbulent transfer.

Figure 1 shows a schematic diagram of a boundary layer in which the velocity u varies from zero at the surface to the free-stream value. The shearing stress at the surface $\tau_w = \mu(\partial u/\partial y)_w$ is the skin friction (force per unit area) exerted by the fluid on the surface in the tangential direction.   The shearing stress then varies continuously throughout the boundary layer from τ_w at $y = 0$ to zero at $y = \delta$.

Momentum transfer also takes place between adjacent fluid elements *along* a streamline through the motion of molecules across the interface. The resulting stress is called a normal viscous stress and is proportional to $\mu \, \partial u/\partial x$.   Since the boundary layer is thin and its thickness changes only slowly with x, $\partial u/\partial x \ll \partial u/\partial y$ and we therefore neglect the viscous normal stress compared with the viscous shearing stress.

12.5 BOUNDARY LAYER EQUATION OF MOTION

In Section 3.2 Newton's second law of motion was applied to a fluid element acted upon only by pressure forces and gravity.   Euler's equation for the equilibrium of an inviscid fluid resulted.   This law, applied to a fluid element of mass $\rho \, \Delta x \, \Delta y \, \Delta z$, may be written

$$\rho \, \Delta x \, \Delta y \, \Delta z \, \frac{\mathfrak{D}\mathbf{V}}{\mathfrak{D}t} = \mathbf{F} \tag{2}$$

The left side of Eq. 2 represents the rate of change of the momentum of a fluid particle of mass $\rho \, \Delta x \, \Delta y \, \Delta z$ and the equation expresses the conservation of momentum of the fluid particle.

The equations expressing conservation of momentum in a viscous compressible fluid are derived in detail in Appendix B.   They are also simplified to apply to boundary layers.   In this section, we shall derive *directly* the approximate equation for flow in the two-dimensional boundary layer.   The equation obtained is identical with that found by the more rigorous analysis of Appendix B.

We consider the forces acting on an element in a two-dimensional boundary layer as shown in Fig. 2.   The element is of unit thickness in

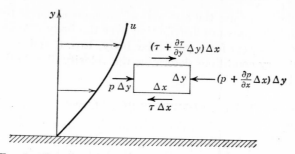

FIG. 2.   Forces acting on an element in the boundary layer.

the z-direction. The sum of the pressure and shear forces on the element give the left side of Eq. 2, that is,

$$\rho\ \Delta x\ \Delta y\ \frac{\mathfrak{D}\mathbf{V}}{\mathfrak{D}t} = \left(-\frac{\partial p}{\partial x} + \frac{\partial \tau}{\partial y}\right)\Delta x\ \Delta y$$

After dividing by $\Delta x\ \Delta y$, expanding the left side and substituting for τ from Eq. 1, we get

$$\rho\left(\frac{\partial u}{\partial t} + u\frac{\partial u}{\partial x} + v\frac{\partial u}{\partial y}\right) = -\frac{\partial p}{\partial x} + \frac{\partial}{\partial y}\left(\mu\frac{\partial u}{\partial y}\right) \tag{3}$$

This equation is the *boundary layer equation of motion*. Then Eq. 3 and the continuity equation

$$\frac{\partial}{\partial x}(\rho u) + \frac{\partial}{\partial y}(\rho v) = -\frac{\partial \rho}{\partial t} \tag{4}$$

which, for incompressible flow, reduces to

$$\frac{\partial u}{\partial x} + \frac{\partial v}{\partial y} = 0 \tag{5}$$

are the equations available for the solution of boundary layer problems.

For an incompressible flow, the variables are u, v, and p, but we have only two equations, Eqs. 3 and 5, to evaluate the three variables. The missing equation expresses conservation of the y-component of momentum, the terms of which become negligible through the assumption that $\partial p/\partial y = 0$ within the boundary layer. As a consequence of the fact that we have only two equations to determine three variables, one of the variables must be given or must be determined independently. The pressure can be determined independently since, as was pointed out in Section 12.3, setting $\partial p/\partial y = 0$ and postulating a thin boundary layer enables us to use the methods of previous chapters for inviscid flows to find the pressure distribution over the body. After we have determined $p = p(x)$ for a particular body, Eqs. 3 and 5 and appropriate boundary conditions determine the velocity distributions in the boundary layer.

12.6 SIMILARITY IN INCOMPRESSIBLE FLOWS

We shall, in this section, demonstrate the importance of Reynolds number in comparing flows about geometrically similar bodies. We could carry out the demonstration with the boundary layer equation, but since the conclusion applies to the entire flow field, we shall use the exact equations of motion. These are the *Navier-Stokes* equations derived in Appendix B; they are the Euler equations of Section 3.2 with the addition of the terms describing the viscous forces on an element. The equations and the continuity equation are

$$\rho \frac{\mathfrak{D}u}{\mathfrak{D}t} = -\frac{\partial p}{\partial x} + \mu \, \nabla^2 u$$

$$\rho \frac{\mathfrak{D}v}{\mathfrak{D}t} = -\frac{\partial p}{\partial y} + \mu \, \nabla^2 v$$

$$\rho \frac{\mathfrak{D}w}{\mathfrak{D}t} = -\frac{\partial p}{\partial z} + \mu \, \nabla^2 w$$

(6)

$$\frac{\partial u}{\partial x} + \frac{\partial v}{\partial y} + \frac{\partial w}{\partial z} = 0$$

where

$$\nabla^2 = \frac{\partial^2}{\partial x^2} + \frac{\partial^2}{\partial y^2} + \frac{\partial^2}{\partial z^2}$$

Let V be a representative velocity (say, that at a great distance from the body) and L be a characteristic length (say, the length of the body). Then Eqs. 6 can be made dimensionless by introducing the following dimensionless variables:

$$x' = \frac{x}{L}, \quad y' = \frac{y}{L}, \quad z' = \frac{z}{L}, \quad u' = \frac{u}{V}$$

$$v' = \frac{v}{V}, \quad w' = \frac{w}{V}, \quad p' = \frac{p}{\rho V^2}, \quad t' = \frac{Vt}{L}$$

Equations 6 then become

$$\frac{\mathfrak{D}u'}{\mathfrak{D}t'} = -\frac{\partial p'}{\partial x'} + \frac{1}{Re}\nabla'^2 u'$$

$$\frac{\mathfrak{D}v'}{\mathfrak{D}t'} = -\frac{\partial p'}{\partial y'} + \frac{1}{Re}\nabla'^2 v' \tag{7}$$

$$\frac{\mathfrak{D}w'}{\mathfrak{D}t'} = -\frac{\partial p'}{\partial z'} + \frac{1}{Re}\nabla'^2 w'$$

$$\frac{\partial u'}{\partial x'} + \frac{\partial v'}{\partial y'} + \frac{\partial w'}{\partial z'} = 0$$

where $Re = VL/\nu$. Now, given two geometrically similar bodies immersed in a moving fluid, Eqs. 7 show that the equations of motion for the two flows are identical, *provided* that the Reynolds numbers are the same. Also the nondimensional boundary conditions for the two flows will be identical.

Therefore, *flows about geometrically similar bodies at the same Reynolds number are completely similar in the sense that u', v', w', and p' are, respectively, the same functions of x', y', z', and t' for the various flows.* Similarity of the bodies must involve not only the shapes but also the roughness; the flows must also be similar as regards turbulence (see Chapter 15).

Another important generalization results when we let the Reynolds number become infinite. Equations 7 then reduce to Euler's equation (Section 3.2) for a perfect fluid. Therefore, the *flow of a perfect fluid is identical with that of a viscous fluid at infinite Reynolds number.* It is important to realize that this statement applies only at infinite Reynolds number; in other words, a finite increase in Reynolds number does not necessarily cause the flow of a viscous fluid to conform more nearly to that of a perfect fluid.

In Chapter 14 it will be shown that for a compressible fluid with heat transfer several more similarity parameters must be taken into account.

Incompressible Laminar Flow in Tubes and Boundary Layers

CHAPTER 13

13.1 INTRODUCTION

In the previous chapter we derived the equations necessary to the solution of the incompressible boundary layer problem. In this chapter we first solve the problem of the steady, incompressible, viscid flow in a tube far from the entrance. Next we solve the boundary layer problem for flow along a flat plate oriented parallel to a flow.

The solutions of these two problems illustrate the importance of the Reynolds number; in fact, all the important quantities in which we are interested, when they are expressed in nondimensional form, are functions only of the Reynolds number. Later sections deal with the momentum relations within the boundary layer and with the flow associated with a pressure gradient. The Kármán-Pohlhausen method of analysis for boundary-layer flow in a streamwise pressure gradient is described.

The results given in this chapter are remarkably good approximations even at relatively high speeds, but a *rigorous* treatment of the boundary layer at high speeds requires that variations of density and temperature be taken into account. The two additional equations needed are the equation of state and the equation expressing conservation of energy in the boundary layer. The latter will be derived in Chapter 14 preliminary to considerations of the compressible boundary layer.

13.2 LAMINAR FLOW IN A TUBE

Consider incompressible flow in the conduit of Fig. 1. The conduit is straight, and, for simplicity of the analysis, a circular cross section is taken. The boundary layer will begin with zero thickness at the

232

entrance and will grow with distance along the tube. At a large distance from the entrance, the outer edge of the boundary layer will have reached the center of the tube, and still further downstream, say for $x \geqq x_1$, all velocity distributions will be identical. Then, by definition, for $x > x_1$, the flow is *fully developed*.*

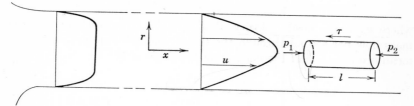

Fig. 1.   Fully developed flow in a tube.

If we sum the forces on the cylindrical element shown in Fig. 1, we have

$$F = \pi r^2 (p_1 - p_2) - 2\pi r l \tau \tag{1}$$

Since the element does not accelerate in a fully developed flow, $F = 0$; that is, the pressure force on the x-faces of any element balance the frictional forces acting on the boundaries parallel to the flow. Further, with the origin at the center of the tube, $\tau = -\mu \, du/dr$, so that Eq. 1 becomes

$$\frac{du}{dr} = -\frac{r}{2\mu}\frac{p_1 - p_2}{l} \tag{2}$$

l is not specified and no other quantity in the equation except $p_1 - p_2$ depends on l. Therefore $-(p_1 - p_2)/l = dp/dx = $ constant. Equation 2 is integrated to obtain:

$$u = \frac{r^2}{4\mu}\frac{dp}{dx} + \text{constant}$$

The constant is evaluated by use of the boundary condition, $u = 0$ at $r = a$. The equation for the velocity distribution in fully developed flow then becomes

$$u = -\frac{1}{4\mu}\frac{dp}{dx}(a^2 - r^2) \tag{3}$$

---

* Boussinesq calculated a formula $x_1 = 0.26rRe$, where x_1 is the distance from the entrance to the point where the flow is fully developed in a tube of circular cross section, r is the radius of the tube, $Re = u_m r/\nu$, and u_m is the mean velocity in the tube. See *Modern Developments in Fluid Dynamics*, edited by Sydney Goldstein, p. 299 ff., Oxford University Press, New York, 1938.

The shape of the velocity profile is seen to be a paraboloid.*   We next obtain the relations between the significant dimensionless parameters. These are the Reynolds number and pressure drop coefficient, defined as follows:

$$Re = \frac{2au_m}{\nu} ; \quad \gamma = \frac{\tau_0}{\frac{1}{2}\rho u_m{}^2} = \frac{-\mu(du/dr)_{r=a}}{\frac{1}{2}\rho u_m{}^2} \tag{4}$$

where u_m is the mean velocity, that is, $u_m = Q/\pi a^2 \rho$ where Q is the mass flow per second through the tube.   Since, for a paraboloid, the mean ordinate is half the maximum, Eq. 3 gives

$$u_m = -\frac{a^2}{8\mu}\frac{dp}{dx}$$

Then

$$\gamma = -\frac{\dfrac{a}{2}\dfrac{dp}{dx}}{\frac{1}{2}\rho u_m{}^2} = \frac{a(dp/dx)}{\rho\left(\dfrac{a^2}{8\mu}\dfrac{dp}{dx}\right)u_m} \tag{5}$$

$$\gamma = \frac{16}{Re} \tag{6}$$

The hyperbola γ versus Re describes the *scale effect* of Reynolds number on the pressure drop coefficient.   The analysis applies only to *laminar flow;* at a critical Reynolds number dependent on factors to be taken up in Chapter 15, *transition* from laminar to *turbulent flow* occurs and time dependent terms associated with the unsteady character of the flow would have to be included if a rigorous solution were to be obtained.

13.3   LAMINAR BOUNDARY LAYER ALONG A FLAT PLATE

The solution of Eq. 3 of Chapter 12 for the steady flow of an incompressible viscous fluid along a flat plate, as shown in Fig. 2, was obtained by Blasius in 1908.   For this case $\partial u/\partial t = \partial p/\partial x = 0$, and the equations of motion and continuity (Eqs. 3 and 5 of Chapter 12) become

$$u\frac{\partial u}{\partial x} + v\frac{\partial u}{\partial y} = \nu\frac{\partial^2 u}{\partial y^2}$$

$$\frac{\partial u}{\partial x} + \frac{\partial v}{\partial y} = 0 \tag{7}$$

---

* Equation 3 may also be obtained as an exact solution of the equation of motion derived in Appendix B.

To solve these equations, we need two boundary conditions for the first and one for the second.   The conditions are

B.C.

$$\text{at } y = 0, u = v = 0$$

$$\text{at } y = \infty, u = U_1 \tag{8}$$

They express the physical conditions that there is no slip at the boundary ($u = 0$ at $y = 0$), that the boundary is a streamline ($v = 0$ at $y = 0$), and that the flow is unaffected at infinity ($u = U_1$ at $y = \infty$).

FIG. 2.   The boundary layer on a flat plate.

We see that in Eqs. 7 we have two equations to determine the two unknown variables.   In order to get a single unknown variable and a single equation, we introduce the *stream function*, which was defined and discussed in Section 2.6.   The stream function ψ is defined as that function of x and y such that

$$u = \frac{\partial \psi}{\partial y}, \quad v = - \frac{\partial \psi}{\partial x} \tag{9}$$

It is clear that the stream function defined in this way satisfies identically the continuity equation.

We now introduce ψ as a function of x and y such that the equation of motion of Eqs. 7 reduces to an ordinary differential equation, that is, the two independent variables are reduced to one.   The reason for seeking an ordinary differential equation is that no general methods exist for solving partial differential equations of the type of the equation of motion.   The most distressing feature of the equation is that it is nonlinear in the dependent variable ψ, as is evident if Eqs. 9 are substituted in Eqs. 7.

We therefore seek to express the equation of motion in terms of a single independent variable η, a function of x and y; that is, the equation of motion will be expressed in a form in which neither x nor y appears explicitly.   Blasius found that if the new variable η were made proportional to $y/\sqrt{x}$, an ordinary differential equation resulted.*

* The *order-of-magnitude* analysis of Appendix B justifies the choice of $y/\sqrt{x}$ as the independent variable.

It is, in general, most convenient to work with dimensionless quantities, and accordingly we define

$$\eta = \frac{y}{2}\left(\frac{U_1}{\nu x}\right)^{1/2}, \quad \psi = (\nu U_1 x)^{1/2} f(\eta) \tag{10}$$

Here η is dimensionless and ψ has the dimensions: velocity $\times$ length.
We next determine, by means of Eqs. 9 and 10, the terms in Eqs. 7.
Differentiations with respect to η are denoted by primes. Then,

$$u = \tfrac{1}{2}U_1 f', \qquad \frac{\partial u}{\partial x} = -\frac{1}{4}\frac{U_1}{x}\eta f''$$

$$\frac{\partial u}{\partial y} = \frac{U_1}{4}\left(\frac{U_1}{\nu x}\right)^{1/2} f'', \qquad \frac{\partial^2 u}{\partial y^2} = \left(\frac{U_1}{8}\right)\left(\frac{U_1}{\nu x}\right) f''' \tag{11}$$

$$v = \frac{1}{2}\left(\frac{U_1 \nu}{x}\right)^{1/2}(f'\eta - f)$$

When these values are substituted in the first of Eqs. 7 the result is
the differential equation

$$f''' + ff'' = 0 \tag{12}$$

and the boundary conditions, Eqs. 8, become

$$\text{at } \eta = 0, \quad f = f' = 0$$
$$\text{at } \eta = \infty, \quad f' = 2 \tag{13}$$

and the solution $f(\eta)$ will, by Eqs. 11, enable the determination of u and
v. The uniqueness of the solution has not been proved, but comparison
with experiment has shown that the solution given is the one that
describes the flow for the case considered. The differential equation,
Eq. 12, appears simple; on the contrary, it is nonlinear and quite difficult. No closed solution has been found and, thus, solution by series
is resorted to. We assume a solution of the form

$$f = A_0 + A_1\eta + \frac{A_2}{2!}\eta^2 + \frac{A_3}{3!}\eta^3 + \cdots + \frac{A_n}{n!}\eta^n + \cdots$$

When the first two boundary conditions are applied to f, we find that
$A_0 = A_1 = 0$. After substituting the series for f into Eq. 12, we get

$$A_3 + A_4\eta + \frac{A_5}{2!}\eta^2 + \cdots$$

$$+ \left(\frac{A_2}{2!}\eta^2 + \frac{A_3}{3!}\eta^3 + \cdots\right)\left(A_2 + A_3\eta + \frac{A_4}{2!}\eta^2 + \cdots\right) = 0$$

The multiplication is carried out and the coefficients of like powers are collected. Then,

$$A_3 + A_4\eta + \left(\frac{A_2{}^2}{2!} + \frac{A_5}{2!}\right)\eta^2 + \cdots = 0$$

Since this equation must hold for all values of η, the coefficients of every power of η must vanish. Hence,

$$A_3 = A_4 = 0, \quad A_2{}^2 + A_5 = 0, \text{ etc.}$$

Then all terms can be expressed as functions of η and A_2:

$$f = \frac{A_2\eta^2}{2!} - \frac{A_2{}^2\eta^5}{5!} + \frac{11A_2{}^3\eta^8}{8!} - \frac{375A_2{}^4\eta^{11}}{11!} + \cdots \tag{14}$$

Equation 14 satisfies the first two boundary conditions of Eqs. 13, and the third will be used to determine A_2.

To accomplish this we write $f(\eta)$ in the equivalent form

$$f = A_2{}^{\frac{1}{3}}\left[\frac{(A_2{}^{\frac{1}{3}}\eta)^2}{2!} - \frac{(A_2{}^{\frac{1}{3}}\eta)^5}{5!} + \frac{11(A_2{}^{\frac{1}{3}}\eta)^8}{8!} - \frac{375(A_2{}^{\frac{1}{3}}\eta)^{11}}{11!} + \cdots\right]$$

$$\equiv A_2{}^{\frac{1}{3}}g(\Gamma)$$

where $\Gamma = A_2{}^{\frac{1}{3}}\eta$. The boundary condition (Eqs. 13) to be satisfied at $\eta = \infty$ is

$$\lim_{\eta \to \infty} f' = 2$$

which may be written

$$\lim_{\Gamma \to \infty} [A_2{}^{\frac{2}{3}}g'(\Gamma)] = 2$$

where the prime refers to differentiation with respect to Γ. But, for $A_2 > 0$ when $\eta \to \infty$, $\Gamma \to \infty$, and we may write instead of the above

$$\lim_{\eta \to \infty} [g'(\eta)] = \frac{2}{A_2{}^{\frac{2}{3}}}$$

or

$$A_2 = \left[\frac{2}{\lim_{\eta \to \infty} g'(\eta)}\right]^{\frac{3}{2}}$$

The right-hand side of this equation is plotted as a function of η, and A_2 can be determined to any desired approximation. Goldstein * found that $A_2 = 1.32824$. The quantities f, f', and f'' are plotted in Fig. 3 for this value of A_2.

* *Modern Developments in Fluid Dynamics*, edited by Sydney Goldstein, p. 135, Oxford University Press, New York, 1938.

The solution shows that the value of u does not reach U_1 until $\eta = \infty$, that is, at $y = \infty$. However, at $\eta = 2.6$, $u/U_1 = 0.994$; therefore, if

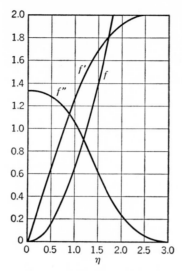

FIG. 3.   The Blasius functions $f(\eta)$, $f'(\eta)$, $f''(\eta)$.

we choose the edge of the boundary layer ($y = \delta$) as the point where u is within 0.6 per cent of U_1, we get from Eqs. 10

$$\delta = 5.2 \sqrt{\frac{\nu x}{U_1}} = \frac{5.2x}{\sqrt{Re_x}} \qquad (15)$$

where $Re_x = U_1 x/\nu$.

Since the definition of the boundary-layer thickness δ is arbitrary, we define a *displacement thickness* δ^* according to the equation

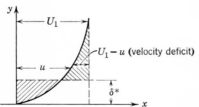

FIG. 4.   Schematic representation of δ^*, the displacement thickness of the boundary layer.

$$\delta^* = \int_0^{\infty} \left(1 - \frac{u}{U_1}\right) dy \qquad (16)$$

Reference to Fig. 4, in which the two cross-hatched areas are equal, shows that the displacement thickness may be interpreted as the thickness of a stagnant fluid layer with the same integrated *velocity deficit* $(U_1 - u)$ as the actual boundary layer. Then the streamline at the outer edge of the boundary layer $(y = \delta)$ is displaced outward a distance δ^* from its location in a frictionless fluid.

We now calculate δ^*, which, according to Eqs. 11 and 16, is given by

$$\delta^* = \int_0^\infty \left(1 - \frac{u}{U_1}\right) dy = \left(\frac{\nu x}{U_1}\right)^{\frac{1}{2}} \int_0^\infty (2 - f')\, d\eta$$

$$= \left(\frac{\nu x}{U_1}\right)^{\frac{1}{2}} [2\eta - f]_0^\infty$$

$$= \left(\frac{\nu x}{U_1}\right)^{\frac{1}{2}} \lim_{\eta \to \infty} (2\eta - f)$$

Since, from Eqs. 13, $f'(\infty) = 2$, the solution for Eq. 12 which must hold for η large is $f = 2\eta + \beta$, where β is a constant; that is, $\lim_{\eta \to \infty} (2\eta - f)$ $= -\beta$. β can be determined from a solution of Eq. 12 by successive approximation.† The result is $\beta = -1.7208$; that is,

$$\delta^* = \frac{1.7208x}{\sqrt{Re_x}} \tag{17}$$

The skin-friction coefficient $c_f = \tau_0 / \frac{1}{2}\rho U_1^2$ is calculated as follows:

$$\tau_0 = \mu \left(\frac{\partial u}{\partial y}\right)_{y=0} = \frac{\mu}{2} U_1 f''(0) \frac{1}{2}\left(\frac{U_1}{\nu x}\right)^{\frac{1}{2}}$$

$$= \frac{1}{4}\mu A_2 U_1 \left(\frac{U_1}{\nu x}\right)^{\frac{1}{2}}$$

Then

$$c_f = \frac{A_2}{2}\left(\frac{\nu}{U_1 x}\right)^{\frac{1}{2}} = \frac{0.664}{Re_x^{\frac{1}{2}}} \tag{18}$$

The average skin-friction coefficient C_f for one side of the flat plate of unit width and of length l is given by

$$C_f = \frac{\int_0^l \tau_0 \, dx}{\frac{1}{2}\rho U_1^2 l} = \frac{1.328}{Re_l^{\frac{1}{2}}} \tag{19}$$

where $Re_l = U_1 l/\nu$. Figures 5 and 6 show excellent agreement between theory and experiment for the velocity profile and for the local skin friction coefficient.

† *Aerodynamic Theory*, Vol. 3, p. 87, edited by W. F. Durand, Durand Reprinting Committee, Pasadena, Calif., 1943.

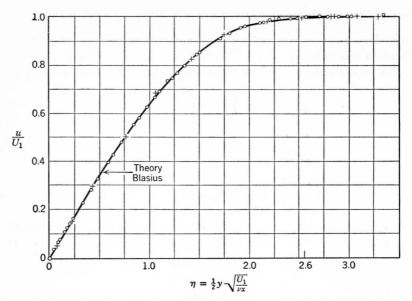

FIG. 5. Comparison between theoretical and experimental velocity distributions in the laminar boundary layer on a flat plate. Experiments by J. Nikuradse (Monograph, *Zentrale f. Wiss. Berichtswesen*, Berlin, 1942) cover Reynolds number range 1.08×10^5 to 7.28×10^5.

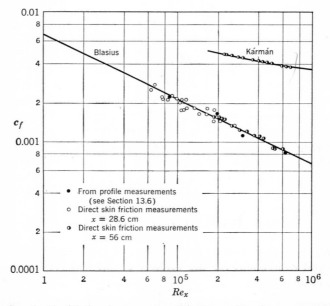

FIG. 6. Local skin friction in incompressible flow. The lower curve refers to laminar flow, the upper to turbulent. Experiments by H. W. Liepmann and S. Dhawan (*Proc. 1st U.S. Nat. Cong. Applied Mech.*, 1951, p. 869; also S. Dhawan, NACA Report 1121, 1953).

240

As is well known, the above solution is valid only below a certain Reynolds number, the value of which is dependent upon various influences (see Chapter 15). At higher Reynolds numbers the flow in the boundary layer becomes *turbulent* and the equation of motion describing the flow must strictly include the transient term $\partial u/\partial t$. The turbulent boundary layer is discussed in Chapter 15. Figure 6 includes a comparison between skin-friction coefficients for laminar and for turbulent flow in the boundary layer.

13.4 FLOW WITH PRESSURE GRADIENT—SEPARATION

The equation of motion for flow in the boundary layer will be analyzed to show some effects, on the flow, of the sign of the pressure gradient along the surface. Some of the facts about flow separation, of which a common example is the stalling of wings, can also be deduced.

Equation 3 of Chapter 12 gives some indication of the effect of pressure gradient on the velocity profile. If we make use of the boundary condition $u = v = 0$ at $y = 0$, the left side of the equation vanishes and we have (for $\mu = $ constant)

$$\mu \left(\frac{\partial^2 u}{\partial y^2}\right)_{y=0} = \frac{\partial p}{\partial x} \tag{20}$$

For the problem of a flat plate parallel to the flow, taken up in the previous section, $\partial p/\partial x = 0$, and hence, from Eq. 20, the profile has an inflection point at the surface. For $\partial p/\partial x < 0$, $(\partial^2 u/\partial y^2)_{y=0} < 0$; that is, the slope, $\partial u/\partial y$, decreases as y increases near the surface. Since $\partial u/\partial y = 0$ at $y = \delta$, we may expect that the decrease which begins at the surface will be *monotonic* to the edge of the boundary layer; in other words, the slope decreases with increasing y at every point within the layer. However, for $\partial p/\partial x > 0$, $(\partial^2 u/\partial y^2)_{y=0} > 0$; that is, $\partial u/\partial y$ *increases* as y increases near the surface. Since $\partial u/\partial y$ must be zero at $y = \delta$, $\partial^2 u/\partial y^2$ must go through zero somewhere within the bouneary layer; in other words, an inflection point appears in the profile.

The physical reason for the appearance of an inflection point in the velocity profile in an *adverse pressure gradient* ($\partial p/\partial x > 0$) lies in the retarding effect, on the flow, of the upstream force associated with the adverse pressure gradient. The resulting loss of momentum of the fluid is especially noticeable near the surface where the velocity is low; hence $\partial u/\partial y$ near $y = 0$ becomes smaller and smaller the longer the distance over which the adverse gradient persists. This effect is shown diagrammatically in Fig. 7. Then, at some distance downstream of the pressure minimum, we reach a point where $(\partial u / \partial y)_{y=0} = 0$, and beyond this point the direction of flow reverses near the surface. The point where $(\partial u / \partial y)_{y=0} = 0$ is the *separation point*. The greater the adverse pressure gradient the shorter will be the distance from point A, the pressure minimum, to the separation point, B.

Immediately downstream of the separation point, the schematic streamlines near the surface in Fig. 7 show a strong curvature, which must be associated with a strong pressure gradient normal to the surface. Accordingly, the reasoning of Section 12.3, which led to the conclusion that $\partial p / \partial y \approx 0$ through the boundary layer, can no longer be valid at, or downstream of, the separation point. The assumption which was the foundation of that analysis, that the boundary layer is thin compared with a characteristic dimension of the body, therefore breaks down, and it would be necessary to use the complete equations of motion to describe the flow. This analysis has not been carried out.

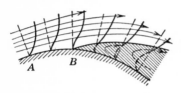

Fig. 7. Velocity distributions in the vicinity of a separation point. A is the point of minimum pressure; B is the separation point.

An additional complication arises from the experimental observation that the flow downstream of the separation point is, in general, quite unsteady. The unsteadiness is confined to a region, extending downstream of the body, called the *turbulent wake*.

It will be seen from the above description that flow separation is a phenomenon associated with the boundary layer and therefore does not occur in an inviscid-fluid flow. The salient facts are that (1) separation occurs only in an adverse pressure gradient and then only if the adverse pressure gradient persists over a great enough length, the length being greater the more gentle the gradient; and (2) at and near the separation point, $\partial p / \partial y \neq 0$ near the surface.

Wherever the boundary layer is thin, Prandtl's hypothesis (Section 12.3) permits us to use the perfect-fluid analysis as a good approximation to the pressure distribution over a body in a viscous flow. But we can no longer employ this principle if an appreciable area of the body is in a region of separated flow; under these circumstances, theoretical and experimental pressure distributions will diverge widely.

The stalling of an airfoil at high angles of attack with its accompanying loss in lift and increase in drag is a separation phenomenon and is completely unpredictable by inviscid-fluid theory. Stalling is discussed in Appendix C.

We are concerned here only with a description of flow separation; the point at which separation occurs is affected by many factors, among them the state of the boundary layer—whether it is laminar or turbulent. It will be pointed out in Section 16.10 that the higher velocities near the surface for a turbulent boundary layer enable it to drive further against an adverse pressure gradient than can the laminar layer; consequently, the effect of changing the boundary layer from laminar to turbulent is to move the separation point rearward.

13.5 SIMILARITY IN BOUNDARY LAYER FLOWS

The general condition for similarity of incompressible viscid flows about geometrically similar bodies was found to be equality of the Reynolds numbers (Section 12.6). Examples of the importance of Reynolds number are found in Sections 13.2 and 13.3, where it is shown that the resistance coefficient for flow in a tube and the skin-friction coefficient on a flat plate are determined by the Reynolds number.

"Similar" solutions of the boundary layer equations are those which yield scale factors that reduce all velocity profiles to a single curve. For instance, the Blasius solution of Section 13.3 predicts that $u/U_1 = f'(\eta)$ where $\eta = \frac{1}{2}y/\sqrt{U_1/\nu x}$. Figure 5 shows excellent agreement with experiment.

A general class of similar profiles was found by Falkner and Skan.* They found that if U_1 varies according to the law

$$U_1(x) = u_1 x^m \tag{21}$$

and

$$\psi(x, y) = \sqrt{\frac{2}{m+1}} \sqrt{\nu u_1}\, x^{(m+1)/2} f(\xi)$$

$$\xi = y \sqrt{\frac{m+1}{2} \frac{U_1}{\nu x}} = y \sqrt{\frac{m+1}{2} \frac{u_1}{\nu}}\, x^{(m-1)/2} \tag{22}$$

the boundary layer equation, Eq. 3, reduces to

$$f''' + ff'' + \beta(1 - f'^2) = 0 \tag{23}$$

where

$$\beta = \frac{2m}{m+1} \tag{24}$$

* W. M. Falkner and S. W. Skan, "Some Approximate Solutions of the Boundary Layer Equations," *Phil. Mag.*, vol. 12, p. 865, 1931; British A.R.C., *Report and Memo.* 1324, 1930.

We see that for $m = 0$ $(\beta = 0)$ Eq. 23 reduces to the Blasius equation Eq. 12, and ψ, ξ, and $u = U_1 f'$ differ only by numerical factors from their counterparts in the Blasius analysis.

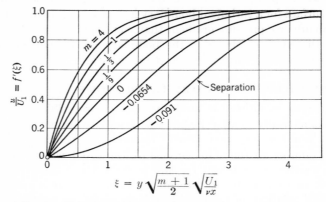

FIG. 8.   Velocity profiles for various values of m in Eq. 21.

Equation 23 shows that similar boundary layer profiles exist everywhere on a body for which the velocity outside the boundary layer can be represented by Eq. 21 with constant m.* The profiles are shown in Fig. 8 for various values of m. The curve for $m = 0$ is the same as that shown in Fig. 5. We note that for $m = -0.091$ the flow is constantly on the verge of separation.

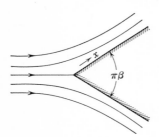

FIG. 9.   Streamlines for potential flow described by Eqs. 21 and 24.

Equation 21 represents the velocity at the surface of a wedge which turns an inviscid flow through an angle $\beta\pi/2$ and therefore represents physically the flow past a wedge as shown in Fig. 9. Then the velocity profiles corresponding to negative values of m have no physical significance. The flows corresponding to $m > 0$, however, occur in many practical applications; for instance, for $m = 1(\beta = 1)$ the boundary layer profile is that which occurs near the stagnation point of a two-dimensional body.

* Other "similar solutions" are given by H. Schlichting, *Boundary Layer Theory*, translated by J. Kestin, Chapter 8, McGraw-Hill, New York, 1955.

13.6 THE VON KÁRMÁN INTEGRAL RELATION

Although solutions of the boundary layer equations for particular pressure distributions are useful, their practical application is limited to specific body shapes. A useful application of the momentum theorem, derived in Chapter 3, was devised by von Kármán * to solve the boundary layer problem for any given pressure distribution. The method will be described here and its uses and limitations will be pointed out.

Consider a two-dimensional region (Fig. 10) bounded by a solid surface, the line $y = \delta$, and two parallel lines perpendicular to the solid

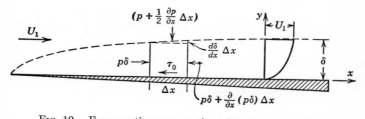

FIG. 10.   Forces acting on a section of the boundary layer.

surface. We analyze the forces acting on the fluid according to the momentum theorem of Section 3.3, which may be stated: _The total rate of increase of momentum within a region is equal in both magnitude and direction to the force acting on the boundary of the region._ Consider the component of momentum parallel to the surface. A friction force $\tau_0 \, \Delta x$ is acting on the surface, and pressure forces are acting on the other three sides; the pressures are constant over the two faces since $\partial p / \partial y = 0$. The total downstream force acting on the boundaries of the element of length Δx is

$$-\tau_0 \, \Delta x + p\delta - \left\{ p\delta + \frac{\partial}{\partial x} (p\delta)\Delta x \right\} + \left(p + \frac{1}{2} \frac{\partial p}{\partial x} \Delta x \right) \frac{d\delta}{dx} \Delta x$$

The last term of this expression is the downstream component of the mean pressure force acting on the sloping boundary $y = \delta$. Since δ is small, we may neglect the term involving $(\Delta x)^2$, and the above expression for the downstream force simplifies to

$$\left(-\tau_0 - \delta \frac{\partial p}{\partial x} \right) \Delta x \tag{25}$$

---

* T. von Kármán, "Über laminare und turbulente Reibung," _Z. angew. Math. u. Mech._, Vol. 1, pp. 233–251, 1921, translated as NACA TM 1092, 1946.

To arrive at the momentum flux consider first the flux of mass through the region. The various contributions are:

$$\text{mass entering at left per second} = \int_0^\delta \rho u \, dy$$

$$\text{mass leaving at right per second} = \int_0^\delta \rho u \, dy + \frac{\partial}{\partial x}\left[\int_0^\delta \rho u \, dy\right]\Delta x$$

Then, from continuity, the mass entering the sloping face must equal the difference between these two values. Thus,

$$\text{mass entering sloping face per second} = \frac{\partial}{\partial x}\left[\int_0^\delta \rho u \, dy\right]\Delta x$$

These expressions are used to find the flux of momentum, that is, the excess momentum leaving at the right over that entering at the left per second. | The flux through the parallel faces is

$$\frac{\partial}{\partial x}\left[\int_0^\delta \rho u^2 \, dy\right]\Delta x \tag{26}$$

and the momentum entering the sloping face per second is the rate at which mass enters the sloping face, given above, multiplied by the free-stream velocity U_1. Thus, the momentum enters the sloping face at the rate

$$U_1 \frac{\partial}{\partial x}\left[\int_0^\delta \rho u \, dy\right]\Delta x \tag{27}$$

The momentum theorem is expressed by means of Eqs. 25, 26, and 27 and a term representing the time rate of increase of momentum within the element. Then

$$\int_0^\delta \frac{\partial}{\partial t}(\rho u)\, dy + \frac{\partial}{\partial x}\left[\int_0^\delta \rho u^2 \, dy\right] - U_1 \frac{\partial}{\partial x}\left[\int_0^\delta \rho u \, dy\right] = -\tau_0 - \delta \frac{\partial p}{\partial x} \tag{28}$$

This is the one form of the *von Kármán integral relation*. It is applicable to an unsteady, compressible, viscid flow. We shall now particularize Eq. 28 to treat the incompressible boundary layer.

Equation 28 is put in a more convenient form by introducing the displacement thickness δ^* defined in Section 13.3 and the *momentum* *thickness* θ of the boundary layer. For an incompressible flow these quantities are defined by the relations

$$\delta^* = \int_0^\delta \left(1 - \frac{u}{U_1}\right) dy \tag{29}$$

$$\theta = \int_0^\delta \frac{u}{U_1}\left(1 - \frac{u}{U_1}\right) dy \tag{30}$$

In Section 13.3, δ^* was interpreted in terms of the velocity deficit in the boundary layer. Likewise, θ is a length associated with the momentum deficit that the air has suffered because of friction. To see this, consider the expression $\rho u(U_1 - u)\, dy$, which is the momentum deficit of the mass $\rho u\, dy$ passing through the layer dy per second, relative to its momentum at velocity U_1. If this quantity is divided by ρU_1^2 and integrated through the boundary layer, we get Eq. 30, which then defines a length associated with the total momentum deficit in the boundary layer.

We may put the pressure term in a more usable form by means of the equation of motion for flow outside the boundary layer. Thus,

$$-\frac{\partial p}{\partial x} = \rho\left(\frac{\partial U_1}{\partial t} + U_1\frac{\partial U_1}{\partial x}\right)$$

and, after integrating from 0 to δ, this equation may be written

$$-\delta\frac{\partial p}{\partial x} = \int_0^\delta \rho\frac{\partial U_1}{\partial t}\, dy + \frac{\partial U_1}{\partial x}\int_0^\delta \rho U_1\, dy \tag{31}$$

Also, the last term on the left in Eq. 28 may be written

$$U_1\frac{\partial}{\partial x}\int_0^\delta \rho u\, dy = \frac{\partial}{\partial x}\left\{U_1\int_0^\delta \rho u\, dy\right\} - \frac{\partial U_1}{\partial x}\int_0^\delta \rho u\, dy \tag{32}$$

After substituting Eqs. 31 and 32 in Eq. 28,

$$\tau_0 = \frac{\partial}{\partial x}\left[\int_0^\delta \rho(U_1 u - u^2)\, dy\right] - \frac{\partial U_1}{\partial x}\int_0^\delta \rho u\, dy + \frac{\partial U_1}{\partial x}\int_0^\delta \rho U_1\, dy$$

$$- \int_0^\delta \rho\frac{\partial}{\partial t}(u - U_1)\, dy \tag{33}$$

and Eqs. 29 and 30 enable us to put this formula in the form

$$\tau_0 = \rho\frac{\partial}{\partial x}(U_1^2\theta) + \rho U_1\frac{\partial U_1}{\partial x}\delta^* + \rho\frac{\partial}{\partial t}(U_1\delta^*) \tag{34}$$

This equation has been the basis for many investigations of the incompressible boundary layer. It is derived here on physical grounds; it could as well be obtained as a first integral of the equation of motion as derived in Section 12.5.

Equation 34 provides a practical means for determining the distribution of shearing stress over a body. If velocity profiles in the boundary layer are measured at various stations, then the quantities occurring in the equation and their derivatives can be determined approximately and the shearing stress calculated. This method has been followed to determine the distribution of shearing stress over the surface of an airfoil.

13.7 THE POHLHAUSEN ANALYSIS OF THE BOUNDARY LAYER

The von Kármán integral relation was applied by Pohlhausen to an approximate investigation of the laminar boundary layer over bodies in steady incompressible flow when the pressure distribution is known. The method involves the evaluation of a polynomial with undetermined coefficients for the velocity distribution. The coefficients are determined as functions of the boundary-layer thickness by means of boundary conditions, and Eq. 34 yields a differential equation for finding the boundary-layer thickness as a function of x.

Since the velocity profile in an adverse pressure gradient has an inflection point (Section 13.4), we must employ at least a third-degree polynomial to represent it. In order to provide for a slightly better fit, Pohlhausen introduced the fourth-degree expression

$$\frac{u}{U_1} = A\,\frac{y}{\delta} + B\left(\frac{y}{\delta}\right)^2 + C\left(\frac{y}{\delta}\right)^3 + D\left(\frac{y}{\delta}\right)^4 \tag{35}$$

where A, B, C, D are undetermined coefficients. The method of solution consists first of expressing these coefficients as functions of δ by means of the boundary conditions, and second, of determining δ as a function of x by means of the von Kármán integral relation. The boundary conditions are

$$\text{at } y = 0, \quad u = 0, \quad \mu\,\frac{\partial^2 u}{\partial y^2} = \frac{\partial p}{\partial x}$$

$$\text{at } y = \delta, \quad u = U_1, \quad \frac{\partial u}{\partial y} = 0, \quad \frac{\partial^2 u}{\partial y^2} = 0 \tag{36}$$

where the second boundary condition at $y = 0$ is Eq. 20, and $\partial p/\partial x$ is considered to be given as a function of x. The three boundary conditions at $y = \delta$ may be considered simply as a definition of δ. They are approximate; we have seen from the Blasius analysis of Section 13.2 that these conditions are exact only at $y = \infty$. Equation 35 already satisfies the condition $u = 0$ at $y = 0$, and so the remaining four serve to determine A, B, C, and D as functions of δ.

If the conditions of Eqs. 36 are applied to Eq. 35, we obtain the following equations:

$$A + B + C + D = 1$$

$$A + 2B + 3C + 4D = 0$$

$$2B + 6C + 12D = 0 \tag{37}$$

$$B = \frac{\delta^2}{2\mu U_1} \frac{\partial p}{\partial x}$$

By Bernoulli's equation for the flow at the edge of the boundary layer, the last of Eqs. 37 may be written

$$B = -\frac{\delta^2}{2\nu} \cdot \frac{dU_1}{dx} = -\frac{\lambda}{2} \tag{38}$$

where

$$\lambda = +\frac{\delta^2}{\nu} \cdot \frac{dU_1}{dx} \tag{39}$$

is known as the *Pohlhausen parameter*. It is dimensionless and is a function of x. We solve Eqs. 37 for the constants A, C, and D in terms of λ and obtain

$$A = 2 + \frac{\lambda}{6}, \quad C = -2 + \frac{\lambda}{2}, \quad D = 1 - \frac{\lambda}{6} \tag{40}$$

and a particular boundary-layer problem resolves itself into finding λ as a function of x; once λ is known we can plot the velocity profiles by means of Eqs. 35 and 40. Velocity profiles for various values of λ are plotted in Fig. 11.

The parameter λ has special significance with regard to the separation point, where the condition is, according to Section 13.4, $(\partial u/\partial y)_{y=0} = 0$. When this condition is applied to Eq. 35 we get $A = 0$ or

$$\lambda = -12 \tag{41}$$

as the condition for flow separation. The velocity profile for $\lambda = -12$ is shown in Fig. 11.

Further, $\lambda = 0$ at the minimum pressure point. If values of λ are substituted in Eq. 35, we get values of $u/U_1 > 1$ if $\lambda > +12$. Since

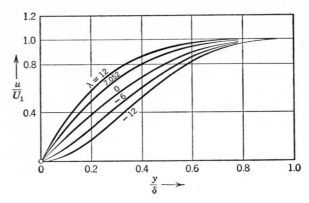

FIG. 11.   Velocity profiles given by the von Kármán-Pohlhausen method.

this type of profile is unreasonable from a physical standpoint, we conclude that

$$-12 < \lambda < 12 \tag{42}$$

Pohlhausen determined λ as a function of x for the problem of the flow past a circular cylinder. He utilized the von Kármán integral relation of Eq. 34, which, when restricted to steady flow, may be written

$$\frac{\tau_0}{\rho} = U_1{}^2 \frac{d\theta}{dx} + (2\theta + \delta^*) U_1 \frac{dU_1}{dx} \tag{43}$$

This expression leads to an ordinary differential equation in δ^2/ν by the following process: Eq. 35 with the coefficients given in Eqs. 38 and 40 is substituted in Eqs. 29 and 30. The expressions for δ^* and θ so determined and

$$\tau_0 = \mu \left(\frac{\partial u}{\partial y}\right)_{y=0} = \frac{\mu A U_1}{\delta} = \frac{\mu U_1}{\delta}\left(2 + \frac{\lambda}{6}\right)$$

are substituted in Eq. 43. After some manipulation, an ordinary differential equation with δ^2/ν as the dependent variable results. The equation involves U_1 and U_1'', where the primes indicate differentiations with respect to x, and so the solution of a particular problem requires that the pressure distribution over the surface be known.

The above method has been applied to determine the boundary layer development of bodies of various shapes. The results have been compared with more exact methods for specific cases, such as the flat plate problem of Section 12.3, the flow in the region of a two-dimensional stagnation point, and the flow past a circular cylinder.*

The various comparisons indicate that the Kármán-Pohlhausen method gives an excellent representation for the displacement and momentum thicknesses of the boundary layer and the skin-friction coefficient everywhere except near the separation point of the flow. A concomitant of this observation is the fact that the method predicts satisfactorily the location of the separation point only if the adverse pressure gradient is severe ($\partial p/\partial x \gg 0$). On the other hand, on streamline shapes with gradual adverse gradients the actual separation point is in general well downstream of the location predicted by the von Kármán-Pohlhausen method.

One of the greatest uses of the method is to show trends of various effects, such as Mach number and local irregularities in pressure distributions.

13.8 THREE-DIMENSIONAL BOUNDARY LAYERS

The two-dimensional boundary layers taken up in previous sections are characterized by a pressure gradient parallel to the flow direction. However, in many applications, such as the yawed cylindrical body in Fig. 12, the pressure gradient along the surface makes an angle with the flow direction outside the boundary layer. The component normal to the streamlines, designated by $\partial p/\partial n$, will cause the streamlines to curve in the planes tangent to the cylinder surface. The streamline curvature will be governed by the condition for equilibrium between the pressure and centrifugal forces on a fluid element (see Section 3.5),

$$\frac{\partial p}{\partial n} = \rho \frac{V^2}{R}$$

where V is the total velocity and R is the radius of curvature of the streamline. Since p is independent of y through the boundary layer, so will $\partial p/\partial n$ be constant. It follows that R will be proportional to V^2, that is, the radius of curvature will be small near the surface and will increase with distance from the surface. This three-dimensional boundary layer is shown schematically in the magnified region in Fig. 12. Typical streamlines very near the surface and near the outer edge of the boundary layer are also shown schematically.

---

* See H. Schlichting, *Boundary Layer Theory*, pp. 213–216. H. Holstein and T. Bohlen (*Boundary Layer Theory*, pp. 206–213) have devised a form of the von Kármán-Pohlhausen method that is particularly well suited to practical calculations.

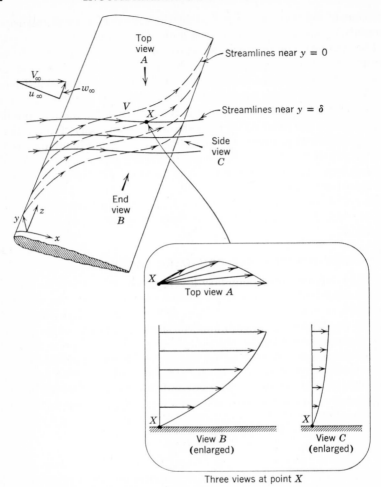

Fig. 12. Streamlines and "blown up" profile for three-dimensional boundary layer on yawed cylinder.

The direction of the curvature of the streamlines can be rationalized as follows. As the streamline approaches the cylinder, it will bend toward the direction of the most rapid pressure decrease, that is, toward the normal to the line of minimum pressure. As the streamline *leaves* the pressure "trough," it will bend *away* from the direction of the most rapid *increase* in pressure. There will therefore be an inflection in the streamlines as they cross the line of minimum pressure. It follows also, as is shown in Fig. 12, that the pressure gradients will deflect the slow-moving air near the surface more than that near the edge of the boundary layer. We might also reason that the shapes of the streamlines will be qualitatively comparable to the paths of balls that traverse a shallow trough cut in a table at an angle to the initial direction of the roll.

Analytically the flow in the boundary layer of a yawed *infinite* cylinder may be treated with respect to the axes designated in Fig. 12. The exact equations of motion and continuity for incompressible flow are derived in Appendix B and were used in the similarity analysis of Section 12.6. They are

$$\rho \frac{\mathfrak{D}u}{\mathfrak{D}t} = -\frac{\partial p}{\partial x} + \mu \nabla^2 u$$

$$\rho \frac{\mathfrak{D}v}{\mathfrak{D}t} = -\frac{\partial p}{\partial y} + \mu \nabla^2 v$$

$$\rho \frac{\mathfrak{D}w}{\mathfrak{D}t} = -\frac{\partial p}{\partial z} + \mu \nabla^2 w$$

$$\frac{\partial u}{\partial x} + \frac{\partial v}{\partial y} + \frac{\partial w}{\partial z} = 0$$

(44)

With the axes designated in Fig. 12, we see that none of the flow properties vary with z; that is, all derivatives with respect to z vanish. With this simplification, the first two equations and continuity contain only u, v, and p as functions of x, y, and t. The boundary conditions are also independent of z. Therefore, these equations may be solved for u, v, and p, and these solutions substituted in the third of Eqs. 44 enable us to solve for w.

It is shown in Appendix B that the boundary layer equation, Eq. 3 of Chapter 12, is a simplified form of the first equation of motion and that all of the terms in the second equation are negligible. Then the u- and v-components in the boundary layer may be found from the boundary layer equation

$$\frac{\partial u}{\partial t} + u \frac{\partial u}{\partial x} + v \frac{\partial u}{\partial y} = -\frac{1}{\rho}\frac{\partial p}{\partial x} + \nu \frac{\partial^2 u}{\partial y^2}$$

(45)

and continuity

$$\frac{\partial u}{\partial x} + \frac{\partial v}{\partial y} = 0$$

(46)

To solve for the spanwise component in the boundary layer, the third of Eqs. 44 simplifies to a form identical with Eq. 45 for u, except that $\partial p/\partial z = 0$. Then,

$$\frac{\partial w}{\partial t} + u\frac{\partial w}{\partial x} + v\frac{\partial w}{\partial y} = \nu\frac{\partial^2 w}{\partial y^2} \tag{47}$$

As was pointed out above, Eqs. 45 and 46 may be solved for u and v and substituting these in Eq. 45 enables us to solve for w.

The above method of solution described is exact for *incompressible* flow over a yawed *infinite* cylinder. For compressible flow, the energy equation (Chapter 14) that must be used to obtain u and v cannot be made independent of w. For a finite yawed cylinder, for example, a finite wing, $\partial(\ )/\partial z$ will not be zero near the tips and w cannot be eliminated from the first two of Eqs. 44.*

* For details, see Franklin K. Moore, "Advances in Applied Mechanics," *Three Dimensional Boundary Layer Theory*, edited by H. L. Dryden and T. von Kármán, Vol. 4, pp. 160–224, Academic Press, New York, 1956.

Laminar Boundary Layer
in Compressible Flow

CHAPTER 14

14.1 INTRODUCTION

We shall consider in this chapter the effects of compressibility on boundary layer phenomena.   The density and temperature, hitherto considered constant, now become variables and so we need two new relations in addition to the equations of motion and continuity to solve the boundary layer problem.   One of these relations is the equation of state, $p = \rho R T$, and the other is the equation expressing conservation of energy.   This latter equation, derived for an adiabatic process in Chapter 8, was found to be $c_p T + \frac{1}{2} V^2 = c_p T_0$.   When we consider the flow in the boundary layer, we need the *general* form of the energy equation, though the above simple form is found to be a useful approximation when there is no heat transfer to the wall.

The variation of temperature through a high-speed boundary layer brings with it not only a variation in density but in viscosity and heat transfer coefficients as well.   In Section 1.6 we found that the thermal conductivity and viscosity coefficient are theoretically connected by the relationship $k \smallfrown c_p \mu$ and that $\mu \smallfrown \sqrt{T}$.   The first of these relations is found to hold quite closely, but in the second the viscosity coefficient actually varies more nearly according to the 0.76 power of the temperature.

A new parameter of considerable significance is the *Prandtl number*, $c_p \mu / k$, which, according to the previous paragraph, should be a constant for a given fluid.   Actually its variation is small; values for air are given in Table 5 at the end of the book.   We show later that the value of the Prandtl number is a measure of the degree to which effectively adiabatic conditions prevail in the boundary layer, and therefore of the limits of variation of the stagnation temperature within the layer.

The buoyancy forces resulting from density variations are neglected in the applications we deal with. This simplification is justified because in high-speed flow the convection currents resulting from the buoyancy forces will invariably be small compared with the velocity of the flow.

The velocity and temperature profiles through the boundary layer are described and the relation between skin-friction and heat transfer coefficients are given. The combined effects of Reynolds and Mach numbers are shown.

The occurrence of flow separation at supersonic speeds is complicated by the presence of shock waves. Whenever a shock wave intersects a surface, there will be a tendency for flow separation because the pressure is always greater on the downstream side of a shock (adverse gradient). Stalling of airfoils and flow separation in channels will be described.

We began the previous chapter on incompressible viscid flow by analyzing fully developed flow. When we realize that the effect of friction is to convert directed energy into heat, it becomes clear that fully developed flow of a gas can only be realized approximately, since as the gas becomes heated its density decreases and the flow never reaches an equilibrium distribution. In fact, as was shown in Chapter 8, the effect of friction is to accelerate a subsonic flow and to decelerate a supersonic flow.

Only a few of the simpler analyses which serve to illustrate the important concepts will be reproduced in this chapter.*

14.2   CONSERVATION OF ENERGY IN THE BOUNDARY LAYER

The conservation of energy principle applied to a group of particles of fixed identity has been given by Eq. 13 of Chapter 8. If this equation is specialized to the two-dimensional element $\rho \, \Delta x \, \Delta y$ shown in Fig. 1, we have

$$\rho \, \Delta x \, \Delta y \, \frac{de}{dt} = \frac{\delta}{\delta t} \iint_{S_1} (q' - w') \, d\hat{S}_1 \qquad (1)$$

where q' and w' represent the heat and work transfers across the surface

* For further details, the reader should consult: H. Schlichting, *Boundary Layer Theory*, translated by H. Kestin, McGraw-Hill, New York, 1955; S. I. Pai, *Viscous Flow Theory*, Van Nostrand, New York, 1956; *Modern Developments in Fluid Dynamics*, edited by L. Howarth, Oxford University Press, 1953.

$\hat{S}_1$ and the internal energy e, given by Eq. 19 of Chapter 8,* represents the average value for element $\rho \, \Delta x \, \Delta y$.

$$e = c_v T + \tfrac{1}{2} u^2 + \text{constant} \qquad (2)$$

In Fig. 1 it is assumed $\partial T / \partial y \gg \partial T / \partial x$. Therefore we may neglect heat transfer through the ends of the element compared with that through the top and bottom faces. Further, we adopt the boundary layer approximations $\partial p / \partial y = 0$ and $\partial u / \partial y \gg \partial u / \partial x$.

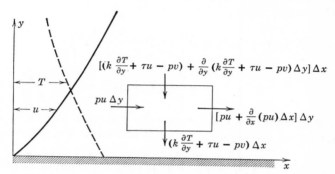

FIG. 1.   Energy balance in the boundary layer.

Heat is transferred through the bottom face at the rate $-k(\partial T / \partial y) \, \Delta x$ and through the top face at the rate

$$\left[-k \frac{\partial T}{\partial y} + \frac{\partial}{\partial y} \left(-k \frac{\partial T}{\partial y} \right) \Delta y \right] \Delta x$$

and the net transfer is

$$\frac{\partial}{\partial y} \left(k \frac{\partial T}{\partial y} \right) \Delta x \, \Delta y \qquad (3)$$

Work performed by the pressure stress p and shearing stress τ is transferred across the horizontal and vertical faces as indicated in Fig. 1. The net rate of work transfer is

$$+ \left[\frac{\partial}{\partial y} (\tau u) - \frac{\partial}{\partial x} (pu) - \frac{\partial}{\partial y} (pv) \right] \Delta x \, \Delta y \qquad (4)$$

* Gravitational energy, $-gz$, has been neglected. Departing from the nomenclature of Chapter 8, the letter u in the following material refers to the x-component of velocity and not to the intrinsic energy.

After substituting Eqs. 2, 3, and 4, into Eq. 1, we obtain

$$\rho \frac{d}{dt}\left(c_v T + \frac{u^2}{2}\right) = \frac{\partial}{\partial y}\left(k \frac{\partial T}{\partial y}\right) + \frac{\partial}{\partial y}(\tau u) - \frac{\partial}{\partial x}(pu) - \frac{\partial}{\partial y}(pv)$$

(5)

Equation 5 expresses the law: the rate of increase of total energy is equal to the sum of the rate at which heat is conducted into the element and the rate at which the stresses at the boundaries do work on the element. It is convenient to express the left side of Eq. 5 in terms of the enthalpy $c_p T + \frac{1}{2}u^2$,

$$\rho \frac{d}{dt}(c_v T + \tfrac{1}{2}u^2) = \rho \frac{d}{dt}\left(c_p T - \frac{p}{\rho} + \frac{1}{2}u^2\right)$$

$$= \rho \frac{d}{dt}(c_p T + \tfrac{1}{2}u^2) - \frac{dp}{dt} + \frac{p}{\rho}\frac{d\rho}{dt}$$

(6)

After substituting from the continuity equation $\rho \operatorname{div} \mathbf{V} = -d\rho/dt$ in the last term and expanding the last two terms, Eq. 6 becomes

$$\rho \frac{d}{dt}(c_v T + \tfrac{1}{2}u^2) = \rho \frac{d}{dt}(c_p T + \tfrac{1}{2}u^2) - \frac{\partial}{\partial x}(pu) - \frac{\partial}{\partial y}(pv)$$

The last two terms of this equation cancel the last two terms of Eq. 5 which now becomes, after substituting $\tau = \mu \, \partial u/\partial y$,

$$\rho \frac{d}{dt}(c_p T + \tfrac{1}{2}u^2) = \frac{\partial}{\partial y}\left(k \frac{\partial T}{\partial y}\right) + u \frac{\partial}{\partial y}\left(\mu \frac{\partial u}{\partial y}\right) + \mu \left(\frac{\partial u}{\partial y}\right)^2$$

(7)

We can simplify this equation further by noting that if we multiply the boundary layer momentum equation (Eq. 3 of Chapter 12) for steady flow by u and subtract it from Eq. 7 we get, with $c_p = $ constant,

$$\rho c_p \frac{dT}{dt} = u \frac{\partial p}{\partial x} + \frac{\partial}{\partial y}\left(k \frac{\partial T}{\partial y}\right) + \mu \left(\frac{\partial u}{\partial y}\right)^2$$

(8)

This equation is the boundary layer energy equation in the form in which it is usually used.

The left side of Eq. 8 represents the rate of increase of enthalpy per unit volume as the element moves with the flow. The three terms on the right side represent, respectively, the rate at which work is done by the pressure forces, the rate at which heat is transferred through the sides of the element and the rate at which viscous stresses dissipate energy of the ordered motion into heat (or enthalpy).

The equations governing the compressible laminar boundary layer are: Eq. 8 above and the equations of motion and continuity, Eqs. 3 and 4 of Chapter 12, respectively. The latter are

$$\rho\left(u\frac{\partial u}{\partial x}+v\frac{\partial u}{\partial y}\right)=-\frac{\partial p}{\partial x}+\frac{\partial}{\partial y}\left(\mu\frac{\partial u}{\partial y}\right)$$

$$\frac{\partial}{\partial x}(\rho u)+\frac{\partial}{\partial y}(\rho v)=0$$

(9)

The boundary conditions are

$$\text{at } y=0: \quad u=v=0, \quad T=T_w(x)$$
$$\text{at } y=\infty: \quad u=U_1(x), \quad T=T_1(x)$$

(10)

In addition p, ρ, and T are connected by the equation of state $p=\rho RT$.

Various simplifications of these equations leading to results of practical value are taken up in succeeding sections.

14.3 ROTATION AND ENTROPY GRADIENT IN THE BOUNDARY LAYER

We shall show here that the rotation in the boundary layer is associated with an entropy gradient normal to the streamlines. From Eq. 33, Chapter 8, the differential of the entropy is given by

$$ds=\frac{\delta q}{T}=d\,(\log T^{c_v}-\log \rho^{R})$$

which becomes

$$ds=c_v\frac{dT}{T}-R\frac{d\rho}{\rho}$$

After introducing $p=\rho RT$

$$\frac{\partial s}{\partial y}=\frac{c_p}{T}\frac{\partial T}{\partial y}-\frac{R}{p}\frac{\partial p}{\partial y}$$

We set $\partial p/\partial y=0$ for boundary layer flow and substitute for $\partial T/\partial y$ from

$$c_pT=c_pT_0-\frac{u^2}{2}$$

Then

$$\frac{\partial s}{\partial y}=-\frac{u}{T}\frac{\partial u}{\partial y}+\frac{c_p}{T}\frac{\partial T_0}{\partial y}$$

In the boundary layer $\partial v/\partial x\simeq 0$ so that $\partial u/\partial y\simeq \mathrm{curl}_z\,\mathbf{V}$. We shall see later that $\partial T_0/\partial y$ is small in the boundary layer over an insulated surface. Then an approximate relation between entropy gradient and vorticity in the boundary layer is

$$\frac{\partial s}{\partial y} \simeq \frac{u}{T} \operatorname{curl}_z \mathbf{V}$$

This relation, with y measured normal to the streamlines, also holds approximately in the free stream. It is known as Crocco's relation and shows that the entropy gradient along a detached shock (Section 10.7) is associated with a rotation in the flow downstream of the shock.

14.4 SIMILARITY CONSIDERATIONS FOR COMPRESSIBLE BOUNDARY LAYERS

We showed in Section 12.6 that the condition for similarity of the incompressible flows around geometrically similar bodies is that the Reynolds numbers be identical. We shall show here what additional parameters are required for a compressible flow. We follow the same procedure as in Section 12.6, introducing the reference quantities L (length), U (velocity), ρ_1 (density), μ_1 (viscosity), and T_1 (temperature); and setting

$$u' = u/U, \quad v' = v/U, \quad x' = x/L, \quad y' = y/L$$

$$\mu' = \mu/\mu_1, \quad \rho' = \rho/\rho_1, \quad T' = T/T_1, \quad p' = p/\rho_1 U^2, \quad Re = \rho_1 UL/\mu_1 \tag{11}$$

Now, if the temperature variation through the boundary layer is not too great, we may for the purposes of the similarity analysis take μ and k as constants. Then the equations of motion reduce to those given in Section 12.6 for incompressible flow. To find the additional parameters introduced by compressibility, we use Eqs. 11 to nondimensionalize the approximate form of the energy equation, Eq. 8. We obtain

$$\frac{UT_1 c_p \rho'}{L} \frac{dT'}{dt'} = \frac{U^3}{L} u' \frac{\partial p'}{\partial x'} + \frac{kT_1}{L^2} \frac{\partial^2 T'}{\partial y'^2} + \frac{\mu U^2}{L^2} \left(\frac{\partial u'}{\partial y'} \right)^2$$

In terms of dimensionless parameters this equation becomes

$$\rho' \frac{dT'}{dt'} - (\gamma - 1) M^2 u' \frac{\partial p'}{\partial x'} = \frac{1}{PrRe} \frac{\partial^2 T'}{\partial y'^2} + \frac{(\gamma - 1) M^2}{Re} \left(\frac{\partial u'}{\partial y'} \right)^2 \tag{12}$$

where $Pr = c_p \mu/k$ is defined as the *Prandtl number*.

We see from Eq. 12 that the similarity of steady compressible boundary layer flows requires identical values of $(\gamma - 1) M^2$, Pr, and Re.

Another parameter which enters, through the boundary conditions, is the *Nusselt number*, derived in Appendix A.

$$Nu = \frac{hL}{k}$$

where h is the rate of heat transfer per unit area per unit temperature difference and L is a characteristic length.

The solution of a particular compressible boundary layer problem may therefore be expressed formally as

$$f(c_f, Re, Nu, Pr, M, \gamma) = 0 \qquad (13)$$

where c_f is the skin friction coefficient $\tau_0/\frac{1}{2}\rho_1 U_1{}^2$. Fortunately γ and Pr are only weak functions of the temperature and they may be taken as constant for a wide range of applications. Hence, for most practical purposes a boundary layer problem reduces to the functional relationship:

$$f(c_f, M, Nu, Re) = 0 \qquad (14)$$

The solutions discussed in the remainder of this chapter are in the form of Eq. 14.

14.5 SOLUTIONS OF THE ENERGY EQUATION FOR PRANDTL NUMBER UNITY

Many applications of boundary layer theory to compressible fluids yield good engineering approximations for air if the Prandtl number

$$Pr = c_p \frac{\mu}{k}$$

is set to unity. We shall in this section show that the problem of the compressible boundary layer is thus greatly simplified. Further, we shall demonstrate that the physical reason for the resulting simplification is that a Prandtl number of unity implies effectively adiabatic flow at every point in the boundary layer.

A physical interpretation of the Prandtl number will help in understanding its role in boundary layer theory. μ represents the rate of momentum transfer per unit area per unit velocity gradient and k/c_p represents the rate of heat transfer per unit area per unit enthalpy gradient. Then the Prandtl number represents the ratio between these two rates of transfer.

We can arrive at another physical interpretation by considering Eq. 7

$$\rho \frac{d}{dt}\left(c_p T + \frac{u^2}{2}\right) = \frac{\partial}{\partial y}\left(k \frac{\partial T}{\partial y}\right) + u \frac{\partial}{\partial y}\left(\mu \frac{\partial u}{\partial y}\right) + \mu \left(\frac{\partial u}{\partial y}\right)^2 \qquad (7)$$

The first term on the right hand side of Eq. 7 represents heat transferred out of the fluid element by conduction. The second and third terms correspond to energy generated through shear at the boundaries of the element and viscous dissipation within. If the heat transferred out of the element is just equal to the total heat generated through the action of viscosity, the right hand side of Eq. 7 is zero. After making this assumption, the integral of Eq. 7 can be written:

$$c_p T + \frac{u^2}{2} = \text{constant} = c_p T_0 \tag{15}$$

Eq. 15 indicates that the quantity $c_p T + \frac{1}{2} u^2$ is constant along a streamline. For the usual case of uniform flow upstream, the stagnation temperature has the same value on every streamline, and it may be concluded that $c_p T + \frac{1}{2} u^2$ is constant throughout the boundary layer.

The significance of this conclusion in terms of the Prandtl number may be seen by assuming the temperature gradient within the boundary layer to be small enough so that μ and k may be taken as constants. Then Eq. 7 may be written

$$\frac{d}{dt} (c_p T + \tfrac{1}{2} u^2) = \frac{k}{\rho c_p} \frac{\partial^2}{\partial y^2} (c_p T + \tfrac{1}{2} u^2 Pr) \tag{16}$$

Equation 15 is a solution of Eq. 16, regardless of the velocity distribution, only if the Prandtl number is unity. Therefore, within the restrictions that μ and k are constant, the above analysis shows that Prandtl number unity implies effectively adiabatic conditions in the sense that the heat generated within an element by viscous work is transferred out of the element by conduction.

Equation 15 is but one of the solutions to Eq. 16 for Prandtl number unity. To determine the properties of the solution, we differentiate Eq. 15 and get

$$c_p \frac{\partial T}{\partial y} = -u \frac{\partial u}{\partial y} \tag{17}$$

We see from this equation that $\partial T/\partial y = 0$ where $u = 0$ $(y = 0)$ and where $\partial u/\partial y = 0$ $(y = \delta)$.

We conclude, therefore, that Prandtl number unity implies that for flow over an insulated surface, defined by $(\partial T/\partial y)_w = 0$, the energy equation reduces to Eq. 15 and that the velocity and temperature boundary layers have the same thickness. Note that this conclusion involves no restrictions on the pressure gradient in the flow direction.

We shall now find the corresponding relation between velocity and temperature with heat transfer at the wall. Here we make the approximation that $\partial p/\partial x = 0$. Then Eq. 8 with Prandtl number unity, is

$$\rho\left(u\frac{\partial T}{\partial x} + v\frac{\partial T}{\partial y}\right) = \frac{\partial}{\partial y}\left(\mu\frac{\partial T}{\partial y}\right) + \frac{\mu}{c_p}\left(\frac{\partial u}{\partial y}\right)^2 \tag{18}$$

We now assume that

$$T = A + Bu + Cu^2 \tag{19}$$

Equation 19 is substituted for T in Eq. 18 and the constants A, B, and C are evaluated by means of the boundary conditions:

$$\begin{aligned} &\text{at } y = 0: \quad u = 0, \quad\;\; T = T_w \\ &\text{at } y = \infty: \quad u = U_1, \quad T = T_1 \end{aligned} \tag{20}$$

Equation 18 with T from Eq. 19 is

$$\rho B\left(u\frac{\partial u}{\partial x} + v\frac{\partial u}{\partial y}\right) + 2\rho Cu\left(u\frac{\partial u}{\partial x} + v\frac{\partial u}{\partial y}\right)$$

$$= \frac{\partial}{\partial y}\left[\mu\left(B\frac{\partial u}{\partial y} + 2Cu\frac{\partial u}{\partial y}\right)\right] + \frac{\mu}{c_p}\left(\frac{\partial u}{\partial y}\right)^2 \tag{21}$$

The momentum equation (Eq. 9) with $\partial p/\partial x = 0$ is

$$u\frac{\partial u}{\partial x} + v\frac{\partial u}{\partial y} = \frac{\partial}{\partial y}\left(\mu\frac{\partial u}{\partial y}\right) \tag{22}$$

We multiply Eq. 22 by B and subtract it from Eq. 21. Then, after expanding the term $\partial/\partial y[2Cu(\partial u/\partial y)]$, Eq. 21 becomes

$$2C\rho u\left(u\frac{\partial u}{\partial x} + v\frac{\partial u}{\partial y}\right) = 2Cu\frac{\partial}{\partial y}\left(\mu\frac{\partial u}{\partial y}\right) + 2C\mu\left(\frac{\partial u}{\partial y}\right)^2 + \frac{\mu}{c_p}\left(\frac{\partial u}{\partial y}\right)^2 \tag{23}$$

Now, if we multiply Eq. 22 by $2Cu$ and subtract from Eq. 23 we get:

$$C = -\frac{1}{2c_p} \tag{24}$$

Then, after using the first boundary condition of Eqs. 20 to give $A = T_w$, Eq. 19 with Eq. 24 becomes:

$$T = T_w + Bu + \frac{u^2}{2c_p}$$

and, with B evaluated by use of the second condition of Eqs. 20,

$$T = T_w + \left[\frac{T_1 - T_w}{U_1} + \frac{U_1}{2c_p} \right] u - \frac{u^2}{2c_p} \tag{25}$$

or

$$\frac{T}{T_1} = \frac{T_w}{T_1} + \left(1 - \frac{T_w}{T_1} \right) \frac{u}{U_1} + \frac{u}{U_1} \left(1 - \frac{u}{U_1} \right) \frac{U_1{}^2}{2c_p T_1}$$

But

$$2c_p T_1 = \frac{2\gamma R T_1}{\gamma - 1} = \frac{2a_1{}^2}{\gamma - 1}$$

where a_1 is the speed of sound outside the boundary layer. Then, with $M_1 = U_1/a_1$, Eq. 25 finally becomes

$$\frac{T}{T_1} = \frac{T_w}{T_1} + \left(1 - \frac{T_w}{T_1} \right) \frac{u}{U_1} + \frac{\gamma - 1}{2} M_1{}^2 \left(1 - \frac{u}{U_1} \right) \frac{u}{U_1} \tag{26}$$

This equation is generally referred to as Crocco's form of the energy equation. It applies strictly for $\partial p/\partial x = 0$, and $Pr = 1$, but k and μ need not be constants.

If we differentiate Eq. 26 we get a relation between the temperature and velocity gradients,

$$\frac{\partial T}{\partial y} = \left[\left(1 - \frac{T_w}{T_1} \right) + \frac{\gamma - 1}{2} M_1{}^2 \left(1 - 2\frac{u}{U_1} \right) \right] \frac{T_1}{U_1} \frac{\partial u}{\partial y} \tag{27}$$

and at $y = 0$ ($u = 0$) and with $c_p\mu = k$ the relation between heat transfer and skin friction at the wall is:

$$k \left(\frac{\partial T}{\partial y} \right)_w = \left\{ \left(1 - \frac{T_w}{T_1} \right) + \frac{\gamma - 1}{2} M_1{}^2 \right\} \frac{T_1 c_p}{U_1} \mu \left(\frac{\partial u}{\partial y} \right)_w \tag{28}$$

We concluded from Eq. 15 that for an insulated plate Prandtl number unity implies that the temperature and velocity boundary layers are of equal thickness. Equation 28 permits us to broaden this conclusion to include arbitrary heat transfer at the wall at zero pressure gradient.

Since the Prandtl number for air is near unity, the above solutions (Eqs. 15 or 26) of the energy equation give satisfactory results for many boundary layer problems in aerodynamics. Before use can be made of these solutions, however, it is necessary to find the velocity distributions by solving the momentum equation.

14.6 TEMPERATURE RECOVERY FACTOR

The *adiabatic, recovery,* or *equilibrium temperature,* designated by T_{ad}, is the temperature of the wall in an airflow in which there is no heat transfer to the wall. Mathematically $T_w = T_{ad}$ for $(\partial T/\partial y)_w = 0$. From the previous section (Eq. 15) we see that when the Prandtl number is unity, $T_{ad} = T_0$, the stagnation temperature in the outside flow. The correction to this result caused by deviations of the Prandtl number from unity will be investigated in this section. The problem of determining the recovery temperature is generally referred to as the "thermometer problem."

The flat plate thermometer problem was solved by Pohlhausen * under the restrictions that the Mach number of the flow is low enough so that we may take ρ, μ, and k as constants. The governing equations are then Eqs. 8, 9, and 10. With $\partial p/\partial x = 0$, these are

$$u\frac{\partial u}{\partial x} + v\frac{\partial u}{\partial y} = \nu\frac{\partial^2 u}{\partial y^2}$$

$$\frac{\partial u}{\partial x} + \frac{\partial v}{\partial y} = 0 \qquad\qquad (29)$$

$$\rho c_p\left(u\frac{\partial T}{\partial x} + v\frac{\partial T}{\partial y}\right) = k\frac{\partial^2 T}{\partial y^2} + \mu\left(\frac{\partial u}{\partial y}\right)^2$$

The boundary conditions are:

$$\text{at } y = 0: \quad u = v = 0, \quad \partial T/\partial y = 0$$
$$\text{at } y = \infty: \quad u = U_1, \quad T = T_1 \qquad\qquad (30)$$

The first two equations of Eqs. 29 and the boundary conditions on the velocities in Eqs. 30 constitute the Blasius problem solved in Section 13.3. The basic independent variable there was:

$$\eta = \frac{1}{2}\sqrt{\frac{U_1}{\nu x}}\,y$$

and

$$(31)$$

$$u = \frac{U_1}{2}f'(\eta); \quad v = \frac{1}{2}\sqrt{\frac{U_1\nu}{x}}\,[\eta f'(\eta) - f(\eta)]$$

* E. Pohlhausen, Der Wärmeaustausch zwischen festen Körpern und Flüssigkeiten mit kleiner Reibung und kleiner Wärmeleitung, *Zeit. f. angew. Math. u. Mech.*, Vol. 1, p. 115, 1921.

We use these expressions for u and v and try to express the third equation of Eqs. 29 as an ordinary differential equation. We first write

$$T = T_1 + \frac{U_1^2}{2c_p}\theta(\eta) \tag{32}$$

and the boundary conditions on the temperature in Eqs. 30 become

$$\theta'(0) = 0 \quad \text{and} \quad \theta(\infty) = 0 \tag{33}$$

When the expressions for u, v, and T in Eqs. 31 and 32 are substituted in the third equation of Eqs. 29, we obtain, after canceling common terms,

$$\theta'' + Prf\theta' + 0.5Prf''^2 = 0 \tag{34}$$

After substituting values of f and f'' as given in Fig. 3 of Chapter 13, Pohlhausen found an approximate solution of Eq. 34. The recovery factor, which we shall call r, was found to be

$$r = \theta(0) = \sqrt{Pr} = 0.845 \text{ (for air)} \tag{35}$$

Figure 2 is a plot of $\theta(\eta)$ through the boundary layer.

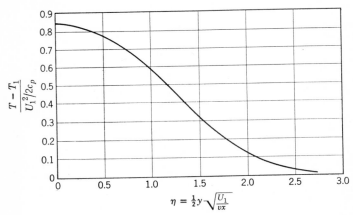

FIG. 2. Pohlhausen solution for temperature distribution in the boundary layer.

Equation 35 states that the air near the wall has lost stagnation enthalpy. Then conservation of energy demands, since we are dealing with an adiabatic process, that somewhere in the boundary layer the air must have *gained* stagnation enthalpy. This increase in stagnation enthalpy is shown clearly in the curves of Fig. 3.*

* E. R. van Driest, *Investigation of Laminar Boundary Layer in Compressible Fluids Using the Crocco Method*, NACA TN 2597, 1952.

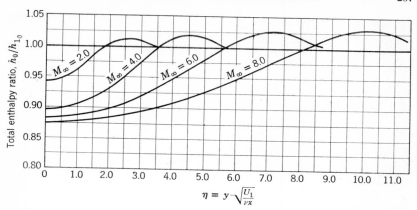

FIG. 3. Distribution of stagnation enthalpy in the boundary layer on an insulated plate.

Accurate calculations * show only small deviations of the laminar recovery factor from $\sqrt{Pr}$ up to Mach numbers of at least 8.

Some experimental results on a cone at various Mach numbers are shown in Fig. 4. The boundary layer at the low Reynolds numbers is

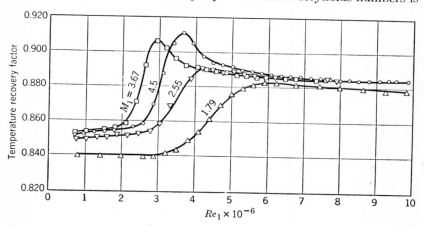

FIG. 4. Measurements of temperature recovery factor (θ (0) of Eq. 35) on 5° cone. Measurements by Leslie M. Mack (Report 20–80, Jet Propulsion Laboratory, Calif. Inst. of Tech., 1954).

laminar and the temperature recovery factor is 0.84 to 0.855 over the range of Mach numbers 1.79 to 4.5. Reference to Eq. 35 shows that the agreement between theory and experiment is remarkably good.

* *Ibid.*

Results from various laboratories give values of the laminar recovery factor of 0.85 ± 0.01 for Mach numbers between 1.2 and 6.

The curves in Fig. 4 begin to rise steeply at Reynolds numbers for which transition to the turbulent boundary layer occurs. These portions will be referred to in the following two chapters.

14.7 HEAT TRANSFER VERSUS SKIN FRICTION

Pohlhausen * also calculated the heat transfer to a flat plate at constant temperature T_w with the same restrictions as applied in calculating the recovery factor in Section 14.6 ($\partial p/\partial x = 0$ and ρ, μ, and k constants), and, in addition, the velocities are assumed to be low enough so that the dissipation term $\mu(\partial u/\partial y)^2$ in the energy equation can be neglected.

The governing equations, Eqs. 8, 9, 10, become

$$u \frac{\partial u}{\partial x} + v \frac{\partial u}{\partial y} = \nu \frac{\partial^2 u}{\partial y^2}$$

$$\frac{\partial u}{\partial x} + \frac{\partial v}{\partial y} = 0 \tag{36}$$

$$\rho c_p \left(u \frac{\partial T}{\partial x} + v \frac{\partial T}{\partial y} \right) = k \frac{\partial^2 T}{\partial y^2}$$

with the boundary conditions

$$\text{at } y = 0: \quad u = v = 0, \quad T = T_w$$

$$\text{at } y = \infty: \quad u = U_1, \quad T = T_1 \tag{37}$$

As in the previous section, we see that the first two equations of Eqs. 36 and the boundary conditions on the velocities in Eqs. 37 constitute the Blasius problem solved in Section 13.3. Then with η, u, and v as given in Eqs. 31 and a new variable

$$\beta(\eta) = \frac{T_w - T}{T_w - T_1} \tag{38}$$

we attempt to obtain an ordinary differential equation from the last equation of Eqs. 36. The derivatives occurring are:

* See reference, Section 14.6.

$$\frac{\partial T}{\partial x} = \frac{\eta}{2x}(T_w - T_1)\beta'$$

$$\frac{\partial T}{\partial y} = -\frac{1}{2}\sqrt{\frac{U_1}{\nu x}}(T_w - T_1)\beta' \qquad (39)$$

$$\frac{\partial^2 T}{\partial y^2} = -\frac{1}{4}\frac{U_1}{\nu x}(T_w - T_1)\beta''$$

The boundary conditions on the temperature, Eqs. 37, become

$$\text{at } \eta = 0: \quad \beta = 0$$
$$\text{at } \eta = \infty: \quad \beta = 1 \qquad (40)$$

We now substitute into the last equation of Eqs. 36 the expressions for u and v from Eqs. 31 and for the temperature derivatives from Eqs. 39. Then the equation becomes, after factoring common terms:

$$\beta'' + Prf\beta' = 0 \qquad (41)$$

where Pr is the Prandtl number $c_p\mu/k$ and f is the Blasius function of the previous section (see Fig. 3 of Chapter 13). Equation 41 is a linear ordinary differential equation in β and with $Pr = $ constant, its solution is of the form

$$\beta' = \alpha \exp\left\{-Pr\int_0^\eta f\, d\eta\right\} \qquad (42)$$

where α is the integration constant. After integrating Eq. 42 and applying the boundary condition $\beta = 0$ at $\eta = 0$ (Eq. 40), we get

$$\beta = \alpha \int_0^\eta \exp\left\{-Pr\int_0^\eta f\, d\eta\right\} d\eta \qquad (43)$$

α is evaluated by the boundary condition $\beta = 1$ at $\eta = \infty$. Thus

$$\alpha = \left[\int_0^\infty \exp\left\{-Pr\int_0^\eta f\, d\eta\right\} d\eta\right]^{-1} \qquad (44)$$

Pohlhausen substituted the Blasius function f shown in Fig. 3 of Chapter 13 and found, approximately

$$\alpha = 0.664 Pr^{1/3} \qquad (45)$$

The heat transfer coefficient is found by evaluating Q, the rate at which heat is transferred to a plate of width b and length l. We may write

$$Q = -kb\int_0^l \left(\frac{\partial T}{\partial y}\right)_w dx \qquad (46)$$

After substituting for $\partial T/\partial y$ from Eq. 39, noting from Eq. 43 that $\beta' = \alpha$ at $y = \eta = 0$ and integrating,

$$Q = kb\alpha(T_w - T_1)\sqrt{\frac{U_1 l}{\nu}} \tag{47}$$

The Nusselt number Nu, derived in Appendix A and mentioned as one of the similarity parameters for boundary layer flow in Section 14.3, is given by:

$$Nu = \frac{hL}{k} = \frac{L}{k}\left(\frac{Q}{S(T_w - T_1)}\right) \tag{48}$$

where L is a characteristic length, h is the rate of heat transfer per unit area per unit temperature difference, and S is the area of the plate ($S = lb$). If we take the length of the plate, l, as the characteristic length and substitute for Q from Eq. 47 and for α from Eq. 45, Eq. 48 becomes

$$Nu = 0.664 \, Pr^{\frac{1}{3}}Re^{\frac{1}{2}} \tag{49}$$

where

$$Re = U_1 l/\nu$$

Another dimensionless heat transfer coefficient, called the Stanton number, St, is defined as

$$St = \frac{h}{\rho c_p U_1} = \frac{Q}{\rho c_p S U_1(T_w - T_1)} \tag{50}$$

When we are dealing with the relation between heat transfer and skin friction, the Stanton number proves to be a convenient similarity parameter. Thus, after substituting for Q and for Nu,

$$St = \frac{Nu}{Pr \cdot Re} = \frac{0.664}{Pr^{\frac{2}{3}}Re^{\frac{1}{2}}} \tag{51}$$

If we compare Eq. 51 with the expression for the average skin-friction coefficient, C_f from Eq. 10 of Chapter 13, we may write

$$St = Pr^{-\frac{2}{3}}C_f/2 \tag{52}$$

If we define the local Stanton number

$$st = \frac{q}{\rho c_p U_1(T_w - T_1)}$$

the analysis similar to that leading to Eq. 52 gives

$$st = Pr^{-\frac{2}{3}}c_f/2 \tag{53}$$

Since the Prandtl number for air does not vary greatly, we have in Eqs. 52 and 53 remarkably simple relations between local and average heat transfer and skin-friction coefficients for a flat plate.

In spite of the approximations inherent in Eqs. 36 the agreement between Eqs. 52 and 53 and experiment is good up to reasonably high Mach numbers.*

14.8 VELOCITY AND TEMPERATURE PROFILES AND SKIN FRICTION

In the previous sections, the approximations made amounted to a neglect of the effect of compressibility on the velocity profile. Although the results so obtained are applicable to some significant problems, their use is limited to moderate Mach numbers. Solutions applicable to high Mach numbers must take into account alterations to the velocity profile resulting from variations of μ and ρ with temperature (and therefore with y).

Many solutions of Eqs. 8, 9, and 10 have been obtained for specific variations of T_w, U_1, and T_1 with x, for various Prandtl numbers, and for various relations between μ and k and T. The analyses, compared with that for incompressible flow, are complicated considerably by the introduction of the new variables and equations. The details of the solutions are beyond the scope of this book. Therefore, only the results of some of those studies which illustrate the important concepts will be described here.

In practically all of the analyses the Prandtl number is assumed constant, so that $k \smallsmile c_p\mu$, but the variation of μ with T takes several forms. The most accurate relation is expressed by the Sutherland equation

$$\frac{\mu}{\mu_r} = \frac{T_r + 216}{T + 216}\left(\frac{T}{T_r}\right)^{\frac{3}{2}} \tag{54}$$

but the difficulty of using this form in any solutions except those employing computing machines precludes its use in most analyses. Most analytical solutions employ the relation

$$\frac{\mu}{\mu_r} = C\left(\frac{T}{T_r}\right)^{\omega} \tag{55}$$

where μ_r and T_r refer to reference values, C is a coefficient which may be a weak function of the temperature and $\frac{1}{2} < \omega < 1$.

* Dean R. Chapman, and Morris W. Rubesin, "Temperature and Velocity Profiles in the Compressible Laminar Boundary Layer with Arbitrary Distribution of Surface Temperature," *J. Aero. Sci.*, Vol. 16, No. 9, pp. 547–566, September 1949.

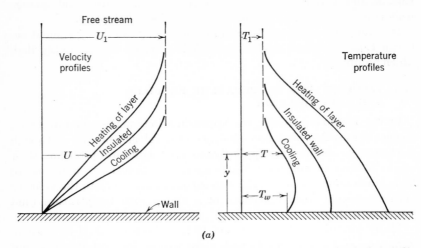

FIG. 5a.   Qualitative effect of wall temperature on temperature and velocity profiles in a boundary layer.

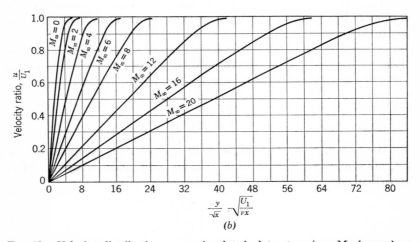

FIG. 5b.   Velocity distributions on an insulated plate at various Mach numbers.

The general features of the velocity and temperature profiles in a compressible boundary layer as affected by heat transfer are shown qualitatively in Fig. 5a. Figure 5b demonstrates the effect of Mach number on the velocity profiles over an insulated plate.* We see that the boundary layer thickness increases with temperature of the surface and with increasing Mach number of the free stream.

Figure 6 † shows the dependence of the mean skin-friction coefficient C_f for a flat plate on Mach number, Reynolds number, and temperature

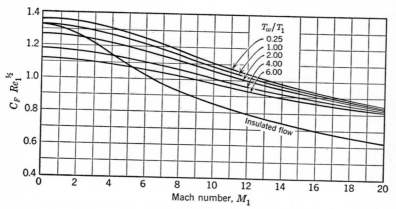

FIG. 6. Mean skin-friction coefficient for flat plate as function of Reynolds number, Mach number, and temperature ratio.

ratio. The effect of Mach number is seen to be quite small until appreciable supersonic Mach numbers are reached.

14.9 EFFECTS OF PRESSURE GRADIENT

The effects of compressibility on the boundary layer in a favorable pressure gradient introduce complications in the solution of the equations, but no new concepts are involved. On a surface which is warped so that the flow is turned away from its original direction, expansion waves form and the accompanying favorable pressure gradient accelerates the boundary layer flow. If expansion waves intersect the body, a similar accelerating effect is experienced by the flow.

On the other hand, if the body is warped so that the flow turns *into* itself, compression waves will appear and these will tend to form an envelope as shown in Fig. 7. The envelope is a shock with intensity

* E. R. van Driest, *Investigation of Laminar Boundary Layer in Compressible Fluids Using the Crocco Method.*
  † *Ibid.*

varying along its length so that there will be an entropy gradient (see Section 10.6) normal to the streamlines in the downstream flow. Further, an adverse pressure gradient will exist on the concave wall with the resulting tendency for flow separation. However, if the curvature continues as shown, there will be a tendency for the flow to *re-attach* after separating.

The behavior of the boundary layer on a body in a supersonic flow in an adverse pressure gradient resolves itself into some phase of *shock*

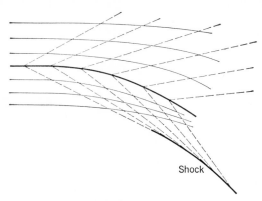

Fig. 7. Formation of a shock as an envelope of weak compression waves.

wave-boundary layer interaction. Considerable theoretical and experimental work has been carried out on two types of interaction: (1) the shock from a wedge intersecting the boundary layer on a flat plate, and (2) the flow over a sharp step.

When a shock wave intersects the boundary layer, its strength decreases steadily as it proceeds into the layer, and it becomes a Mach line at the streamline where the flow is sonic. The high pressure behind the wave provides a steep adverse pressure gradient which makes itself felt upstream through the subsonic portion of the layer. *Transition* to turbulent boundary layer (Chapter 15) or flow separation may result, depending on the intensity of the adverse gradient, that is, on the intensity of the shock.

Intuitively, it is logical that the thicker the subsonic portion of the boundary layer, the farther upstream the effects of the adverse gradient will be felt. Also, $\partial u/\partial y$ near $y = 0$ will be small for a thick subsonic portion, and hence a small adverse gradient (small shock intensity) will suffice to cause flow separation. In general, a laminar boundary layer will have a thicker subsonic portion than will the turbulent layer. Since this is the only fact we need know to rationalize the differences between the interaction of a shock with a laminar or turbulent layer, both types will be discussed here. It is recommended that the student reread this section after studying the turbulent boundary layer.

In Fig. 8,* the incident shock, generated by a 4.5° wedge, intersects a laminar boundary layer on a flat plate. The shock wave configuration

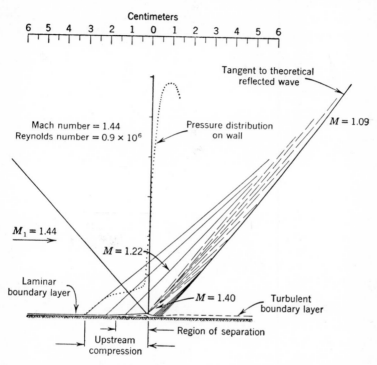

Fig. 8. Model of reflection of shock wave from laminar boundary layer (NACA Report 1100). Expansion waves are shown by broken lines. (Figure reproduced by courtesy of NASA.)

was identified by schlieren photographs, the boundary layer was studied with a total-head tube, and the pressure distribution was measured at the surface of the plate. The figure shows that the pressure rise has propagated upstream a distance of 3 cm or about 50 times the thickness of the boundary layer. The resulting adverse pressure gradient causes a thickening of the laminar layer followed by a "bubble" of separated flow and finally by transition to a turbulent boundary

* H. W. Liepmann, A. Roshko, and S. Dhawan, *On Reflection of Shock Waves from Boundary Layers*, NACA Report 1100, 1952.

FIG. 9.   Schlieren photographs of the shock wave configuration on the upper surface of an airfoil at a free-stream Mach number of 0.843.   For the upper photograph the Reynolds number is 10^6 and the boundary layer is laminar; for the lower the Reynolds number is 2×10^6 and the boundary layer is turbulent.   Measurements at GALCIT (courtesy H. W. Liepmann).

layer. The waves associated with the thickening and subsequent thinning of the layer are shown in the figure. The final reflected wave is parallel to the direction computed for reflection from a plane surface in an inviscid fluid. The initial Mach number given is measured; the others are computed from the wave configuration.

If the boundary layer is turbulent, the pressure rise propagates only about one-tenth as far upstream as for the laminar layer. In the experiments described, no flow separation was observed when the boundary layer was turbulent.

It was pointed out in Chapter 11 that for an airfoil in transonic flow the pressure recovery over the upper surface is generally accomplished by means of a shock wave. The interaction between this shock wave and the boundary layer has been the subject of many theoretical and experimental investigations. Figure 9 shows two schlieren photographs of the flow over an airfoil at a free-stream Mach number of 0.843; in the upper picture the boundary layer upstream of the shock wave is laminar; in the lower it is turbulent. In both pictures the flow direction is from left to right.

Studies of the intensity of the shock wave required to cause flow separation on a flat plate have been carried out. * These indicate that the value of $\Delta p/q_1$, where Δp is the pressure rise across the shock and q_1 is the dynamic pressure ahead of the shock, required to cause separation of the laminar layer is proportional to $Re_x^{-\frac{1}{2}}$. For the turbulent layer the critical value of $\Delta p/q_1$ is proportional to $Re_x^{-\frac{1}{5}}$. These dependencies on Reynolds number indicate that, for a given Mach number and temperature ratio, the shock strength required to cause flow separation is proportional to the local skin friction (see Fig. 6 of this chapter and Eq. 28 of Chapter 16). The conclusion seems intuitively reasonable when we reflect that the skin-friction coefficient for both laminar and turbulent flow is proportional to $(\partial u/\partial y)_w$ and that the adverse pressure gradient, which is proportional to the shock intensity, must be great enough to reduce $(\partial u/\partial y)_w$ to zero.

* Coleman duP. Donaldson and Roy H. Lange, *Study of the Pressure Rise across Shock Waves Required to Separate Laminar and Turbulent Boundary Layers*, NACA TN 2770, 1952.

Transition from Laminar
to Turbulent Flow

CHAPTER 15

15.1 INTRODUCTION

In the preceding two chapters we have treated the laminar boundary layer, represented mathematically as the "steady flow solution" of the equations of conservation of mass, momentum, and energy of a gas under conditions of no-slip at the surface of the body. As is well known, the laminar layer is realized near the forward stagnation point of a body. However, where the boundary layer Reynolds number exceeds a critical value the layer becomes unstable, in the sense that a small disturbance to the flow, such as that caused by a small surface irregularity, grows with time. If all disturbances can be prevented, the laminar layer will persist over the entire surface. On the other hand, if the disturbance occurs and grows, transition to *turbulent* boundary layer follows.

This chapter treats the circumstances affecting the occurrence of boundary layer transition. A brief description of a turbulent flow field and the hot-wire method for measuring turbulence is followed by a description of transition and discussions of the factors affecting transition, methods of detecting transition, and of the flow around spheres and cylinders as affected by Reynolds number. The latter topic is included because it provides a spectacular example of the effect of boundary layer transition on the drag of bluff bodies.

A thorough understanding of the transition phenomenon must rest on a detailed knowledge of turbulent flow. A brief introduction to this subject is given in Section 15.2, and it is recommended that the student reread this chapter after studying Chapter 16.

15.2 DESCRIPTION OF TURBULENT FLOW

The qualitative description of turbulence will be based on Fig. 1, which is sketched from photographs of the surface of a water tank on which powdered mica has been sprinkled. The grid shown at the right is being drawn through the tank at constant speed and the lines shown are approximate streamlines of the flow. Immediately behind the grid, the wake of each rod, in the form of a regular succession of vortices, can be seen. This regular succession of vortices is called the *von Kármán vortex street* and will be described in Section 15.6. The wakes of the individual rods gradually merge into each other until at the left a

Fig. 1. Schematic representation of the approximate streamlines behind a grid moving from left to right at uniform velocity through a fluid.

turbulent field is shown in which the turbulence is *homogeneous;* that is, the turbulence in one part of the field has no average features distinguishing it from that in any other part.

The distance between the rods, called the *mesh length*, is a characteristic length of the turbulent field; 15 or 20 mesh lengths downstream of the grid, homogeneity is approximately established. If a speed-measuring instrument, moving with the grid, were placed at any cross-stream location in the stream at about 20 mesh lengths behind the grid, the record would look qualitatively like the trace in Fig. 2. The mean

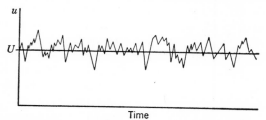

Time

Fig. 2. Schematic representation of the velocity fluctuations in a turbulent flow.

speed would be the speed of the grid, but at any particular instant the speed may deviate appreciably from the mean. These fluctuations have no definite frequency, and their amplitudes may have values anywhere between very small and fairly large values. The velocity distribution in space associated with these fluctuations is a *turbulent field*, such as exists in the free-stream of a wind tunnel, or in the atmosphere.

A quantitative measure of turbulence is taken as the root-mean-square value of the fluctuations. Thus,

$$\sigma = \frac{100}{V} \sqrt{\frac{1}{T} \int_0^T \frac{(u_1{}^2 + v_1{}^2 + w_1{}^2)}{3} \, dt} \tag{1}$$

where T is large, compared with the duration of any excursion from the mean value (Fig. 2), and u_1, v_1, and w_1 are, respectively, the deviations of the x-, y-, z-components of the velocity from their mean values, is a statistical measure of the magnitude of the turbulence in per cent of the mean speed V.

The magnitude of the turbulence, σ, will determine its *diffusing* effe t, that is, the rate at which a drop of coloring matter, for instance, will spread throughout the flow behind the grid in Fig. 1. It follows intuitively that the greater the disturbance behind the grid (large σ) the greater will be the rate at which the coloring matter will spread throughout the flow. If, on the other hand, the color were added to the water ahead of the grid, it would diffuse throughout the flow at an extremely slow rate. Ahead of the grid, the coloring is spread by molecular diffusion; behind, turbulence plays the major role in the diffusion.

In general, it follows that turbulent diffusion tends to destroy gradients in any property, whether it be color, momentum, heat, or density of particles in suspension.

Consider now the laminar boundary layer and assume that through some combination of circumstances, turbulence is generated in the layer. The intense mixing effect of the turbulence will tend to flatten the velocity profile, but it cannot carry this effect to the wall because of the

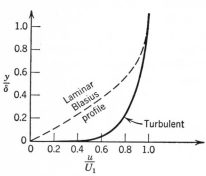

FIG. 3. Comparison between laminar and turbulent velocity profiles for the same boundary-layer thickness.

no-slip condition there. Therefore, the effect of the turbulence will be qualitatively as shown in Fig. 3; the velocity gradient becomes smaller in the outer region and greater near the wall.

The process of change from laminar to turbulent boundary layer shown in Fig. 3 is called *transition*. The change from the laminar profile to the mean velocity profile for turbulent flow takes place over a downstream interval which is called the *transition region*.

The practical importance of transition and therefore of the factors that affect it are threefold: (1) since $(\partial u/\partial y)_w$ is greater for the turbulent than for the laminar layer, the shearing stress $\tau_w = \mu(\partial u/\partial y)_w$ will increase greatly through the transition region (see Fig. 6 of Chapter 13); (2) reference to Section 14.7 indicates that there will be a corresponding increase in heat transfer rate at the wall; (3) flow separation will be delayed because $(\partial u/\partial y)_w$ is greater in the turbulent layer.

15.3 METHOD OF MEASUREMENT OF TURBULENCE

Many methods for measuring turbulence have been proposed, but the hot-wire anemometer * has so far proved superior to all others. The instrument utilizes a platinum or tungsten wire 0.0001 in. to 0.0003 in. in diameter and about $\frac{1}{16}$ in. to $\frac{1}{4}$ in. long. The wire is mounted between two fine needles, placed in the windstream and heated electrically to about 200° F above room temperature. The rate of heat loss from the wire as a function of the wind speed in steady flow is given by King's formula,

$$H = (A + B\sqrt{U})(T - T_a)$$

where H is the rate of heat generation in the wire ($H = i^2 R$, i being the current, R the resistance), $T - T_a$ is the difference between the temperature of the wire and that of the fluid, and A and B are constants that are determined experimentally. The fluctuations in wind speed in a turbulent flow cause a fluctuation in the temperature, resistance, and voltage drop across the wire. The fluctuations in voltage drop are impressed across the input of an amplifier, the output of which is connected to an oscillograph or mean square voltmeter. A continuous record from the oscillograph gives a record similar to Fig. 2, and after suitable calibration the reading of the mean square meter can be converted to the value of $\overline{u_1^2}$. A simplified diagram of one arrangement is shown in Fig. 4, in which the Wheatstone bridge provides means for measuring the heating current and resistance of the wire.

A single hot wire, normal to the flow, is sensitive to changes in the total velocity q; since $u = U + u_1 = q \cos \theta$, where θ is the angle be-

* A review of methods for measuring turbulence is given by L. S. G. Kovasznay, in Section F of *Physical Measurements in Gas Dynamics and Combustion*, Vol. 9, of High Speed Aerodynamics and Jet Propulsion, Princeton University Press, Princeton, 1954.

tween the instantaneous velocity and the mean velocity U, it follows that v_1 and w_1 can have fairly large values before q will depart appreciably from u. Therefore, the single hot wire is sensitive mainly to u_1.

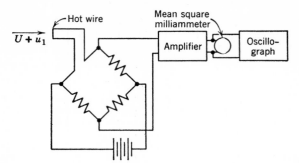

FIG. 4.   Simplified schematic circuit for the measurement of the component of the velocity fluctuations in the direction of the main flow.

To measure v_1 and w_1 an X arrangement shown in Fig. 5 is used. The X formed by the two wires is in the plane of the main flow and the component to be measured. Its effectiveness depends on the fact that when the velocity vector tilts, signifying a cross-component of the flow,

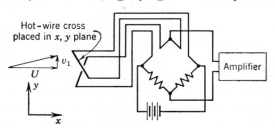

FIG. 5.   Simplified schematic circuit for the measurement of the component of the velocity fluctuations in the direction normal to the main flow.

the wires are differentially cooled, and the difference between their temperatures is a measure of the angle of tilt and therefore of the cross-component.

15.4   DESCRIPTION OF TRANSITION

The classical experiments of Osborne Reynolds demonstrated the fact that under certain circumstances the flow in a tube changes from laminar to turbulent over a given region of the tube.* The experi-

* Osborne Reynolds, "An Experimental Investigation of the Circumstances Which Determine Whether the Motion of Water Shall Be Direct or Sinuous, and of the Laws of Resistance in Parallel Channels," *Phil. Trans. Roy. Soc, London,* Vol 174, pp. 935–982, 1883.

mental arrangement involved a water tank and an outlet through a small tube, at the end of which was a stopcock for varying the speed of the water through the tube. The junction of the tube with the tank was nicely rounded, and a filament of colored fluid was introduced at the mouth. When the speed of the water was low, the filament remained distinct throughout the entire length of the tube, as shown in Fig. 6a; when the speed was increased, the filament broke up at a given point and diffused throughout the cross section, as shown in Fig. 6b.

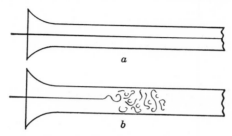

FIG. 6. Schematic representation of Reynolds' experiment.

Reynolds identified a governing parameter as $U_m d/\nu$, where U_m is the mean velocity through the tube of diameter d, and this number has since been known as the Reynolds number.

Reynolds found that transition occurred at Reynolds numbers between 2000 and 13,000, depending upon the smoothness of the entry conditions. When extreme care is taken to obtain smooth flow, the transition can be delayed to Reynolds numbers as high as 40,000; on the other hand, a value of 2000 appears to be about the lowest value obtainable regardless of how rough the entrance conditions are made. The fact that the transition Reynolds number can be varied by disturbing the flow indicates that the transition Reynolds number is affected by the turbulence in the stream.

The actual mechanism of transition, though far from completely understood, has been greatly illuminated by recent investigations, both theoretical and experimental. Tollmien, and later Schlichting, Lin, and others,[†] showed that for Reynolds numbers, $Re_{\delta*} = U_1 \delta^*/\nu$, above a definite minimum value, disturbances in a certain band of frequencies will tend to grow with time. Hot-wire records made by Schubauer and Skramstad [‡] at various distances behind the leading edge of a flat plate are shown in Fig. 7. These show the sequence of events following the

---

[†] A review of the subject is given by C. C. Lin, *Hydrodynamic Stability*, Cambridge University Press, Cambridge, 1955.

[‡] G. B. Schubauer and H. K. Skramstad, "Laminar Boundary Layer Oscillations and Stability of Laminar Flow," *J. Aero. Sci.*, Vol. 14, pp. 69–78, 1947.

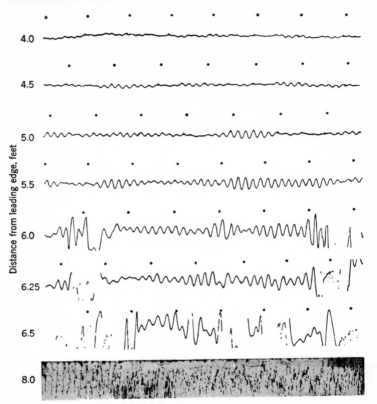

Fig. 7.   Oscillograms by Schubauer and Skramstad showing fluctuations in the laminar boundary layer on a flat plate.   Distance from surface $= 0.025$ in., $U_1 = 80$ ft/sec, time interval between dots $= 0.033$ sec.   (Figure reproduced courtesy National Bureau of Standards.)

generation of a disturbance in the laminar boundary layer.   The oscillations, which represent fluctuations in the wind speed at 0.025 in. from the surface, are seen to grow as the distance from the leading edge increases.   At $x = 6$ ft, however, some irregularities occur in the waves. These are "bursts" of high-frequency fluctuations ordinarily associated with turbulent flow.   The bursts become more frequent and of longer duration with increasing x until, at 8 ft, the entire record is turbulent.

The Tollmien disturbances shown in Fig. 7 are two-dimensional and streamlines are shown in Fig. 8.   The streamlines shown are those seen by an observer moving downstream at the speed of propagation of the disturbance.   This speed of propagation is about one-third of the flow speed at the edge of the boundary layer.

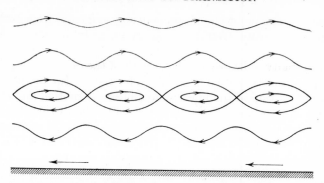

Fig. 8. Streamline pattern of Tollmien disturbances in laminar boundary layer on a flat plate. C. C. Lin, *Quart. Appl. Math.*, Vol. 3, No. 3, 1945.

The overall response of the laminar boundary layer to two-dimensional disturbances is shown in Fig. 9, where β is the frequency of the fluctuations. The theoretical "neutral curve" and some of the experimental neutral points of Schubauer and Skramstad are shown. For $Re_{\delta*} > 575$ only those disturbances for which $\beta v / U_1^2$ lies inside of the neutral curve will amplify. Thus the laminar layer selects for amplification a narrow band of frequencies from whatever disturbances

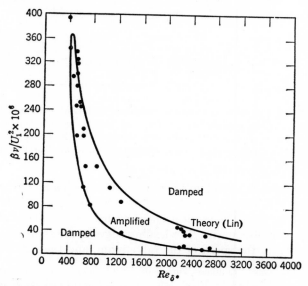

Fig. 9. Measurements by Schubauer and Skramstad of the neutral curve for the velocity fluctuations in the laminar boundary layer on a flat plate compared with the theoretical curve by Lin.

are present. The disturbances present may originate from turbulence in the outside stream, from pressure waves, or from roughness at the surface.

The instability indicated by the growth of the disturbances is only a first step in the transition process. The theoretical predictions are based on a solution of the linearized equation of motion and therefore do not provide for any distortion of the sinusoidal disturbances shown in Fig. 7, much less for the appearance of the bursts of turbulence.

Emmons * suggested that the bursts occur when "turbulent spots" pass the hot-wire location and that the spots are regions of turbulent

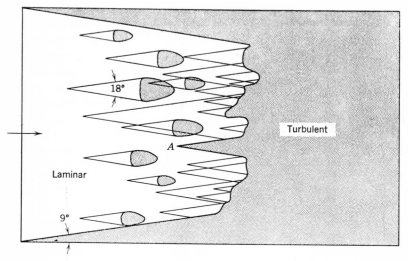

Fig. 10. Transition resulting from the growth of turbulent spots and transverse contamination. Vertices of the wedges represent sources of turbulent spots. End of transition region is marked by the line along which the spots have merged. Transverse contamination occurs from roughness element at A and from edges of plate.

flow which appear at random in the transition region and grow in area as they move downstream with the flow. The process is shown qualitatively in Fig. 10. The vertices of the wedges represent the sources of the turbulent spots shown. The leading edges of the spots move downstream at nearly the speed of the full stream, and their growth in the

* H. W. Emmons, "Laminar Turbulent Transitions in a Boundary Layer," Part I, *J. Aero. Sci.*, Vol. 18, No. 7, 1951; Part II, *Proceedings*, 1st National Conference for Applied Mechanics, Edwards Brothers, Ann Arbor, Mich., 1952. See also, S. Dhawan and R. Narasimha, "Some Properties of Boundary Layer Flow During Transition," *J. Fluid Mechanics*, Vol. 3, Part 4, pp. 418–436, January 1958.

lateral direction subtends an angle of about 18°. In Fig. 7 the spots first appear at $5.5 < x < 6$ ft and they have merged into a completely turbulent layer at $6.5 < x < 8$ ft.*

The reason for the appearance of the turbulent spots, as for the appearance of the initial instability waves, probably lies with turbulence in the outside stream, pressure waves, or surface roughness. It is presumed that when the instability waves have grown to sufficient amplitude, a slight further disturbance has an explosive effect in generating the high-frequency fluctuations characteristic of turbulent flow. The range of validity of the linearized theory leading to the results in Figs. 8 and 9 is obviously exceeded when the bursts occur.

Figure 10 also shows transition occurring as a result of "transverse contamination" from the edges of the plate or behind a roughness element (e.g., at point A). The turbulent boundary layer grows laterally to subtend an angle of 18° behind the roughness element and at about 9° from the leading edge at the corners. Note that the roughness element causes a wedge of turbulent flow, whereas behind the spots the flow is again laminar.

15.5 FACTORS AFFECTING TRANSITION

The factors affecting transition will be listed separately here, though they are in no sense independent of each other. Under circumstances in which more than one factor is involved, the results given here show, in general, the trend of the effect of each factor, but they permit only qualitative conclusions for the combined effect.

1. REYNOLDS NUMBER. The influence of Reynolds number on the boundary layer along a plate was described in the previous section and is illustrated in Fig. 9. Theory shows that the amplification rate within the unstable region increases as the Reynolds number increases, so that a disturbance of a given magnitude whose frequency has a value such that $\beta \nu / U_1{}^2$ lies in the unstable region will presumably cause transition much sooner at high than at low Reynolds number. It follows that in order to maintain larger and larger regions of laminar boundary layer, extraordinary care must be taken to keep the disturbances small. Further, for a given magnitude of disturbance, as the Reynolds number increases we would expect the transition point to move forward.

2. PRESSURE GRADIENT. The influence of downstream pressure gradient on transition is demonstrated in the Schubauer-Skramstad

---

* For a detailed study of the shape and rate of growth of turbulent spots, see G. B. Schubauer and P. S. Klebanoff, *Contributions to the Mechanics of Boundary Layer Transition*, NACA TN 3489, 1955.

results shown in Fig. 11. A curved plate with the pressure distribution shown at the left was used. The figure shows a favorable pressure gradient ($\partial p/\partial x < 0$) over the forward portion and an unfavorable gradient over the rear portion. We see from the traces that disturbances

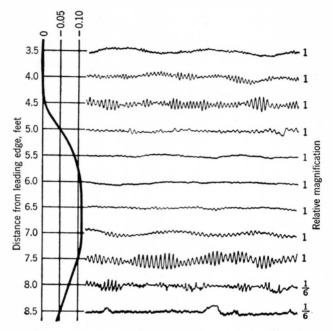

Fig. 11. Oscillograms by Schubauer and Skramstad showing fluctuations in the laminar boundary layer on a surface with the pressure distribution indicated at the left, where the numbers refer to values of $(p - p_\infty)/\frac{1}{2}\rho U^2$. Distance from surface = 0.021 in., $U_1 = 95$ ft/sec. (Figure reproduced courtesy of National Bureau of Standards.)

which amplify in a region of zero pressure gradient are damped in a favorable gradient; when the gradient becomes adverse, they are again amplified.

We conclude from these phenomena that a favorable pressure gradient tends to retard transition and an unfavorable gradient tends to hasten it. The reason lies in the theoretical prediction that a velocity profile with an inflection point, that is, one which occurs in an unfavorable pressure gradient (Section 13.4), tends to be more unstable than one in which no inflection occurs.

The stabilizing effect of a favorable pressure gradient is exploited in the design of *low-drag airfoils* (Appendix C) and in the application of suction to an airfoil surface described below.

Transition in an adverse pressure gradient may also occur as a result of local separation of the laminar boundary layer. If the adverse pressure gradient is large, *permanent* flow separation occurs; if it is small, instead of permanent separation, a *bubble* of separated flow may form. The flow rejoins the surface behind the bubble in the form of a turbulent boundary layer.

Where a compression wave intersects a laminar boundary layer, the strong adverse pressure gradient accompanying it causes an inflection point in the profile or flow separation (Section 14.9). It is to be expected then that even a relatively weak compression may induce transition where it intersects a laminar layer.

On the other hand, the strong favorable pressure gradient in the expansion associated with supersonic flow around a corner can cause "reverse transition," that is, transition from turbulent to laminar flow in the boundary layer.[†]

3. SUCTION. The application of suction to the surface of a body decreases the boundary layer thickness and hence its Reynolds number. This fact alone would, according to Fig. 9, tend to retard transition; in addition, the resulting velocity profile has a stability limit $Re_{\delta*}$ of about 70,000, compared with a value of 575 without suction. Both of these tendencies indicate that suction has a strong stabilizing effect on the laminar boundary layer.

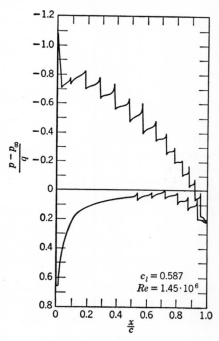

FIG. 12. Pressure distribution by Pfenninger over an airfoil with suction applied through slots in the surface.

Many investigations, primarily on wing sections, have been made in which suction is applied through slots in the surface. One of the most complete studies is that by Pfenninger.[‡] In this work many

[†] Joseph Sternberg, *The Transition from a Turbulent to a Laminar Boundary Layer*, Ballistics Research Laboratory Report 908, 1954.

[‡] Werner Pfenninger, *Investigations on Reductions of Friction on Wings in Particular by Means of Boundary Layer Suction*, NACA TM 1181, 1947.

carefully shaped suction slots span the airfoil at various chordwise stations; if they are closely spaced, they have the effect, shown in Fig. 12, of maintaining a favorable pressure gradient over practically the entire wing.   Each slot acts as a spanwise line sink accelerating the flow upstream and causing a stagnation point to form at the lip, as shown in Fig. 13.   A pressure rise then takes place at the slot from tne

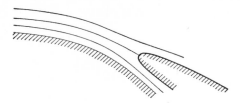

FIG. 13.   Streamlines near a suction slot.

static pressure just ahead to the stagnation pressure of the streamline that terminates at the stagnation point.   If the velocity profile is known, it is possible to calculate the discontinuous pressure rise at the slot as a function of the rate at which air is drawn from the flow.* If enough air is drawn off, and if the slots are closely enough spaced, a *stepwise* favorable pressure gradient results.   Pfenninger found that, for the pressure distributions shown in Fig. 12, the boundary layer was laminar at least as far as the last slot.   He found that, depending on Reynolds number, it was necessary to remove only from 15 to 20 per cent of the displacement thickness of the boundary layer.

4. TURBULENCE.   The effect of the magnitude of the free-stream turbulence on transition has been completely investigated for flow over a smooth flat plate by Schubauer and Skramstad.   Their results are shown in Fig. 14, in which Re_x is plotted against the turbulence number σ (Eq. 1).   They show that as the turbulence increases, transition occurs earlier, and that the width of the transition region changes very little over the range of turbulence investigated.

According to these measurements, the width of the transition region as well as its position remain fixed on the plate for all values of σ below 0.08.   As the turbulence increases, the transition region moves toward the leading edge.   However, if we adopt the concept of the growth of turbulent spots as forming the transition region (Section 15.4), it follows that the downstream edge of that region, shown in Fig. 10, never quite reaches the leading edge, even for very high turbulence.

* Sydney Goldstein, "Low-Drag and Suction Airfoils," *J. Aero. Sci.*, Vol. 15, p. 189, 1948.

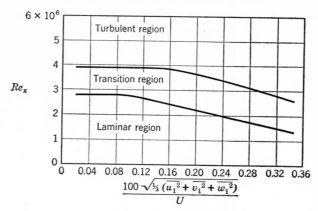

Fig. 14. Measurements by Schubauer and Skramstad of the Reynolds number of transition as a function of the free-stream turbulence for flow over a flat plate.

5. ROUGHNESS. The effect of roughness will, of course, be qualitatively in the same direction as that of increasing turbulence. Both influences introduce disturbances in the laminar flow and the transition Reynolds number will tend to decrease. Although there are several types of roughness—single two- or three-dimensional roughness elements, distributed sand roughness, etc.—their general effect on transition is represented in Fig. 15.†

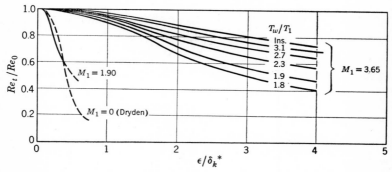

Fig. 15. Effect of roughness, surface temperature, and Mach number on transition on a flat cone.

The ratio of the boundary layer Reynolds number at transition Re_t to that for the smooth body Re_0 is plotted versus the ratio of the roughness height, ϵ, to the displacement thickness of the laminar layer at

† E. R. van Driest and J. C. Boison, "Experiments on Boundary Layer Transition at Supersonic Speeds," *J. Aero. Sci.*, vol. 24, No. 12, pp. 885–900, December 1957.

transition, δ^*. These results show that the transition Reynolds number associated with a given roughness height increases with Mach number and decreases with cooling of the surface. The effect will be rationalized later where the influence of compressibility on boundary layer stability is described.

6. CURVATURE. Transition due to curvature takes place in an entirely different way from that due to the factors previously discussed. The cause can be illustrated simply by means of Fig. 16, which represents boundary-layer profiles for flow over curved surfaces. Consider a

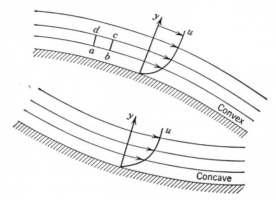

FIG. 16.   Schematic representation of the flow along concave and convex surfaces.

small element of fluid $abcd$; it must be in equilibrium under the actions of pressure and centrifugal forces. Equating these forces,

$$-\frac{\partial p}{\partial n} \cdot dr \cdot r \, d\theta = \rho r \, dr \, d\theta \cdot \frac{u^2}{r}$$

or

$$-\frac{\partial p}{\partial n} = \rho \frac{u^2}{r} \tag{2}$$

where r is the radius of curvature (positive for concave, negative for convex) and u is the velocity. For equilibrium, $\partial p/\partial n$ will be positive for a convex and negative for a concave surface; that is, the pressure force will be toward the surface for convex curvature and away from the surface for concave curvature. For the convex surface, if a small element of fluid is disturbed (by turbulence or roughness) so that it moves outward, its velocity will be less than that of the surrounding air, and hence the centrifugal force tending to carry it farther out will be less than the pressure force tending to return it to its layer of origin. Thus, it will tend to return to its layer of origin; in other words, the effect of convex curvature is to stabilize the flow. For the concave flow, if a particle is displaced outward, the centrifugal force is less than that on the surrounding air because its velocity is less; hence the pressure force, which is just sufficient to balance the centrifugal force on the surrounding air, will carry the particle farther from its layer of origin. Therefore, concave curvature has a destabilizing effect, whereas convex curvature has a stabilizing effect. Although the above analysis is somewhat rough, the conclusion agrees qualitatively with the theoretical investigation by Goertler.

Goertler * found that laminar flow over a concave surface is unstable if the parameter, $Re_\theta \sqrt{\theta/r}$, where θ is the momentum thickness of the boundary layer, exceeds 0.83. Experimentally, H. W. Liepmann † found that the parameter had values between 6 and 9 at transition, depending on the turbulence level in the free stream. There is a considerable discrepancy between theoretical and experimental values of the parameter, but it must be remembered that the theoretical value refers to instability and therefore must be somewhat lower than the experimental value, which refers to transition.

An essential difference exists between the Tollmien waves shown in Fig. 8 and the disturbances found by Goertler, shown in Fig. 17. The

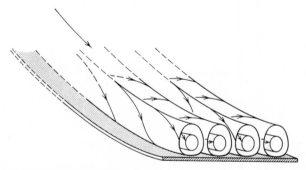

Fig. 17. Streamline pattern of Goertler disturbances in laminar boundary layer on a concave surface.

latter type consists essentially of vortices oriented in the stream direction; they are similar to the disturbances found by G. I. Taylor ‡ in his investigation of the instability of the flow between rotating cylinders.

* See C. C. Lin, *Hydrodynamic Stability;* see also papers by H. Goertler and G. Haemmerlin in *50 Jahre Grenzschichtforschung,* edited by H. Goertler and W. Tollmien, Friedr. Vieweg & Sohn, Braunschweig, 1955.

† See C. C. Lin, *op. cit.*

‡ *Ibid.*

7. HEAT. The analyses of the stability of the laminar boundary layer described in Section 15.4 indicate that the effect of an inflection point in the laminar-boundary layer velocity profile is to increase appreciably the rate of amplification of disturbances. We can show quite simply that if a surface is heated the velocity profile develops an inflection point. This analysis is analogous to that of Section 13.4, which shows the effect of an adverse pressure gradient on the velocity profile.

It was shown in Chapter 1 that the viscosity coefficient μ is theoretically proportional to the square root of the absolute temperature. If a temperature gradient exists in the y-direction (normal to the surface), μ will vary with y, and the boundary-layer equation of motion becomes

$$\rho\left(u\frac{\partial u}{\partial x} + v\frac{\partial u}{\partial y}\right) = -\frac{\partial p}{\partial x} + \frac{\partial}{\partial y}\left(\mu\frac{\partial u}{\partial y}\right) \tag{3}$$

At the surface $u = v = 0$ and Eq. 3 becomes

$$\frac{\partial p}{\partial x} = \left[\frac{\partial}{\partial y}\left(\mu\frac{\partial u}{\partial y}\right)\right]_{y=0}$$

This may be written

$$\left(\frac{\partial^2 u}{\partial y^2}\right)_{y=0} = \frac{1}{\mu}\left[\frac{\partial p}{\partial x} - \left(\frac{\partial \mu}{\partial y}\cdot\frac{\partial u}{\partial y}\right)_{y=0}\right] \tag{4}$$

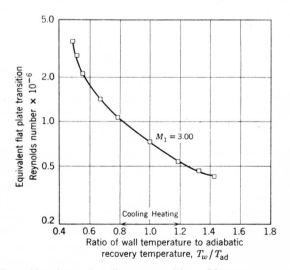

FIG. 18. Effect of heating and cooling on transition. Measurements made on cone and converted to "equivalent flat plate." (J. R. Jack and N. S. Diaconis, NACA TN 3562, 1955.)

Consider first a heated flat plate ($\partial p/\partial x = 0$). Then the temperature and therefore μ will decrease with y. Since $(\partial u/\partial y)_{y=0} > 0$, Eq. 4 shows that for this case $(\partial^2 u/\partial y^2)_{y=0} > 0$. But near the outer edge of the boundary layer $\partial^2 u/\partial y^2 < 0$. Therefore, at some point within the layer $\partial^2 u/\partial y^2 = 0$; that is, the velocity profile has an inflection point.

As was pointed out earlier, a velocity profile with an inflection point is unstable. The measurements of Fig. 18 are in qualitative agreement with these predictions, that is, transition is delayed by cooling and is hastened by heating.

8. COMPRESSIBILITY. Lees, Lin, and Dunn * studied the effect of Mach number on the stability of the laminar layer on a flat plate. The

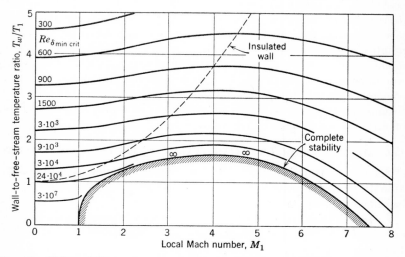

FIG. 19. Effect of Mach number and temperature ratio on stability of boundary layer on a flat plate. $Re_{\delta_{\min}\text{ crit}}$ is the minimum critical Reynolds number based on x and on ν at $y = \delta$. See Van Driest and Boison, *op. cit.*

minimum critical value of Re_θ where θ is the momentum thickness of the boundary layer, for $M = 0$ and an insulated plate, was 200; at $M = 1.3$ the value was 82, indicating an appreciable destabilizing effect of compressibility. The effect on transition of heating or cooling which in most practical cases accompanies high Mach numbers was described in the preceding paragraph. The theoretical *combined* effects on stability are shown in Fig. 19, where all combinations of cooling and Mach number inside the loop indicate complete stability. The insulated plate lies well within the unstable region. We see that the

* See C. C. Lin, *op. cit.*

minimum critical Reynolds number, shown in Fig. 9 for incompressible flow, depends strongly on the degree of cooling and on the Mach number. The region of complete stability (infinite minimum critical Reynolds number) is realized only if the disturbances to the flow are small. If appreciable surface roughness or stream turbulence exists, the disturbance may exceed the limit of validity of the theory and cause transition even though the Mach number and surface temperature place the flow inside the "completely stable" region of Fig. 19.

In fact, the experiments shown in Fig. 15 indicate that on a *rough* plate the effect of cooling is to *decrease* the transition Reynolds number. The reason probably lies in the circumstance that, as the surface is cooled, the kinematic viscosity in the immediate vicinity of the surface decreases and the Reynolds number of the flow past a roughness element therefore increases. Associated with this increase in Reynolds number, there is an increase in the magnitude of the disturbance in momentum (ρu) in the wake of the roughness element. The result would be a decrease in the transition Reynolds number. We may conclude then that the validity of the results shown in Fig. 19 is limited to smooth surfaces and if a surface is rough enough, the indicated effect of surface cooling may be reversed.

15.6   METHODS FOR EXPERIMENTALLY DETECTING TRANSITION

Some understanding of the difference between laminar and turbulent boundary layers can be gained from a consideration of the methods that have been devised for locating transition.

1. HOT-WIRE ANEMOMETER. The difference between hot-wire records in the laminar and turbulent boundary layers is demonstrated in Fig. 7 and is described in Section 15.4.

2. TOTAL HEAD NEAR SURFACE. If a total head tube of small dimensions is moved upstream near the surface, when it passes from the turbulent to the laminar layer, there will be an appreciable drop in the total head. The reason for this drop is that the velocity very near the surface, and hence the total head, is much less in a laminar layer than in a turbulent. This method was demonstrated in flight by Jones;* Fig. 20 shows some results obtained by it.

3. STETHOSCOPE. If a standard medical stethoscope is applied to short tubes leading from a total-head tube in the boundary layer, irregular pulses shown in the transition region in the hot-wire records of Fig. 7 can be detected. A steady noise is heard when the total-head tube is in the turbulent boundary layer.

* B. M. Jones, "Flight Experiments on the Boundary Layer," *J. Aero. Sci.*, Vol. 5, pp. 81–96, 1938.

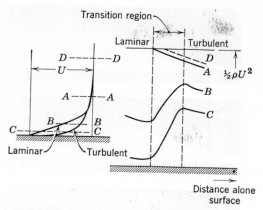

FIG. 20. Schematic representation of the variation of stagnation pressure through the transition region at various heights above the surface.

4. SUBLIMATION. This method utilizes a coating of a volatile substance on the surface; the rate of sublimation depends upon whether the boundary layer is laminar or turbulent. The greater velocity gradient at the surface in the turbulent layer causes a higher rate of sublimation than if the layer is laminar. Consequently, behind the transition region the surface will clean more rapidly than ahead, and the line of demarcation marks the transition point. One application * utilizes a mixture of ether and camphor which is sprayed on the surface; as soon as it has dried, the windstream is started and is continued until a portion of the surface is clean.

5. SURFACE TEMPERATURE. Figure 4 of Chapter 14 shows a marked increase of the temperature recovery factor in the transition region; thus measurements of the equilibrium temperature of an insulated surface provide a practical means for determining the transition region. For flows of short duration, the surface will not reach the equilibrium temperature, but since the skin friction is markedly greater in the turbulent region than in the laminar (Fig. 6, Chapter 13 and Fig. 4 of Chapter 16), the rate of heat transfer to the surface will be much greater in the transition region (see Eq. 53, Chapter 14).

6. SCHLIEREN PHOTOGRAPHS. Magnified schlieren photographs, sensitive to the density gradients normal to the surface, provide an accurate means of locating transition.† Figure 21 reproduces a series of photographs with various degrees of surface cooling.

---

* R. C. Pankhurst and D. W. Holder, *Wind-Tunnel Technique*, Pitman and Sons, London, 1952. See Chapter 3 on "Methods of Flow Visualization."

† E. R. van Driest and J. C. Boison, *op. cit.*

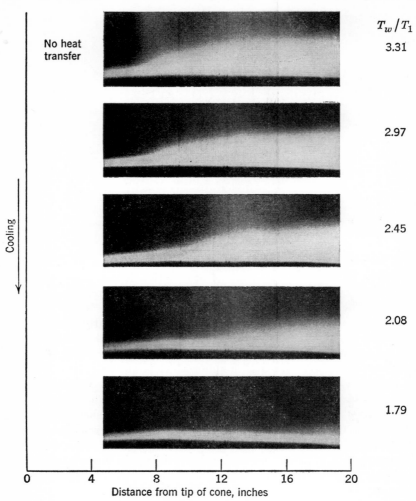

FIG. 21.   Typical schlieren photographs showing the effect of surface cooling on transition on a smooth 10° cone for $M_1 = 3.65$.

15.7   FLOW AROUND SPHERES AND CIRCULAR CYLINDERS

The flow around circular cylinders and spheres are described here because of the marked effect that boundary layer transition has on the flow configuration.   Figure 22 is the curve of drag coefficient of a sphere $C_D = \text{drag}/qD^2$ versus Reynolds number UD/ν, where D is the sphere diameter.   This is an experimental curve with data from various laboratories, and the three dotted branches of the curves are

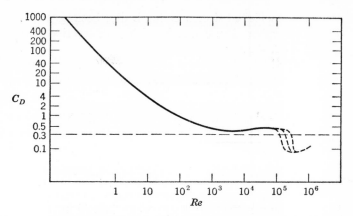

FIG. 22.   Drag coefficient for spheres as a function of Reynolds number.

taken from data obtained at the National Bureau of Standards for different magnitudes of turbulence.

Four different flow configurations are identifiable for different ranges of Reynolds number.

(a) The *Stokes* range extends up to a Reynolds number of about 40. The flow closely resembles that of a perfect fluid to the extent that no separation is evident. The drag coefficient varies inversely with the Reynolds number.

(b) The quadratic resistance law range, in which the drag coefficient is approximately constant, extends from a Reynolds number of about 200 to a point where the curve of Fig. 22 begins to break downward. The boundary layer is laminar and flow separation occurs at about 83° from the forward stagnation point. The break occurs at a Reynolds number between 100,000 and 400,000, depending on the magnitude and scale of turbulence in the main stream and on the roughness of the surface.

(c) This range starts at the upper limit of range *b* and extends over a Reynolds number interval of around 150,000. At the beginning of the interval the Reynolds number is just high enough so that a short distance aft of the laminar separation point the flow rejoins the surface as a turbulent boundary layer (Section 15.5, Factor 2). The velocity profile for the turbulent boundary layer, as shown in Fig. 3, is much "fuller" near the surface and the flow will therefore follow the surface for some distance before the adverse pressure gradient can cause separation. Thus, the separation point moves continuously rearward with increasing Reynolds number, from 83° to around 110°. As a result, the drag coefficient decreases markedly, because the turbulent wake behind the sphere is much reduced in cross section by the rearward movement of the separation point.

(d) This is the high Reynolds number range (beyond 400,000) and the small amount of data available indicate that the drag coefficient increases with increasing Reynolds number.

As mentioned above, the Reynolds number at which the sharp break in the drag coefficient occurs in Fig. 22 is a function of the turbulence in the airstream.* The Reynolds number corresponding to the approximate center of the break, that is, to a drag coefficient of 0.3, is defined as the critical Reynolds number of the sphere. The critical Reynolds number decreases with increasing turbulence. The highest values measured are around 400,000; they occur in low turbulence wind tunnels and in the atmosphere.

Pressure distributions over a sphere in the subcritical (range b) and supercritical (range d) ranges of Reynolds number are shown in Fig. 23.

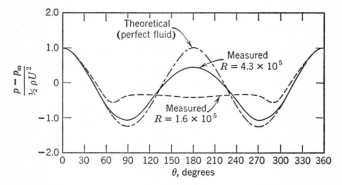

FIG. 23. Pressure distributions over a sphere at two Reynolds numbers compared with perfect fluid theory.

They show that the drop in drag coefficient through the critical range is due to a reduction in the *pressure drag* or *form drag*, obtained by integrating the pressure distributions. As the separation point moves rearward, the skin friction must increase, but the *reduction* in form drag associated with the smaller wake overshadows this contribution.

The flow past a circular cylinder is qualitatively similar to that past a sphere in that there are again four ranges of the Reynolds number and the critical value is sensitive to the turbulence. One difference lies

* H. L. Dryden and A. M. Kuethe, *Effects of Turbulence in Wind Tunnel Measurements*, NACA TR 342, 1929.

in the flow configuration in range b, in which a regular succession of vortices, shown qualitatively in Fig. 1, is given off by the cylinder, whereas for the sphere a spiral vortex trail develops. For the cylinder, the vortices are shed at regular intervals, first from the one side, then from the other. This phenomenon is known as the *von Kármán vortex street*.* Von Kármán investigated the problem theoretically, and good agreement has been found with experiment.

The *Strouhal number*, U/nD, where n is the frequency of the vortex shedding, has a constant value of 5 throughout the von Kármán vortex street range of Reynolds numbers. The Strouhal number, in one form or another, occurs in several practical problems in aeronautics; among these problems are the flutter and buffeting of aircraft lifting and control surfaces.

* The von Kármán vortex street accounts for *aeolian tones*, an example of which is the singing of electric wires in a high wind. By the Helmholtz vortex laws, when a vortex of a given sign is shed, the change in circulation around the cylinder must be equal and opposite to that of the vortex; therefore, a change in the lateral force equal to $\rho U \Gamma$ per foot, where Γ is the circulation of the vortex, acts on the cylinder. The cylinder, therefore, oscillates with the same frequency as that at which the vortices are shed. When the frequency of shedding equals the natural frequency of the cylinder, a tone of appreciable intensity results. A complete investigation of the vortex street has been made by L. S. G. Kovasznay, "Hot-Wire Investigation of the Wake behind Cylinders at Low Reynolds Numbers," *Proc. Roy. Soc.* A, Vol. 198, pp. 174–190, 1949.

Turbulent Flow in Tubes
and Boundary Layers

CHAPTER 16

16.1 INTRODUCTION

In the chapters on laminar flow we were able to solve some problems and to indicate in a straightforward manner a variety of solutions. When the flow becomes turbulent, however, as will be pointed out in Section 16.5, the number of dependent variables exceeds the number of equations available. As a result, we cannot solve the simplest problems in turbulent flow unless additional conditions are imposed, and we must depend on experimental results to suggest these conditions.

In the current chapter we continue the description of turbulent flow begun in the previous chapter and describe flow in tubes and boundary layers. The analyses depend greatly on similarity conditions for the form of the solutions and on experiment for numerical factors. Effects of roughness and of pressure gradient are described. Compressibility and heat transfer effects are described.

16.2 QUANTITATIVE DESCRIPTION OF TURBULENCE

The instantaneous velocity vector in a turbulent field will differ from the mean velocity vector in both magnitude and direction. If the x-axis is taken in the direction of the mean velocity U, the velocity components at any particular instant are designated by $U + u_1$, v_1, and w_1, where u_1, v_1, and w_1, are, respectively, the x-, y-, and z-components of the instantaneous deviation of the velocity from its mean value. The values of these components will fluctuate with time about a zero value in the same way as the speed fluctuates about its mean value in Fig. 2 of Chapter 15. Hence u_1, v_1, and w_1 at a given point are functions of the time and are characterized by zero mean values; that is, the integral of the area between the trace in Fig. 2 of Chapter 15 and the line representing the mean value is zero. Mathematically,

$$\frac{1}{T}\int_0^T u_1\, dt = \frac{1}{T}\int_0^T v_1\, dt = \frac{1}{T}\int_0^T w_1\, dt = 0 \qquad (1)$$

where T is a time that is very long in comparison with the duration of any of the individual excursions from the mean value. In order to simplify the notation, a bar placed over a quantity signifies the mean value of the quantity with respect to the time, and Eq. 1 may be written $\overline{u_1} = \overline{v_1} = \overline{w_1} = 0$.

Theoretical analyses show that a significant quantity in a turbulent field is the root mean square value of the fluctuations defined in Eq. 1 of Chapter 15. In terms of the above notation,

$$\sigma \equiv \frac{100}{U}\sqrt{\frac{\overline{u_1}^2 + \overline{v_1}^2 + \overline{w_1}^2}{3}} \qquad (2)$$

In the main stream of a wind tunnel (outside of the boundary layer) the quantities $\overline{u_1}^2$, $\overline{v_1}^2$, and $\overline{w_1}^2$ are very nearly equal, and so the definition generally employed for the turbulence number is

$$\sigma \equiv \frac{100\sqrt{\overline{u_1}^2}}{U} = \frac{100}{U}\sqrt{\frac{1}{T}\int_0^T u_1^2\, dt} \qquad (3)$$

The effect of the turbulence number on aerodynamic phenomena in wind tunnels, was discussed in Section 15.7, and will be discussed further in Appendix C.

The above description of turbulence characterizes it as a *statistical phenomenon*, which means that the significant properties of a turbulent field are expressed in terms of the mean square value of the fluctuations rather than as instantaneous values.

When turbulent fluctuations are generated in a flow, as for instance by the grid in Fig. 1 of Chapter 15, some of the energy of the flow is transformed into turbulent energy. This energy loss by the main flow would be evidenced by a drop in stagnation pressure through the grid; in the water flow of Fig. 1 of Chapter 15 a drop in the water level would occur through the grid. Then the energy lost by the main stream must equal the mean kinetic energy of the turbulent fluctuations. This amount can be calculated by considering the mean kinetic energy of the fluctuations per unit volume, given by

$$\text{K.E.} = \tfrac{1}{2}\rho[\overline{\{(U + u_1)^2 + (V + v_1)^2 + (W + w_1)^2\} - \{U^2 + V^2 + W^2\}}]$$

From the integral definition of mean values above it is clear that

$$\overline{a + b} = \overline{a} + \overline{b}$$

$$\overline{Uu_1} = U\overline{u_1} = 0, \text{ etc.}$$

Using these relations we get

$$\overline{\text{K.E.}} = \tfrac{1}{2}\rho(\overline{u_1{}^2} + \overline{v_1{}^2} + \overline{w_1{}^2}) \tag{4}$$

Comparison with Eq. 2 shows that the square of the turbulence number, σ, is proportional to the ratio between the kinetic energy of the turbulence and that of the main stream.

As the disturbances caused by the grid are carried downstream the turbulent fluctuations gradually dissipate and their energy is transformed into heat, that is, into molecular agitation. This process, by which energy is drawn from the main stream and converted into heat, must be associated with an increase in entropy of the flow system (see Chapter 8).

We have so far encountered three aerodynamic phenomena in which the gas suffers an increase in entropy. They are, shock waves, the laminar boundary layer, and turbulence. In the laminar boundary layer and in the shock wave the energy of the main flow is transformed directly into random energy, or heat. In turbulence, however, energy is first drawn from the main flow into disturbances or eddies. The viscous stresses occurring within the eddies cause them to decay, and their energy is eventually transformed completely into heat. This process is responsible for the major portion of the entropy increase in the turbulent boundary layer.

16.3 TURBULENT SHEARING STRESS

Just as we defined the laminar shearing stress (Section 12.4) in terms of the lateral transfer of momentum by *molecular* motions, we shall now define the turbulent shearing stress in terms of the lateral transfer of momentum by *turbulent* motions. From the qualitative description of turbulence in Section 15.2 it follows that the turbulent motions are a powerful means for the lateral transfer of properties of a fluid or of a flow. In Section 12.4 the rate of lateral transfer of momentum per unit area carried out by the random molecular motions was identified as the laminar shearing stress; its value was $\mu\,du/dy$, where μ is the coefficient of viscosity and is a property of the fluid. By analogy the turbulent shearing stress is sometimes defined as $\epsilon\,dU/dy$, where U is the mean velocity at a point and ϵ is the coefficient of *turbulent viscosity*.

This definition, however, is of little immediate help since ϵ is not simply a property of the fluid, as is μ, but rather it has a complicated dependence on the properties of the *flow* as well.

We can set up an expression for the rate of lateral transfer of momentum in a two-dimensional turbulent flow in much the same way as it was done for laminar flow in Chapter 1. To do so we analyze a mean velocity distribution as shown in Fig. 1. The turbulent motions carry

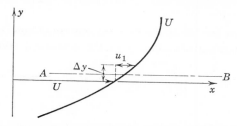

Fig. 1.   Lateral momentum transport in a turbulent flow.

downstream momentum across the plane AB; the fluid crossing the plane from below carries with it on the average a deficit in momentum relative to the fluid above AB, and, conversely, the fluid crossing the plane from above carries with it a surplus of momentum. The momentum transferred per unit time per unit area of AB is the shearing stress. Since we are considering turbulent transfer we concern ourselves with masses of air that are relatively large compared with the mass of a molecule.

The component of velocity normal to AB is the y-component of the fluctuation, v_1, and so the instantaneous rate of mass flow across AB per unit area is ρv_1. The mass moving up from below AB has on the average an x-component equal to the value of U at the point of origin, and after it has moved a lateral distance Δy its x-component has not changed but its value is less than the mean velocity at the new location by the amount $(dU/dy)\,\Delta y$. Then $u_1 = (dU/dy)\,\Delta y$ is, as shown in Fig. 1, negative for the fluid moving in the positive y-direction; a positive ρv_1 is associated with the negative u_1. Conversely, a positive u_1 is associated with a negative ρv_1 for the fluid moving in the negative y-direction. The instantaneous rate of momentum transfer per unit area is positive and is therefore $-\rho u_1 v_1$. The *mean* rate of momentum transfer is a shearing stress and is designated as a *Reynolds stress*,

$$\tau_t = -\overline{\rho u_1 v_1} = -\rho \overline{u_1 v_1} \qquad (5)$$

The bar, as in the previous sections, signifies a mean value with respect to time and, for an incompressible fluid, the bar need extend only over u_1v_1.

As indicated previously, the turbulent fluctuations represent a random process, and it is therefore to be expected that a fluid element moving upward, for instance, will not invariably carry with it a deficit in momentum. In other words, at any given instant $-\rho u_1 v_1$ may be positive or negative; its value will, however, be positive more often than negative, so that if the mean value is taken over a long time $-\rho u_1 v_1 > 0$.

This fact, that not all of the fluctuations contribute to the shearing stress is expressed mathematically by the numerical value of a *correlation factor*:

$$R(u_1, v_1) = \frac{-\overline{u_1 v_1}}{\sqrt{\overline{u_1^2}}\ \sqrt{\overline{v_1^2}}} \tag{6}$$

Clearly, if $u_1 \backsim -v_1$ all of the fluctuations contribute to the shearing stress and $R(u_1, v_1) = 1$. The fact that such is not the case in the turbulent boundary layer, for instance, is indicated by the hot-wire measurements of Schubauer and Klebanoff [*] in which $R(u_1, v_1)$ is found to have a nearly constant value between 0.45 and 0.55 throughout the turbulent boundary layer.

The total shearing stress acting at any point will be the sum of the mean laminar stress and the turbulent stress. Thus,

$$\tau = \mu \frac{\partial U}{\partial y} - \overline{\rho u_1 v_1} \tag{7}$$

Because the velocity components will vanish at the wall, Eq. 7 reduces to $\tau_w = \mu(\partial U/\partial y)_w$ at $y = 0$. Except for very small values of y, however, the turbulent mixing is responsible for nearly all of the momentum transfer. Therefore, $\tau = -\rho u_1 v_1$ is a good approximation to Eq. 7 except in the immediate vicinity of the wall.

16.4   BOUNDARY LAYER EQUATION FOR TURBULENT FLOW

We can derive the approximate form of the boundary layer equation for two-dimensional turbulent flow by substituting fluctuating quantities for u, v, and p in the boundary layer equation of Chapter 12. As in Section 16.2, we write

$$u = U(x, y) + u_1(x, y, z, t); \quad v = V(x, y) + v_1(x, y, z, t)$$

$$p = P(x) + p_1(x, y, z, t)$$

[*] G. B. Schubauer and P. S. Klebanoff, *Investigations of the Separation of Turbulent Boundary Layers*, NACA Rep. 1030, 1951.

After substituting these values, Eqs. 3 and 5 of Chapter 12 become

$$\rho \left\{ (U + u_1) \frac{\partial}{\partial x} (U + u_1) + (V + v_1) \frac{\partial}{\partial y} (U + u_1) \right.$$

$$= -\frac{\partial}{\partial x} (P + p_1) + \frac{\partial}{\partial y} \left\{ \mu \frac{\partial}{\partial y} (U + u_1) \right\}$$

$$\frac{\partial}{\partial x} (U + u_1) + \frac{\partial}{\partial y} (V + v_1) = 0$$

We are interested in the *mean* flow rather than in that as a function of time, so we take the mean value of each term and the above equations become

$$\rho \left\{ \overline{U \frac{\partial U}{\partial x}} + \overline{\frac{\partial}{\partial x} \left(\frac{u_1{}^2}{2} \right)} + \overline{\frac{\partial}{\partial x} (Uu_1)} + \overline{V \frac{\partial U}{\partial y}} + \overline{V \frac{\partial u_1}{\partial y}} + \overline{v_1 \frac{\partial U}{\partial y}} \right.$$

$$\left. + \overline{v_1 \frac{\partial u_1}{\partial y}} \right] = -\frac{\overline{\partial P}}{\partial x} - \frac{\overline{\partial p_1}}{\partial x} + \overline{\frac{\partial}{\partial y} \left(\mu \frac{\partial U}{\partial y} \right)} + \overline{\frac{\partial}{\partial y} \left(\mu \frac{\partial u_1}{\partial y} \right)}$$

$$\frac{\overline{\partial U}}{\partial x} + \frac{\overline{\partial V}}{\partial y} + \frac{\overline{\partial u_1}}{\partial x} + \frac{\overline{\partial v_1}}{\partial y} = 0$$

And, after applying the rule (Section 16.2) that the mean value of any term linear in a fluctuation component or its derivative is zero, we obtain

$$\rho \left(U \frac{\partial U}{\partial x} + V \frac{\partial U}{\partial y} \right) = -\frac{\partial P}{\partial x} + \frac{\partial}{\partial y} \left(\mu \frac{\partial U}{\partial y} - \rho \overline{u_1 v_1} \right) - \frac{\partial}{\partial x} (\rho \overline{u_1{}^2})$$

$$\frac{\partial U}{\partial x} + \frac{\partial V}{\partial y} = 0$$

The last term of the first equation represents a turbulent *normal* stress on an element and if this stress is neglected in comparison with the *shearing* stress, the equations become

$$\rho \left(U \frac{\partial U}{\partial x} + V \frac{\partial U}{\partial y} \right) = -\frac{\partial P}{\partial x} + \frac{\partial}{\partial y} \left(\mu \frac{\partial U}{\partial y} - \rho \overline{u_1 v_1} \right) \qquad (8)$$

$$\frac{\partial U}{\partial x} + \frac{\partial V}{\partial y} = 0 \qquad (9)$$

We see that the term in parantheses on the right side of Eq. 8 represents the total shearing stress given in Eq. 7 and the meanings of the various terms are the same as those for the laminar equations, Eqs. 3 and 5, Chapter 12.

A straightforward solution of Eqs. 8 and 9, analogous to that carried out by Blasius for laminar flow along a flat plate (Section 13.3), is not possible because we have introduced a new dependent variable $\overline{u_1 v_1}$ without supplying a new equation. Therefore, in order to solve the problem of the turbulent boundary layer we require assumptions or hypotheses connecting $\overline{u_1 v_1}$ with the other variables in Eqs. 8 and 9. The hypotheses made and their agreement with experiment is taken up in the following sections.

16.5 THE MIXING-LENGTH HYPOTHESIS

In the absence of a straightforward solution of the equations of motion, our knowledge of turbulent flow in boundary layers and in tubes rests to a great extent on physical reasoning by Prandtl, von Kármán, and others, supplemented by experimental data by Nikuradse, Dryden, Schubauer, and others.

The rudiments of the mixing-length hypothesis proposed by Prandtl in 1925 can be described quite simply. In Section 16.3 the mechanism assumed for describing the Reynolds stress shows that u_1 at a particular point in the boundary layer, due to the motion of a fluid element lateral to the main flow, is proportional to dU/dy, where $U = U(y)$ is the mean velocity profile. Then, if the assumption is made that v_1 is also proportional to dU/dy, the expression for the Reynolds stress (Eq. 5) is,

$$\tau_t = -\rho \overline{u_1 v_1} = \rho l^2 \frac{dU}{dy} \left| \frac{dU}{dy} \right| \tag{10}$$

where $l(y)$ is a length and is defined as the *mixing length;* since it is really the product of two proportionality factors, it is not fruitful to attempt to visualize it as a length connected with the body or with the boundary layer. The absolute value sign is introduced on the right so that the shearing stress will have the sign of the velocity gradient, in conformity with the expression for the laminar shearing stress $\mu dU/dy$.

If we write Eq. 7,

$$\tau = \tau_l + \tau_t = \mu \frac{\partial U}{\partial y} - \rho \overline{u_1 v_1} \tag{11}$$

then, by means of Eq. 10, Eq. 8 becomes

$$\rho \left(U \frac{\partial U}{\partial x} + V \frac{\partial U}{\partial y} \right) + \frac{\partial P}{\partial x} = \frac{\partial \tau}{\partial y} = \frac{\partial}{\partial y} \left(\mu \frac{\partial U}{\partial y} + \rho l^2 \frac{\partial U}{\partial y} \left| \frac{\partial U}{\partial y} \right| \right) \tag{12}$$

This equation is similar to that for laminar flow except for the last term in the parentheses on the right, which represents τ_t. In order to solve Eq. 12 it is first necessary to make an assumption for the mixing length, $l = l(x, y)$. Such an assumption is made in the next section in deriving the formula for the velocity distribution in a tube.

16.6 FULLY DEVELOPED FLOW IN A TUBE

Fully developed flow, as described for laminar flow in Section 13.2, is achieved at points far from the entrance of a tube. It is characterized by the fact that all mean velocity profiles are identical and hence that $V = \partial U/\partial x = 0$. Thus, the equation of motion, Eq. 12, for flow in a two-dimensional channel reduces to

$$\frac{dP}{\partial x} = \frac{d\tau}{dy} \tag{13}$$

Equation 13 becomes, after integration and application of the boundary condition $\tau = \tau_w$ at $y = 0$,

$$\tau = \tau_w + y\frac{dP}{dx} \tag{14}$$

and since from symmetry $\tau = 0$ at $y = b/2$, where b is the breadth of the channel,

$$\tau_w = -\frac{b}{2}\frac{dP}{dx} \tag{15}$$

We shall now consider, instead of a two-dimensional channel, a tube of circular cross section, as was analyzed in Section 13.2. The equilibrium of the pressure and shearing forces on an element (Eq. 1, Chapter 13) gives

$$2\pi r\tau = -\pi r^2\frac{dP}{dx}$$

where $dP/dx = (p_2 - p_1)/l$. Then,

$$\tau = -\frac{1}{2}r\frac{dP}{dx} \tag{16}$$

with the origin at the center of the tube. For this case the skin-friction coefficient γ at the wall, as in Section 13.2, is given by

$$\gamma = \frac{\tau_w}{\frac{1}{2}\rho U_m{}^2} = \frac{a}{\rho U_m{}^2}\left(-\frac{dP}{dx}\right) \tag{17}$$

where U_m is the mean speed over the cross section and a is the radius of the tube. By means of this formula it is particularly easy to determine the skin-friction coefficient experimentally; it is necessary only to measure the discharge through the tube to get U_m and to measure dP/dx by means of pressure taps in the wall.

It will be noted that Eqs. 13 through 17 are valid for either laminar or turbulent flow. Figure 2 shows schematically a comparison between fully developed laminar and turbulent flow in a tube as given by experiment for the same mean velocity over the cross section. In both flows the shearing-stress distribution is linear, but in laminar flow its magnitude is much less. The shearing stress is, by Eq. 11, the sum of

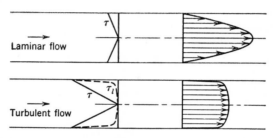

FIG. 2. Schematic representation of fully developed laminar and turbulent flow in a tube, for the same mean velocity.

the laminar (τ_l) and the Reynolds (τ_t) stresses. As was pointed out in Section 16.3, τ_l represents the entire stress at the wall, since the no-slip condition requires that $\overline{u_1 v_1}$ be zero at that point. However, $-\rho \overline{u_1 v_1}$ far overshadows the laminar stress everywhere *except* in the immediate vicinity of the wall.

The method given below for finding the velocity distribution is justified, not by its rigor, but rather by the fact that it provides a systematic framework for the analysis of experimental data. We first neglect the laminar shearing stress and, as a consequence, the velocity distribution cannot possibly hold in the immediate vicinity of the wall. Second, we set $\tau = \tau_w = $ constant. The consequence of the two assumptions is that any agreement between theory and experiment could be expected to be limited to a layer near, but not extending to, the wall, throughout which the shearing stress does not vary much from its value at the wall. The fact that the derived velocity distribution actually agrees with experiment over the entire tube, except in the immediate vicinity of the wall, is simply a fortunate circumstance.

The significant variables that must determine the mean velocity distribution are τ_w, ρ, μ, L, and y. However, experimental results indicate that, rather than consider τ_w as a separate variable, we should employ

$\sqrt{\tau_w/\rho}$, which has the dimensions of a velocity and is called the *friction velocity* U_τ. Then the variables are U_τ, μ, ρ, L, and y. By the Π theorem (Appendix A), we can form only two dimensionless parameters from these five quantities. Accordingly, we may write

$$\frac{U}{U_\tau} = f\left(\frac{U_\tau y}{\nu}, \frac{L}{y}\right) \tag{18}$$

With $\tau = \tau_w$ we assume the simple relation $l/y = \text{constant} = k$. Then Eq. 10 becomes

$$U_\tau^2 = k^2 y^2 \left(\frac{dU}{dy}\right)^2 = \text{constant} \tag{19}$$

which integrates to give

$$U = \frac{U_\tau}{k} \log_e y + \text{constant} \tag{20}$$

The integration constant and the functional dependence of Eq. 18 permits us to put Eq. 20 in the form

$$\frac{U}{U_\tau} = A + \frac{1}{k} \log_e \frac{U_\tau y}{\nu} \tag{21}$$

The experimental results obtained by Nikuradse * and shown in Fig. 3 are employed to evaluate A and $1/k$. The straight line has the equation

$$\frac{U}{U_\tau} = 5.5 + 5.75 \log_{10} \frac{y U_\tau}{\nu} \tag{22}$$

The agreement with experiment is good from $y U_\tau/\nu = 30$ to the center of the channel.†

It was pointed out earlier that neglecting the laminar shearing stress precludes agreement between theory and experiment very near the wall. There is, therefore, a thin layer near the wall in which the shearing stress is for the most part laminar. This layer is termed the *laminar sublayer*, and the velocity distribution in it cannot be represented by Eq. 22. In fact, according to Eq. 19, $(dU/dy)_w$ is infinite, an impossible situation.

* J. Nikuradse, "Gesetzmässigkeiten der turbulenten Strömung in glatten Rohren," *Forschungsheft* 356, *Ver. deutsch. Ing.*, 1932.

† Nikuradse's measurements were made in a circular pipe. More recent measurements also verify the general form of Eq. 21 for flow through a channel with a height to width ratio of 12:1. See John Laufer, "Some Recent Measurements in a Two-Dimensional Channel," *J. Aero. Sci.*, Vol. 17, pp. 277–288, 1950.

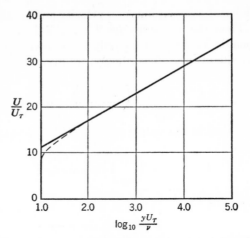

Fig. 3. Measurements by Nikuradse in fully developed turbulent flow in a tube are represented by the dashed curve for small values of $\log_{10}(yU_\tau/\nu)$ and by the straight line over the remainder of the range shown. The measurements cover the range of Reynolds numbers from 4×10^3 to 3.24×10^6.

An example will illustrate how small y is for $yU_\tau/\nu = 30$ for a practical case. Figure 7 shows values of the resistance coefficient for various magnitudes of roughness in a pipe. The curves will be described in Section 16.9; the only purpose in referring to them here is to pick a reasonable value for γ. Taking $\log_{10} 400\gamma = 0.5$, $\gamma = 0.008$; then, if the mean velocity through the pipe U_m is 100 ft/sec, $U_\tau = 6.3$ ft/sec, and, for air ($\nu = 0.0001567$), $y = 0.00075$ ft for $yU_\tau/\nu = 30$. We see, therefore, that for reasonable Reynolds numbers Eq. 22 is a good approximation over by far the greater portion of the channel.

To determine the resistance coefficient, we observe from Eq. 21

$$\frac{U_c}{U_\tau} = A + \frac{1}{k}\log_e \frac{U_\tau a}{\nu}$$

where U_c is the velocity at the center $y = a$. Experiments over a wide range of Reynolds numbers indicate that

$$\frac{U_c - U_m}{U_\tau} = \text{constant}$$

where U_m is the mean velocity over the cross section of the tube. Hence, we may write

$$\frac{U_m}{U_\tau} = A' + B'\log_e \frac{aU_\tau}{\nu}$$

or, if we write

$$\gamma = \frac{\tau_w}{\frac{1}{2}\rho U_m{}^2} = 2\frac{U_\tau{}^2}{U_m{}^2}; \quad Re = \frac{2aU_m}{\nu}$$

we have

$$\sqrt{2}\gamma^{-\frac{1}{2}} = A_1 + B' \log_e Re\gamma^{\frac{1}{2}}$$

The constants A_1 and B' are evaluated from experiments, giving

$$\frac{U_m}{U_\tau} = 0.29 + 5.66 \log_{10} \frac{2aU_\tau}{\nu}$$

$$\gamma^{-\frac{1}{2}} = -0.40 + 4.00 \log_{10} Re\gamma^{\frac{1}{2}} \tag{23}$$

for the resistance of smooth pipes.

The theory leading up to Eqs. 23 is, to be sure, rough and is qualitative to the extent that two empirically determined constants are required. However,

$$B' = k^{-1} \log_e 10$$

which gives a value for k of 0.408, as compared with a value of 0.417 derived from the expression for the velocity distribution Eq. 22. Von Kármán * first introduced the quantity k and pointed out that it has a very nearly constant value for all cases considered. In Section 16.9 it will be shown that the formula that describes the effect of roughness on the velocity distribution agrees with experiment for $k = 0.40$.

In spite of its rough features the theory presents a consistent picture of the physical characteristics of the mean flow in fully developed flow in a tube.

16.7   THE TURBULENT BOUNDARY LAYER ON A FLAT PLATE

The dimensional reasoning in the previous section led to Eq. 18 for the functional dependence of the velocity distribution on the variables involved. For the boundary layer on a flat plate $(dP/dx = 0)$, another parameter, connected with the boundary-layer thickness δ, must be included. For the velocity distribution in the boundary layer von Kármán therefore writes

$$\frac{U}{U_\tau} = \frac{1}{k}\left[\log_e \frac{yU_\tau}{\nu} + h\left(\frac{y}{\delta}\right)\right]$$

He proceeds to determine the unknown function $h(y/\delta)$ and obtains the formula

$$c_f{}^{-\frac{1}{2}} = 1.7 + 4.15 \log_{10} (Re_x c_f) \tag{24}$$

* T. von Kármán, "Mechanische Ähnlichkeit und Turbulenz," *Proc. 3rd Internat. Cong. Applied Mech.*, Stockholm, pp. 90–92, 1930.

where $c_f = \tau_w / \frac{1}{2} \rho U_1{}^2 = 2(U_\tau / U_1)^2$, U_1 is the velocity at the outer edge of the boundary layer, and $Re_x = U_1 x / \nu$, where x is the distance from the leading edge to the point under consideration. The numerical constants were again determined by experiment.

The corresponding formula for the coefficient of mean friction on one side of a flat plate is given by Schoenherr.*

$$C_f{}^{-\frac{1}{2}} = 4.13 \log_{10}(Re_l C_f) \tag{25}$$

where $C_f = F / \frac{1}{2} \rho U_1{}^2 l$, F is the friction per unit width of a plate of length l, and $Re_l = U_1 l / \nu$. Another formula,

$$C_f = 0.455 (\log_{10} Re_l)^{-2.58} \tag{26}$$

which is more convenient for numerical calculations, is given by Prandtl † on the basis of experimental results. The values it gives are practically indistinguishable from those given by Eq. 25.

Equation 25 is plotted in Fig. 4 along with Eq. 19 of Chapter 13 for the laminar boundary layer on a plate of length l. The transition

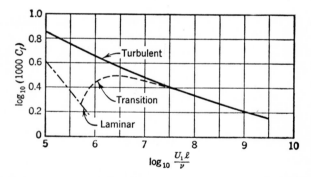

FIG. 4. The skin-friction coefficient for flow over a flat plate with completely laminar boundary layer, with completely turbulent boundary layer, and with transition occurring at a distance from the leading edge dependent on Reynolds number.

curve sketched in the figure represents the total skin-friction coefficient with the boundary layer laminar up to a certain point x and turbulent thereafter. The layer is laminar over the entire plate up to the Reynolds number at which the laminar and transition curves intersect; as the Reynolds number increases further, the transition point moves

* Schoenherr, *Trans. Soc. Naval Architects Marine Engrs.*, Vol. 40, pp. 279–313, 1932.

† L. Prandtl, "The Mechanics of Viscous Fluids," article in *Aerodynamic Theory*, edited by W. F. Durand, Div. G., p. 153, Durand Reprinting Committee, Pasadena, Calif., 1943.

toward the leading edge and the skin-friction coefficient approaches asymptotically that for a completely turbulent boundary layer.

For purposes of calculation, Prandtl * assumes that transition takes place at a point x and that in the turbulent layer behind that point the skin friction is the same as it would be if the layer were turbulent from the leading edge. Then the skin friction over the plate of length l is given by the total turbulent skin friction over the length l minus the correction term made up of the difference between the turbulent and laminar friction over the length x. The correction term is, accordingly, $\frac{1}{2}\rho U_1{}^2 x (C_{f_t} - C_{f_L})_{Re_x}$, where the coefficients of mean laminar and turbulent skin friction C_{f_L} and C_{f_t} are evaluated at Re_x. Then the coefficient of mean skin friction may be written

$$C_f = C_{f_t} - \frac{Re_x}{Re_l}(C_{f_t} - C_{fL})_{Re}$$

or

$$C_f = C_{f_t} - \frac{A}{Re_l}$$

where $A = Re_x(C_{f_t} - C_{f_L})_{Re_x}$ is a function of Re_x. A transition curve for $A = 1800$ is shown in Fig. 4.

Convenient approximate formulas derived by Blasius from experimental results are

$$\frac{U}{U_1} = \left(\frac{y}{\delta}\right)^{\frac{1}{7}}$$

$$\delta = \frac{0.37x}{Re_x{}^{0.2}} \tag{27}$$

$$c_f = 0.296\left(\frac{U_\infty x}{\nu}\right)^{-0.2} = 0.0128\left(\frac{U_\infty \theta}{\nu}\right)^{-0.25} \tag{28}$$

where θ is the momentum thickness of the boundary layer. These hold fairly well up to $Re_x = 10^5$. Use of Eqs. 27 and 28 assumes that the boundary layer is turbulent almost from the leading edge; if this is not so, x is measured from some point between the leading edge and the transition point.

16.8 SIMILARITY CONSIDERATIONS

In the preceding sections, the analyses have involved a combination of the mixing-length hypothesis, a rough approximation to the shearing stress distribution, and similarity considerations, with a strong assist

* *Ibid.*

from experimental results. Here we shall go more closely into the details of the velocity distributions in turbulent boundary layers. Our object will be to delineate the extent to which similarity, in the sense discussed in Section 13.5 for the laminar boundary layer, is realized in the turbulent layer.

Measurements by many investigators have shown that the turbulent boundary layer is made up of two distinct regions: an inner region adjacent to the wall in which the conditions *at* the wall have the determining effect; and an outer region in which the velocity at any position is governed solely by the friction velocity. These regions are separated by an "overlapping region" in which the laws governing the flow in the inner and outer regions are both valid. The regions are described in more detail below.

1) Very near the wall, within the region defined as the *laminar sub-layer* (Eq. 36), there is a linear relation between U and y. This relation may be written

$$\frac{U}{U_\tau} = \frac{U_\tau y}{\nu}$$

(29)

Then

$$\frac{U}{U_\tau} = f\left(\frac{U_\tau y}{\nu}\right)$$

(29a)

characterizes the "inner region" of the turbulent layer, that is, the region within which the velocity profile is determined by the friction at the wall. Equation 29a is generally termed Prandtl's *law of the wall*.

2) The "outer region," comprising approximately the outer 97 per cent of the layer at low speeds, is that portion of the boundary layer in which the velocity distribution is independent of the viscosity, but is dependent on the friction velocity, U_τ. This dependence, first recognized by von Kármán, is known as the "velocity defect law" and is expressed

$$\frac{U_1 - U}{U_\tau} = f\left(\frac{y}{\delta}\right)$$

(30)

Figure 6 shows the experimental points for flow at various distances from the leading edge of a flat plate. All of the observations, except those very near the wall (region 1), fall on a single curve. At $y = 0$ ($U = 0$) Eq. 30 shows that the ordinate is $U_1/U_\tau = \sqrt{2/c_f}$. Since this quantity is a function of x, it is clear that the similarity must fail in the immediate vicinity of the wall.

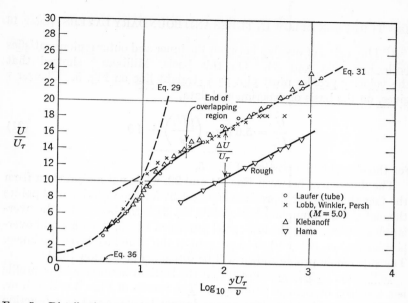

FIG. 5. Distribution of mean velocity near wall in turbulent flow. Effects of roughness and compressibility are shown. The Lobb et al. data are plotted using values of ρ and μ at the wall.

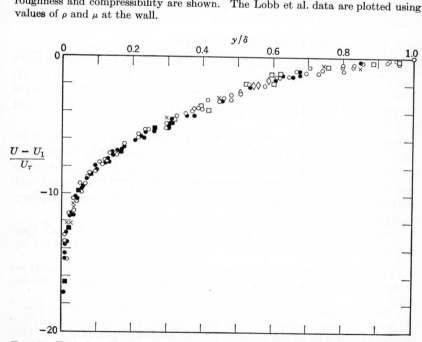

FIG. 6. Turbulent boundary layer profiles on a flat plate. Incompressible flow, smooth and rough surfaces.

(3.) The region of overlap between the inner and outer regions satisfies both Eqs. 29a and 30. On this basis, Millikan * showed that the velocity profiles must plot as a straight line on Fig. 5. Clauser † gives, on the basis of experimental data,

$$\frac{U}{U_\tau} = 5.6 \log_{10}\left(\frac{yU_\tau}{\nu}\right) + 4.9 \qquad (31)$$

for the straight-line portion of Fig. 5.

The differences between Eqs. 31 and 22, while not major, stem from the fact that Eq. 22 represents the best fit for the experimental points throughout the boundary layer while Eq. 31 is the best fit for the overlapping region. For the low-speed profiles of Fig. 5, the inner and overlapping regions cover 10 to 15 per cent of the boundary layer thickness. The supersonic profile shown will be discussed in Section 16.11.

In Section 13.5, it was shown that the laminar boundary layer profile is a function of a single parameter. The results of Figs. 5 and 6 show, however, that the turbulent profile cannot be expressed as a function of a single parameter, but rather must be treated piecemeal, according to the parameters of Eqs. 29 and 30.

16.9   EFFECTS OF SURFACE ROUGHNESS

Roughness of a surface has, in general, two effects on boundary layer flow; it influences the location of boundary layer transition, and it affects the skin friction on that portion of the plate over which the layer is turbulent. The first effect was discussed in Section 15.5; the second will be discussed here.

Reference to the experimental results shown in Figs. 5 and 6 indicates the extent to which the similarity rules described in the previous section hold for rough or smooth walls. In Fig. 5, the overlapping region for the rough wall would coincide with that for a smooth wall with a very small displacement of the origin of y; such a small displacement would not be discernible on Fig. 6.

It will be noticed that in Fig. 5 the curves for smooth and rough walls are displaced by the interval $\Delta U/U_\tau$. Prandtl ‡ gave a relation be-

* C. B. Millikan, "A Critical Discussion of Turbulent Flows in Channels and Tubes," *Proc. 5th Internat. Cong. Applied Mech.*, Cambridge, Mass., pp. 386–392, 1938.

† Francis Clauser, "Turbulent Boundary Layers in Adverse Pressure Gradients," *J. Aero. Sci.*, Vol. 21, No. 2, pp. 91–108, February 1954; *Advances in Applied Mechanics*, edited by T. von Kármán, Vol. IV, Academic Press, New York, 1956.

‡ Ludwig Prandtl, "The Mechanics of Viscous Fluids," p. 153; see also: Francis H. Clauser, "Turbulent Boundary Layers in Adverse Pressure Gradients."

tween the height of the roughness and corresponding value of $\Delta U / U_\tau$ and showed that the effect of roughness on the skin-friction coefficient may be expressed by

$$\sqrt{\frac{2}{c_f}} = 5.6 \log \left(\frac{U_1 \delta^*}{\nu} \right) + 4.3 - \frac{\Delta U}{U_\tau} \tag{32}$$

where δ^* is the displacement thickness of the boundary layer and the numerical values are those given by Clauser.[†] Another equivalent interpretation of the effect of roughness on skin friction is given below.

The effect of roughness in a turbulent boundary layer will be clarified by an understanding of the laminar sublayer mentioned briefly in Section 16.6. The laminar sublayer is defined as that layer adjacent to the surface in which the magnitude of the laminar shearing stress ($\mu \, dU/dy$) is large compared with the turbulent ($-\rho \overline{u_1 v_1}$); Fig. 5 shows graphically that such a layer does exist and that it is extremely thin. We reason that if the peaks of the roughness elements do not project beyond the laminar sublayer of a turbulent layer their effect on the skin friction should be negligible.

Nikuradse's measurements of the resistance coefficient in tubes [‡] are shown in Fig. 7. The surface of the tube was sprinkled with sand of various grain sizes a/ϵ, where a is the radius of the tube and ϵ is the mesh size of the screen through which the sand will *just* pass. The straight lines shown are those for fully developed laminar flow (Eq. 6 of Chapter 13) and an empirical formula given by Blasius for turbulent flow in smooth pipes,

$$\gamma = 0.0655 \left(\frac{U_m a}{\nu} \right)^{-\frac{1}{4}}$$

This formula is in good agreement with Eq. 23 up to a Reynolds number of about 10^6. We see that the agreement with the laminar-flow theory is good up to $\log_{10} \text{Re} = 3.3$, at which point transition begins. Further, for each roughness there is a Reynolds number beyond which γ is constant.

If we confine ourselves to the range of Reynolds numbers for which γ is constant, in the vicinity of the wall the height of the roughness elements is the most important linear dimension. Therefore, we write $U/U_\tau = f(y/\epsilon)$, and Eq. 20 becomes

$$\frac{U}{U_\tau} = k^{-1} \log_e \left(\frac{y}{\epsilon} \right) + \text{constant}$$

† *Loc. cit.*

‡ J. Nikuradse, "Strömungsgesetze in Rauhen Rohren," *Forschungsheft* 361, *Ver. deutsch. Ing.*, 1933.

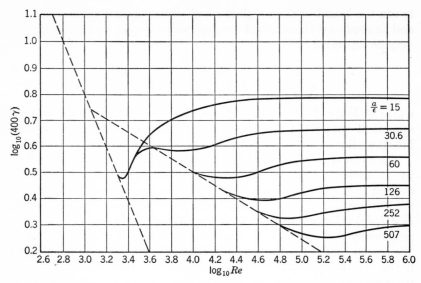

FIG. 7.   Measurements by Nikuradse of the resistance coefficient for fully developed flow through a tube of radius a with various sizes of the roughness elements a/ϵ are represented by the solid curves.   The dashed lines represent theory for laminar and for turbulent flow in a smooth tube.

The constants are determined again from Nikuradse's experiments,

$$\frac{U}{U_\tau} = 8.48 + 5.75 \log_{10}\left(\frac{y}{\epsilon}\right) \tag{33}$$

which indicate a value of $k = 0.400$.   Now, a procedure identical with that leading to Eq. 29 for a smooth pipe gives

$$\frac{U_m}{U_\tau} = k^{-1} \log_e\left(\frac{a}{\epsilon}\right) + \text{constant} \tag{34}$$

in the range for which γ is independent of the Reynolds number.   Comparison with Nikuradse's experiments shows that

$$\frac{U_m}{U_\tau} = \sqrt{\frac{2}{\gamma}} = 4.9 + 5.66 \log\frac{a}{\epsilon} \tag{35}$$

for values of $\epsilon U_\tau/\nu > 100$.   Further analysis shows that for $\epsilon U_\tau/\nu < 4$, Eq. 23 for smooth pipes agrees with the results in Fig. 7.   We now define the *laminar sublayer* as follows: If the roughness elements project through the laminar sublayer, they cause an increase in skin friction;

if they are embedded in the sublayer, the surface is *aerodynamically smooth*. Then the thickness of the laminar sublayer is defined as

$$\delta_l = \frac{4\nu}{U_\tau}$$ (36)

This point is designated in Fig. 5.

Von Kármán * applied the above results on flow through tubes to flow along a surface and obtained for the rough condition ($\epsilon U_\tau/\nu > 100$) the formula

$$c_f{}^{-\frac{1}{2}} = 5.8 + 4.15 \log_{10}\left(\frac{c_f{}^{\frac{1}{2}}x}{\epsilon}\right)$$ (37)

where $c_f = \tau_0/\frac{1}{2}\rho U_1{}^2$, U_1, is the velocity at the outer edge of the boundary layer, and x is the distance from the leading edge, assuming that the boundary layer is turbulent from the leading edge. On the other hand, in the aerodynamically smooth pipe the formulas of Section 16.7 apply.

According to Eq. 37, as x increases, c_f and therefore U_τ will decrease. Hence, by Eq. 36, δ_L, which represents the height of the *maximum allowable roughness*, will increase with x. Also, Eq. 37 shows that for the rough condition if ϵ increases linearly with x the resistance coefficient remains constant.

16.10 TURBULENT BOUNDARY LAYER IN A PRESSURE GRADIENT— FLOW SEPARATION

In Section 13.4 the effect of pressure gradient on the flow in the laminar boundary layer is described. The retarding effect of an adverse pressure gradient and eventual flow separation are described quantitatively by the von Kármán-Pohlhausen analysis of Section 13.6. Although some progress has been made toward establishing hard-and-fast criteria for predicting flow separation for the turbulent boundary layer, no rational theory is at hand. We shall confine ourselves here to some qualitative observations and to some of the similarity considerations.

The fact that the turbulent boundary layer will resist flow separation through a more severe adverse pressure gradient than will the laminar is brought out briefly in Sections 15.2 and 15.4. Comparison of the turbulent velocity profile with the laminar profile of the same thickness (Fig. 3, Chapter 15) shows that for the former the velocity near the surface is greater, and hence we would expect the turbulent layer to

* T. von Kármán, "Skin Friction and Turbulence," *J. Aero. Sci.*, Vol. 1, No. 1, p. 18, 1934.

drive further than the laminar against an adverse pressure gradient. The underlying reason for the higher velocity near the surface is the effect of the turbulence in bringing high velocity air from the outside flow near to the surface where it counteracts the tendency of the adverse pressure gradient to cause reverse flow.

Some qualitative observations may be made on flow separation by analogy with the important factors for laminar flow. The von Kármán-Pohlhausen analysis of Section 13.7 indicates that for the laminar boundary layer

$$\lambda = \frac{\delta^2}{\nu}\frac{dU_1}{dx} = -12$$

is a criterion for flow separation. Although the numerical value of λ given above has no significance for a turbulent boundary layer, it is still undoubtedly true that decreasing δ or increasing dU_1/dx will delay turbulent separation. δ may be reduced and hence separation delayed by applying suction at the surface or by blowing along the surface in the stream direction, thus accelerating the flow in the boundary layer near the surface.

The theories and experiments described in the previous sections of this chapter are restricted to flow along flat plates and to fully developed flow in tubes. When we come to deal with the turbulent

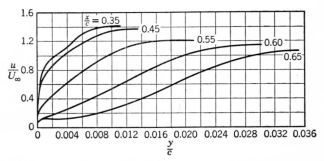

FIG. 8. Velocity distributions in the turbulent boundary layer at various distances from the nose of an airfoil. x is the distance along the airfoil, y is the distance normal to the surface, and c is the chord.

boundary layer on a surface with a pressure gradient, great complications enter. However, considerable progress has been made in systematizing the available experimental results. Figure 8 shows NACA measurements * of velocity profiles at various positions on a wing.

* Albert E. von Doenhoff and Neal Tetervin, *Determination of General Relations for the Behavior of Turbulent Boundary Layers*, NACA TR 772, 1943.

U_∞ is the velocity at a great distance from the wing, x and y are measured along and normal to the surface, respectively, and c is the wing chord. These curves show a rapid increase in the boundary layer thickness and a change in the shape of the profile with distance along an adverse pressure gradient.

The effect of pressure gradient on shearing stress may be correlated approximately with the effect of the pressure gradient on the momentum deficit and hence on the momentum thickness of the boundary layer. This dependence is illustrated by the fact that a relation of the form of Eq. 28 (with U_∞ and θ functions of x) gives a fair representation of the experimental results in an adverse pressure gradient. The determination of $\theta(x)$ is carried out by means of the von Kármán integral relation of Section 13.6.

Various attempts have been made to predict the separation point of the turbulent boundary layer in incompressible flow. The methods are semi-empirical and their adequate treatment would require too much space for inclusion here.*

Investigations of the separation of supersonic flow caused by shock-wave intersection are described in Section 14.9. The intensity of the shock, $\Delta p/q$, required to cause separation of the turbulent boundary layer on a flat plate is found to be proportional to $Re_x^{-\frac{1}{5}}$, which by Eq. 28 is proportional to the skin-friction coefficient in the absence of the shock.

16.11 EFFECTS OF COMPRESSIBILITY

The first estimate of the effect of compressibility on the turbulent skin friction on a flat plate was made by von Kármán.† He assumed that Eq. 25 is valid for a compressible boundary layer provided that properties at the wall, ρ_w and μ_w are used in the calculation of C_f and Re. He further assumed a Prandtl number of unity and then calculated the ratio C_f/C_{fi}, where the subscript i refers to incompressible flow, as a function of the free-stream Mach number. The curve plotted in Fig. 9 was the result. Many other more involved calculations have been made, using some form of the mixing-length hypothesis of Section 16.6 and introducing compressibility by means of the energy equation of Section 14.5. Those theoretical curves which bracket the available

---

* A complete bibliography is given by H. Schlichting, *Boundary Layer Theory*, translated by J. Kestin, McGraw-Hill, New York, 1955. See also 2nd edition, 1959 (in German).

† T. von Kármán, "The Problem of Resistance in Compressible Fluids," Reale Accademia d'Italia, *V. Convegno della Fondazione Alessandro Volta*, Roma, pp. 226–290, 1935.

experimental results are shown in Fig. 9. Hayes and Probstein *
found, by a method similar to that used by von Kármán, that an
excellent fit for the experimental results is given by

$$\frac{C_f}{C_{fi}} = (1 + 0.144M_1{}^2)^{-0.65}$$

The theoretical and experimental results in Fig. 9 refer to the insulated
plate. Three different techniques were used to obtain the experimental

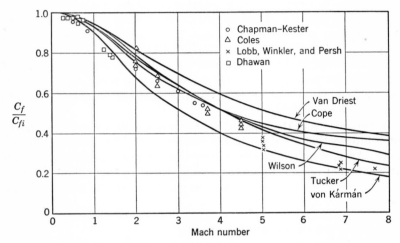

FIG. 9. Ratio of compressible to incompressible skin-friction coefficients for flat
plate as function of Mach number of external flow.

results shown: (1) by analyzing measured velocity profiles by the von
Kármán momentum integral taken up in Section 13.6; (2) by subtracting the measured total drags of bodies of different length; and (3)
by measuring the drag on a small section of a flat plate suspended on a
sensitive balance. There is some effect of Reynolds number in the
measurements and in the theories but the major variation is with the
Mach number.

Figure 5 provides some justification for von Kármán's assumption,
since in plotting the measurements of Lobb et al. for a free-stream Mach
number of 5.0 ρ_w and μ_w were used. Excellent agreement with the
low-speed measurements is shown. A remarkable feature of these results is the relatively large part of the boundary layer that conforms

* Wallace D. Hayes and Ronald F. Probstein, *Hypersonic Flow Theory*, p. 329,
Academic Press, New York, 1959.

approximately with the law of the wall. The edge of the boundary layer is at $\log yU_\tau/v = 2.4$, whereas in the low-speed boundary layer this point represents only 10 to 15 per cent of the boundary layer thickness. Further, results taken over a wide range of values of heat transfer from the wall to the stream show that the law of the wall is valid throughout the entire heat transfer range. Outside of the inner or laminar sublayer region, the velocity profile closely satisfied a power law $U/U_1 = (y/\delta)^{1/n}$ where n decreased from 7 to 5.5 as the Mach number increased from 5 to 7.7.

16.12   REYNOLDS ANALOGY—HEAT TRANSFER AND TEMPERATURE RECOVERY FACTOR

The relation between heat transfer and skin friction in the laminar boundary layer (Section 14.7) rests on the proportionality between the heat transfer and viscosity coefficients, $k \frown c_p\mu$. For the turbulent boundary layer, the *Reynolds Analogy* provides the corresponding relation between skin friction and heat transfer.

Reynolds analogy rests on the assumption that the mechanisms of turbulent transfer of heat and momentum are similar. In Section 16.3 we showed that the mean rate of momentum transfer by turbulence is given by

$$\tau_t = -\rho\,\overline{u_1v_1} \tag{38}$$

By the same reasoning as that used there, ρv_1 is the mass of air crossing unit area of a plane normal to the *temperature* gradient, and it carries with it a temperature deficit or surplus of $\partial T/\partial y\,dy = \theta_1$. Then the turbulent rate of heat transfer per unit area is

$$q_t = \rho c_p\,\overline{v_1\theta_1} \tag{39}$$

Now, if we assume that the rate of heat transfer per unit enthalpy gradient is equal to the rate of momentum transfer per unit momentum gradient, we write,

$$\frac{\rho c_p\overline{v_1\theta_1}}{c_p\,\partial T/\partial y} = \frac{-\rho\overline{u_1v_1}}{\partial U/\partial y} \tag{40}$$

With $q_t = k_t\,\partial T/\partial y$ and $\tau_t = \mu_t\,\partial U/\partial y$, Eq. 40 becomes

$$k_t = c_p\mu_t \tag{41}$$

that is, Eq. 41 implies a *turbulent* Prandtl number of unity.

Now $\partial T/\partial y$ and $\partial U/\partial y$ at any given point in the boundary layer will be proportional respectively to $T_w - T_1$ and to U_1, so Eq. 40 may be written

$$\frac{\rho c_p \overline{v_1 \theta_1}}{c_p(T_w - T_1)} = \frac{-\overline{\rho u_1 v_1}}{U_1} \tag{42}$$

where $c_p(T_w - T_1)$ and U_1, are proportional to the enthalpy and momentum gradients, respectively, at a given point. Then, from Eq. 42 and Eqs. 38 and 39 we form the dimensionless coefficients,

$$\frac{q_t}{\rho c_p U_1 (T_w - T_1)} = \frac{\tau_t}{\rho U_1^2}$$

The left side is the local Stanton number, st (Section 14.7), and the right side is $c_f/2$. Then the Reynolds analogy is

$$st = c_f/2 \tag{43}$$

More detailed studies * predict, instead of Eq. 43,

$$st = 0.6c_f \tag{44}$$

practically independent of Mach number up to about 5.

The *effective* Prandtl number of the turbulent boundary layer, comprising turbulent and laminar contributions, respectively, from the outer region and the laminar sublayer, determines the temperature recovery factor. Many measurements indicate that the recovery factor r for the turbulent boundary layer may be expressed in terms of the *molecular* Prandtl number as

$$r = Pr^{\frac{1}{3}} \cong 0.89 \tag{45}$$

for air over a wide range of Mach numbers.

Figure 3 of Chapter 14 shows experimental recovery factors for laminar and turbulent boundary layers. The agreement between the experimental data and Eq. 35 of Chapter 14 for laminar flow and Eq. 45 above for turbulent flow are seen to be good.

---

* Morris Rubesin, *A Modified Reynolds Analogy*, NACA TN 2917, 1953.   For charts, see Dorothy B. Lee and Maxime A. Faget, *Charts Adapted from Van Driest's Turbulent Flat-Plate Theory for Determining Values of Turbulent Aerodynamic Friction and Heat-Transfer Coefficients*, NACA TN 3811, 1956.

Dimensional Analysis

If an algebraic equation expresses a relation among physical quantities, it can have meaning only if the terms involved are alike dimensionally. For example, two numbers may be equal, but if they represent unlike physical quantities they may not be equated. This requirement of dimensional homogeneity in physical equations is useful in determining the combinations in which the variables occur. Specifically, let it be required that all the terms in an equation be pure numbers. Then the variables involved may occur only in combinations that have zero dimensions. Any physical equation can be expressed in terms of dimensionless combinations of the variables. The formal statement of this fact is embodied in the Π theorem, which may be stated as follows:*

Any function of N variables

$$f\{P_1, \quad P_2, \quad P_3, \quad P_4, \cdots P_N\} = 0 \tag{1}$$

may be expressed in terms of $(N - K)$ Π products

$$f\{\Pi_1, \quad \Pi_2, \quad \Pi_3, \cdots \Pi_{N-K}\} = 0 \tag{2}$$

where each Π product is a dimensionless combination of an arbitrarily selected set of K variables and one other; that is,

$$\Pi_1 = f\{P_1, \quad P_2, \cdots P_K, \quad P_{K+1}\}$$

$$\Pi_2 = f\{P_1, \quad P_2, \cdots P_K, \quad P_{K+2}\}$$

$$\Pi_{N-K} = f\{P_1, \quad P_2, \cdots P_K, \quad P_N \quad\}$$

---

* A proof of the Π theorem may be found in W. F. Durand, *Aerodynamic Theory*, Vol. 1, Durand Reprinting Committee, Pasadena, Calif., 1943.

K is equal to the number of fundamental dimensions required to describe the variables P. If the problem is one in mechanics, all quantities P may be expressed in terms of mass, length, and time, and $K = 3$. In thermodynamics, all quantities may be expressed in terms of mass, length, time, and temperature, and $K = 4$. The arbitrarily selected set of K variables may contain any of the quantities P_i with the restriction that the K set itself may not form a dimensionless combination.

To illustrate the application of the Π theorem to a problem in mechanics, we consider the force experienced by a body that is in motion through a fluid. We assume that the force will depend upon the following parameters:

$$F = f\{\rho, \quad V, \quad l, \quad \mu, \quad a\} \tag{3}$$

where the symbols and their dimensions are as tabulated.

Symbol	Name	Dimensions
F	Force	MLT^{-2}
ρ	Density	ML^{-3}
V	Velocity	LT^{-1}
l	A length characterizing the size of the body	L
μ	Coefficient of viscosity	$ML^{-1}T^{-1}$
a	Speed of sound	LT^{-1}

Let us write Eq. 3 in the form of Eq. 1:

$$g\{F, \quad \rho, \quad V, \quad l, \quad \mu, \quad a\} = 0 \tag{4}$$

There are six variables and three fundamental dimensions. Therefore, there are three Π products. If we choose ρ, V, and l as the K set, the Π products are

$$\Pi_1 = f_1\{F, \quad \rho, \quad V, \quad l\}$$

$$\Pi_2 = f_2\{\mu, \quad \rho, \quad V, \quad l\}$$

$$\Pi_3 = f_3\{a, \quad \rho, \quad V, \quad l\}$$

The Π theorem guarantees that the Π products above can be made dimensionless. As an example, we find a dimensionless combination of the variables in Π_1, in the form $F\rho^a V^b l^c$. We write the quantity in terms of its dimensions

$$(MLT^{-2})(ML^{-3})^a(LT^{-1})^b(L)^c$$

The exponents of M, L, and T must be zero. This process leads to the three equations

$$1 + a = 0$$

$$1 - 3a + b + c = 0$$

$$-2 - b = 0$$

from which

$$a = -1$$

$$b = -2$$

$$c = -2$$

and Π_1 becomes

$$\Pi_1 = \frac{F}{\rho V^2 l^2}$$

Proceeding in the same manner with Π_2 and Π_3, we get

$$\Pi_2 = \frac{\rho V l}{\mu}$$

$$\Pi_3 = \frac{V}{a}$$

Then Eq. 4 may be written

$$f\left\{\frac{F}{\rho V^2 l^2},\ \frac{\rho V l}{\mu},\ \frac{V}{a}\right\} = 0 \tag{5}$$

To illustrate the application of the Π theorem to a problem that includes thermal effects, we consider the heat transferred between a solid and the surrounding fluid when the solid is in motion through the fluid. The heat per second transferred through the boundary layer is given by

$$\frac{\partial Q}{\partial t} = hA(\theta_2 - \theta_1) \tag{6}$$

where A is the area through which the heat is transferred and $\theta_2 - \theta_1$ is the temperature difference between the solid and the fluid. The symbol θ is used in this appendix to represent temperature because the symbol T is reserved for the dimension *time*. The constant h is the heat-transfer coefficient, and we assume that it will be a function of the following parameters:

$$h = f\{\rho,\ \mu,\ k,\ l,\ a,\ c,\ V\} \tag{7}$$

c is the specific heat of the fluid and is defined as the heat required to raise unit mass one degree.* k is the thermal conductivity of the fluid and is defined by the equation

$$\frac{\partial Q}{\partial t} = kA \frac{\partial \theta}{\partial s} \tag{8}$$

where the derivative of the temperature is in a direction normal to the area through which the heat is being transferred. Notice that the thermal conductivity is the proportionality constant in an equation that expresses the rate of heat transfer through a continuous medium, whereas the heat transfer coefficient is the proportionality constant in an equation that expresses the rate of heat transfer between two different media. The dimensions of h and k may be found from the defining Eqs. 6 and 8. The thermal parameters c, h, and k have the following dimensions:

SYMBOL	NAME	DIMENSIONS
c	Specific heat	$L^2 T^{-2} \theta^{-1}$
h	Heat transfer coefficient	$M T^{-3} \theta^{-1}$
k	Thermal conductivity	$MLT^{-3} \theta^{-1}$

Equation 7 contains eight parameters, and, since four dimensions are needed to describe the eight parameters, the number of Π products will be four. If we choose ρ, μ, k, and l as the K set, the Π products are

$$\Pi_1 = f\{h, \quad \rho, \quad \mu, \quad k, \quad l\} \qquad \Pi_3 = f\{c, \quad \rho, \quad \mu, \quad k, \quad l\}$$

$$\Pi_2 = f\{V, \quad \rho, \quad \mu, \quad k, \quad l\} \qquad \Pi_4 = f\{a, \quad \rho, \quad \mu, \quad k, \quad l\}$$

A dimensionless combination of the variables in Π_1, in the form $h\rho^a\mu^b k^c l^d$, is found by the method employed in the preceding example. We write the quantity in terms of its dimensions.

$$(MT^{-3}\theta^{-1})(ML^{-3})^a(ML^{-1}T^{-1})^b(MLT^{-3}\theta^{-1})^c L^d$$

The exponents of M, L, T, and θ must be zero. Thus we obtain the four equations

$$1 + a + b + c = 0$$

$$-3a - b + c + d = 0$$

$$-3 - b - 3c = 0$$

$$-1 - c = 0$$

---

* The specific heats c_p and c_v have been defined in terms of the fluid characteristics in Section 8.2. The definition given here is equivalent.

from which

$$a = 0$$

$$b = 0$$

$$c = -1$$

$$d = 1$$

and Π_1 becomes

$$\Pi_1 = \frac{hl}{k}$$

A similar procedure for Π_2, Π_3, and Π_4 leads to the result

$$\Pi_2 = \frac{\rho V l}{\mu}$$

$$\Pi_3 = \frac{c\mu}{k}$$

$$\Pi_4 = \frac{a\rho l}{\mu} = \Pi_2 \frac{a}{V}$$

Then Eq. 7 may be written

$$f\left\{\frac{hl}{k}, \frac{\rho V l}{\mu}, \frac{c\mu}{k}, \frac{a}{V}\right\} = 0 \tag{9}$$

Two specific heats of a fluid are commonly used: the specific heat at constant pressure c_p and the specific heat at constant volume c_v. If each of these is included in Eq. 7, then both Π products that involve them will be of the form of Π_3. Therefore, one Π product could be taken as

$$\Pi_3 = \frac{c_p\mu}{k}$$

and the other as

$$\Pi_5 = \frac{c_v}{c_p}\Pi_3$$

In place of $c\mu/k$ in Eq. 9, we would write the two quantities γ and $c_p\mu/k$, where γ is the ratio of the specific heats.

Dimensional analysis has application in many other problems that arise in aeronautical engineering. It is commonly employed to isolate the important dimensionless parameters in propeller theory and stability problems of the airplane as a whole. Much of the intuitive reasoning that leads to the laws of skin friction variation in a turbulent boundary layer can be aided by dimensional considerations.

Derivation of the Navier-Stokes
and the Energy Equations

---

1. INTRODUCTION

It is the object here to develop the equations of motion * and energy
for unsteady compressible viscous flow. Special forms of the general
equations have been used in various sections of the book. To derive
the general equations we follow a procedure analogous to that employed
in the theory of elasticity and assume that, with respect to the *principal
axes*, the stress is proportional to the rate of extension and to the rate
of increase of specific volume of the fluid element.

Consider the stress τ exerted across a fluid surface A. If both shear
and normal stresses are assumed to be acting, their resultant will be
oblique to the surface. Let the surface be the oblique face of the small
tetrahedron shown in Fig. 1. Then, if $\mathbf{n}$ is the unit normal to A, the
areas of the tetrahedron faces that are normal to the x-, y-, and z-coordi-
nate axes will be $(\mathbf{n} \cdot \mathbf{i})A$, $(\mathbf{n} \cdot \mathbf{j})A$, and $(\mathbf{n} \cdot \mathbf{k})A$, respectively. The stress
on the x-face of the tetrahedron may be resolved into three components,
of which one is normal to the face and is given the symbol τ_{xx} and the
other two, τ_{xy} and τ_{xz}, are shearing stresses and lie in the x-face. The
notation for the stress components is as follows. The first subscript
represents the face on which the stress acts, and the second subscript
represents the direction in which the stress acts. The stresses on the
x-, y-, and z-faces of the tetrahedron are thus resolved into nine components.

---

* The equations of motion were derived by Navier in France in 1827 and by
Stokes in England in 1845. The general form of the derivation given here for both
the equations of motion and the energy equation follow that of H. Lamb, *Hydrodynamics*, Cambridge University Press, 1932 (Dover Reprint 1945).

For equilibrium of the tetrahedron

$$
\left.
\begin{aligned}
\boldsymbol{\tau \cdot i} &= (\mathbf{i}\tau_{xx} + \mathbf{j}\tau_{yx} + \mathbf{k}\tau_{zx}) \cdot \mathbf{n} = \mathbf{f_1 \cdot n} \\
\boldsymbol{\tau \cdot j} &= (\mathbf{i}\tau_{xy} + \mathbf{j}\tau_{yy} + \mathbf{k}\tau_{zy}) \cdot \mathbf{n} = \mathbf{f_2 \cdot n} \\
\boldsymbol{\tau \cdot k} &= (\mathbf{i}\tau_{xz} + \mathbf{j}\tau_{yz} + \mathbf{k}\tau_{zz}) \cdot \mathbf{n} = \mathbf{f_3 \cdot n}
\end{aligned}
\right\} \qquad (1)
$$

Only three of the six shear stresses are independent, because conservation of angular momentum requires that the torque arising from the shear stresses acting on a fluid element be equal to the time rate of

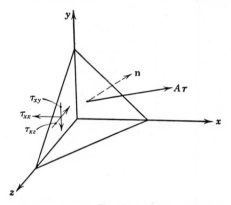

FIG. 1.

change of angular momentum of the element. If the law is applied to an element $\Delta x\, \Delta y\, \Delta z$, it is easily shown that in the limit, as $\Delta x\, \Delta y\, \Delta z$ approaches zero, we have *

$$
\tau_{xy} = \tau_{yx}
$$

$$
\tau_{xz} = \tau_{zx}
$$

$$
\tau_{yz} = \tau_{zy}
$$

It is shown in the next section that a set of axes can be found such that the shearing stresses vanish when referred to them. In deriving the equations of motion it is convenient to express the stresses in this *principal* system of coordinates. Then the basic assumption relating normal stresses to the extension derivatives is applied. A transformation back to the arbitrary coordinate system yields the six components of stress in terms of the rates of extension and strain of the fluid ele-

---

* If these relations are used in Eqs. 1, then the vectors $\mathbf{f_1}$, $\mathbf{f_2}$, and $\mathbf{f_3}$ may be interpreted as the net forces per unit area on the x-, y-, and z-faces, respectively.

ment. The rates of extension and strain of a fluid element have been discussed in Chapter 2.

2. PRINCIPAL AXES

It will be shown that the stresses at a point can be represented by pure normal stresses when referred to the *principal axes*. This property will, for simplicity, be demonstrated in two dimensions; the conclusions hold for three dimensions as well. Consider the element ABC in Fig. 2.

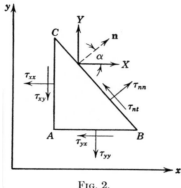

FIG. 2.

Both shear and normal stresses act on the x- and y-faces; the stresses on the inclined face are dictated by the equilibrium condition. If the area of the side BC is A and if X and Y are the stress components indicated,

$$AX = A \cos \alpha\, \tau_{xx} + A \sin \alpha\, \tau_{yx}$$

$$AY = A \sin \alpha\, \tau_{yy} + A \cos \alpha\, \tau_{xy}$$

We may solve for τ_{nn} and τ_{nt} on the BC face. These values are

$$\tau_{nn} = X \cos \alpha + Y \sin \alpha$$
$$= \tau_{xx} \cos^2 \alpha + \tau_{yy} \sin^2 \alpha + 2\tau_{xy} \sin \alpha \cos \alpha$$

$$\tau_{nt} = -X \sin \alpha + Y \cos \alpha$$
$$= \tau_{xy}(\cos^2 \alpha - \sin^2 \alpha) + (\tau_{yy} - \tau_{xx}) \sin \alpha \cos \alpha$$

Now, if we choose the angle α so that $\tau_{nt} = 0$, we get

$$\frac{\tau_{xy}}{\tau_{xx} - \tau_{yy}} = \frac{\sin \alpha \cos \alpha}{\cos^2 \alpha - \sin^2 \alpha} = \frac{1}{2} \tan 2\alpha \qquad (2)$$

and hence there will be two perpendicular directions such that $\tau_{nt} = 0$.

These are the *principal directions*. The corresponding normal stresses are the *principal stresses*.

The extension of the foregoing analysis to three dimensions leads to the following conclusion. Through any point in a flow, three principal planes can be found over which the shearing stresses vanish. Since only normal stresses act on principal planes, there are no stresses acting which can cause a rate of strain of the fluid in these planes (see Section 2.7). We therefore set the rate of strain of the principal planes equal to zero. This property of principal planes is used to advantage in the next section in expressing the rates of strain in terms of the extension derivatives.

3. TRANSFORMATION EQUATIONS

Consider two sets of orthogonal axes x, y, z and x', y', z' that are rotated with respect to each other. The primed set refers to the principal axes. The direction cosines connecting the two sets are given in the following table:

$$
\begin{array}{c|ccc}
 & x & y & z \\
\hline
x' & l_1 & m_1 & n_1 \\
y' & l_2 & m_2 & n_2 \\
z' & l_3 & m_3 & n_3
\end{array}
\tag{3}
$$

It is desired to transform the following quantities to the primed system of coordinates

$$\frac{\partial u}{\partial x}, \qquad \gamma_x = \frac{\partial w}{\partial y} + \frac{\partial v}{\partial z}$$

$$\frac{\partial v}{\partial y}, \qquad \gamma_y = \frac{\partial u}{\partial z} + \frac{\partial w}{\partial x}$$

$$\frac{\partial w}{\partial z}, \qquad \gamma_z = \frac{\partial v}{\partial x} + \frac{\partial u}{\partial y}$$

It was shown in Sections 2.4 and 2.7 that the quantities above represent the rates of extension and strain of a fluid element. The same combinations with the primes represent the rates of extension and strain referred to the principal axes. As explained in the last section,

$$\gamma'_x = \gamma'_y = \gamma'_z = 0 \tag{4}$$

To carry out the transformation, we may, for example, write

$$\frac{\partial u}{\partial x} = \left(l_1 \frac{\partial}{\partial x'} + l_2 \frac{\partial}{\partial y'} + l_3 \frac{\partial}{\partial z'} \right) (l_1 u' + l_2 v' + l_3 w')$$

and

$$\gamma_x = \left(m_1 \frac{\partial}{\partial x'} + m_2 \frac{\partial}{\partial y'} + m_3 \frac{\partial}{\partial z'} \right) (n_1 u' + n_2 v' + n_3 w')$$

$$+ \left(n_1 \frac{\partial}{\partial x'} + n_2 \frac{\partial}{\partial y'} + n_3 \frac{\partial}{\partial z'} \right) (m_1 u' + m_2 v' + m_3 w')$$

Similar expressions hold for the other rates of extension and strain. After we have performed the indicated operations and made use of Eqs. 4, the rates of extension and strain become

$$\left. \begin{array}{l} \dfrac{\partial u}{\partial x} = l_1{}^2 \dfrac{\partial u'}{\partial x'} + l_2{}^2 \dfrac{\partial v'}{\partial y'} + l_3{}^2 \dfrac{\partial w'}{\partial z'} \\[2mm] \dfrac{\partial v}{\partial y} = m_1{}^2 \dfrac{\partial u'}{\partial x'} + m_2{}^2 \dfrac{\partial v'}{\partial y'} + m_3{}^2 \dfrac{\partial w'}{\partial z'} \\[2mm] \dfrac{\partial w}{\partial z} = n_1{}^2 \dfrac{\partial u'}{\partial x'} + n_2{}^2 \dfrac{\partial v'}{\partial y'} + n_3{}^2 \dfrac{\partial w'}{\partial z'} \end{array} \right\} \quad (5)$$

$$\left. \begin{array}{l} \gamma_x = 2 \left(m_1 n_1 \dfrac{\partial u'}{\partial x'} + m_2 n_2 \dfrac{\partial v'}{\partial y'} + m_3 n_3 \dfrac{\partial w'}{\partial z'} \right) \\[2mm] \gamma_y = 2 \left(n_1 l_1 \dfrac{\partial u'}{\partial x'} + n_2 l_2 \dfrac{\partial v'}{\partial y'} + n_3 l_3 \dfrac{\partial w'}{\partial z'} \right) \\[2mm] \gamma_z = 2 \left(l_1 m_1 \dfrac{\partial u'}{\partial x'} + l_2 m_2 \dfrac{\partial v'}{\partial y'} + l_3 m_3 \dfrac{\partial w'}{\partial z'} \right) \end{array} \right\} \quad (6)$$

Thus, the rates of strain referred to arbitrary axes are expressed in terms of the extension derivatives taken with respect to principal axes. If the three relations in Eq. 5 are added, and the equation

$$l^2 + m^2 + n^2 = 1$$

is used, it appears that the sum of the three extension derivatives in the arbitrary coordinate system is equal to the sum of the three derivatives in the principal system. This is to be expected, because the sum of these derivatives is simply div **V**, which is invariant to the choice of coordinate systems.

4. THE STRESSES AT A POINT

The principal stresses at a point are denoted by τ_1, τ_2, and τ_3 normal, respectively, to the x'-, y'-, and z'-planes. The plane BCD in Fig. 3 is

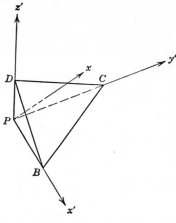

Fɪɢ. 3.

taken normal to the x-axis; according to the table (Eq. 3) the direction cosines of its normal are l_1, l_2, and l_3, and

$$A\tau_{xx} = \tau_1 l_1 A l_1 + \tau_2 l_2 A l_2 + \tau_3 l_3 A l_3$$

After analyzing in a similar way the normal stresses on planes normal to the y- and z-axes, we may write

$$\tau_{xx} = \tau_1 l_1{}^2 + \tau_2 l_2{}^2 + \tau_3 l_3{}^2$$
$$\tau_{yy} = \tau_1 m_1{}^2 + \tau_2 m_2{}^2 + \tau_3 m_3{}^2 \qquad (7)$$
$$\tau_{zz} = \tau_1 n_1{}^2 + \tau_2 n_2{}^2 + \tau_3 n_3{}^2$$

To find τ_{xy} we observe that the y-direction has, respectively, the direction cosines m_1, m_2, and m_3 with respect to the x'-, y'-, and z'-axes. Then,

$$A\tau_{xy} = \tau_1 l_1 A m_1 + \tau_2 l_2 A m_2 + \tau_3 l_3 A m_3$$

The other shearing stresses follow by analogy, so that

$$\tau_{yz} = \tau_1 m_1 n_1 + \tau_2 m_2 n_2 + \tau_3 m_3 n_3$$
$$\tau_{zx} = \tau_1 n_1 l_1 + \tau_2 n_2 l_2 + \tau_3 n_3 l_3 \qquad (8)$$
$$\tau_{xy} = \tau_1 l_1 m_1 + \tau_2 l_2 m_2 + \tau_3 l_3 m_3$$

For a fluid at rest or in uniform motion the three normal stresses in the principal directions τ_1, τ_2, and τ_3 all will have the same value. They will be equal to the static pressure in the fluid $-p$. If, however, the fluid has an arbitrary motion, the stresses τ_1, τ_2, and τ_3 will differ from the static pressure $-p$ by an amount dependent upon the extension derivatives $\partial u'/\partial x'$, $\partial v'/\partial y'$, and $\partial w'/\partial z'$. At this point it is necessary to make an assumption relating the normal stresses and the rates of extension. It is assumed that the stress and rates of extension are related in the following manner:*

$$\tau_1 = -p + \lambda \left(\frac{\partial u'}{\partial x'} + \frac{\partial v'}{\partial y'} + \frac{\partial w'}{\partial z'} \right) + 2\mu \frac{\partial u'}{\partial x'}$$

$$\tau_2 = -p + \lambda \left(\frac{\partial u'}{\partial x'} + \frac{\partial v'}{\partial y'} + \frac{\partial w'}{\partial z'} \right) + 2\mu \frac{\partial v'}{\partial y'} \qquad (9)$$

$$\tau_3 = -p + \lambda \left(\frac{\partial u'}{\partial x'} + \frac{\partial v'}{\partial y'} + \frac{\partial w'}{\partial z'} \right) + 2\mu \frac{\partial w'}{\partial z'}$$

λ is the coefficient of viscosity that relates normal stress to div $\mathbf{V}$. From the equation of continuity

$$\text{div } \mathbf{V} = -\frac{1}{\rho} \frac{\mathfrak{D}\rho}{\mathfrak{D}t} \qquad (10)$$

and therefore div $\mathbf{V}$ may be thought of as the time rate of change of specific volume of the fluid per unit specific volume. λ is of the nature of a *bulk modulus*. μ is the coefficient of viscosity that relates normal stress to the rates of extension. The factor 2 is inserted for convenience in the operations that follow.

To find the normal stresses in the original coordinate system, Eqs. 9 are substituted in Eqs. 7. The first of Eqs. 7 becomes

$$\tau_{xx} = (l_1{}^2 + l_2{}^2 + l_3{}^2)(-p + \lambda \text{ div } \mathbf{V})$$

$$+ 2\mu \left(l_1{}^2 \frac{\partial u'}{\partial x'} + l_2{}^2 \frac{\partial v'}{\partial y'} + l_3{}^2 \frac{\partial w'}{\partial z'} \right)$$

---

* In the theory of elasticity the assumption for the principal stresses τ_i ($i = 1, 2, 3$) are

$$\tau_i = \lambda^*(e'_1 + e'_2 + e'_3) + 2\mu^* e'_i$$

where λ^* is the bulk modulus, μ^* is the modulus of rigidity of the material, and e'_1, e'_2, and e'_3 are the extensions along the principal axes. The familiar quantities, Poisson's ratio and Young's modulus, are algebraic functions of λ^* and μ^*. See, for instance, S. Timoshenko and J. N. Goodier, *Theory of Elasticity*, McGraw-Hill, New York, 1951.

But

$$l_1{}^2 + l_2{}^2 + l_3{}^2 = 1$$

and from the first of Eqs. 5

$$\frac{\partial u}{\partial x} = l_1{}^2 \frac{\partial u'}{\partial x'} + l_2{}^2 \frac{\partial v'}{\partial y'} + l_3{}^2 \frac{\partial w'}{\partial z'}$$

Similar operations with the second and third of Eqs. 7 lead to the following result for the normal stresses:

$$\tau_{xx} = -p + \lambda \operatorname{div} \mathbf{V} + 2\mu \frac{\partial u}{\partial x}$$

$$\tau_{yy} = -p + \lambda \operatorname{div} \mathbf{V} + 2\mu \frac{\partial v}{\partial y} \qquad (11)$$

$$\tau_{zz} = -p + \lambda \operatorname{div} \mathbf{V} + 2\mu \frac{\partial w}{\partial z}$$

The shearing stresses in the original coordinate system are found by substituting Eqs. 9 into Eqs. 8. The first of Eqs. 8 becomes

$$\tau_{yz} = (m_1 n_1 + m_2 n_2 + m_3 n_3)(-p + \lambda \operatorname{div} \mathbf{V})$$

$$+ 2\mu \left(m_1 n_1 \frac{\partial u'}{\partial x'} + m_2 n_2 \frac{\partial v'}{\partial y'} + m_3 n_3 \frac{\partial w'}{\partial z'} \right)$$

But

$$m_1 n_1 + m_2 n_2 + m_3 n_3 = 0$$

and from the first of Eqs. 6

$$\mu \gamma_x = 2\mu \left(m_1 n_1 \frac{\partial u'}{\partial x'} + m_2 n_2 \frac{\partial v'}{\partial y'} + m_3 n_3 \frac{\partial w'}{\partial z'} \right)$$

Therefore,

$$\tau_{yz} = \mu \gamma_x$$

Similar operations with the second and third relations in Eqs. 8 lead to the following result for the shear stresses:

$$\tau_{yz} = \mu \gamma_x = \mu \left(\frac{\partial w}{\partial y} + \frac{\partial v}{\partial z} \right)$$

$$\tau_{zx} = \mu \gamma_y = \mu \left(\frac{\partial u}{\partial z} + \frac{\partial w}{\partial x} \right) \qquad (12$$

$$\tau_{xy} = \mu \gamma_z = \mu \left(\frac{\partial v}{\partial x} + \frac{\partial u}{\partial y} \right)$$

The viscosity coefficients λ and μ may be related in the following manner. We add Eqs. 11 and obtain

$$\tau_{xx} + \tau_{yy} + \tau_{zz} = -3p + (3\lambda + 2\mu)\ \text{div } \mathbf{V}$$

from the continuity equation

$$\text{div } \mathbf{V} = -\frac{1}{\rho}\frac{\mathfrak{D}\rho}{\mathfrak{D}t}$$

so that

$$\tau_{xx} + \tau_{yy} + \tau_{zz} = -3p - (3\lambda + 2\mu)\frac{1}{\rho}\frac{\mathfrak{D}\rho}{\mathfrak{D}t} \tag{13}$$

This equation states that the average of the normal stresses differs from the static pressure by a quantity proportional to the substantial derivative of the density. Therefore, if we make the usual assumption that the pressure is a function only of the density and not of the rate of change of the density as the element moves through the flow, the coefficient of the last term in Eq. 13 must vanish; that is,

$$\lambda = -\tfrac{2}{3}\mu \tag{14}$$

The validity of this assumption is discussed elsewhere.* For air, measurements indicate that $-\lambda$ is of the same order as μ. Therefore, the error involved in using Eq. 14 could be appreciable only if $\mathfrak{D}\rho/\mathfrak{D}t$ is very large. This could happen within a shock wave.

5. CONSERVATION OF MOMENTUM—NAVIER-STOKES EQUATIONS

Let a local region $\hat{R}$ in a fluid be bounded by a surface $\hat{S}$. According to the conservation of momentum principle (Section 3.3), the time rate of increase of momentum within $\hat{R}$ is equal to the rate at which momentum is flowing into $\hat{R}$ plus the forces acting on the fluid within $\hat{R}$. These forces are the force of gravity $\rho\mathbf{g}$ acting on each unit volume and the force applied to the fluid at the boundary by the surface stress $\boldsymbol{\tau}$. The mathematical expression for the conservation of momentum in the x-direction is

$$\frac{\partial}{\partial t}\iiint_{\hat{R}}\rho u\, d\hat{R} = -\iint_{\hat{S}}(\rho\mathbf{V}\cdot\mathbf{n})u\, d\hat{S} + \iiint_{\hat{R}}\rho\mathbf{g}\cdot\mathbf{i}\, d\hat{R} + \iint_{\hat{S}}\boldsymbol{\tau}\cdot\mathbf{i}\, d\hat{S} \tag{15}$$

where $\mathbf{n}$ is the unit vector normal to $\hat{S}$. $\boldsymbol{\tau}\cdot\mathbf{i}$ is given by the first of Eqs. 1. The surface integrals in Eq. 15 are transformed to volume integrals

---

* L. Tisza, "Supersonic Absorption and Stokes' Viscosity Relation," *Phys. Rev.*, Vol. 61, pp. 531–536, 1942; A. Kantrowitz, *Effects of Heat Capacity Lag in Gas Dynamics*, NACA ARR 4A22, 1944.

by means of the divergence theorem (Section 2.4), and after a slight rearrangement Eq. 15 becomes

$$\iiint_{\hat{R}} \left\{ \frac{\partial \rho u}{\partial t} + \text{div } \rho u \mathbf{V} - \rho \mathbf{g} \cdot \mathbf{i} - \text{div } (\mathbf{i}\tau_{xx} + \mathbf{j}\tau_{yx} + \mathbf{k}\tau_{zx}) \right\} d\hat{R} = 0 \quad (16)$$

Equation 16 is true for all regions no matter how small, and therefore the integrand must vanish. After expanding and regrouping the terms in the integrand of Eq. 16, we have

$$u \left\{ \rho \text{ div } \mathbf{V} + \frac{\mathfrak{D}\rho}{\mathfrak{D}t} \right\} + \rho \frac{\mathfrak{D}u}{\mathfrak{D}t} = \rho X + \frac{\partial \tau_{xx}}{\partial x} + \frac{\partial \tau_{yx}}{\partial y} + \frac{\partial \tau_{zx}}{\partial z} \quad (17)$$

where X is the force of gravity per unit mass. According to the equation of continuity, the first term in Eq. 17 must vanish. What remains is the statement of conservation of momentum in the x-direction. Conservation of momentum in the y- and z-directions are found in a similar fashion. The three equations may be written

$$\rho \frac{\mathfrak{D}u}{\mathfrak{D}t} = \rho X + \frac{\partial \tau_{xx}}{\partial x} + \frac{\partial \tau_{yx}}{\partial y} + \frac{\partial \tau_{zx}}{\partial z}$$

$$\rho \frac{\mathfrak{D}v}{\mathfrak{D}t} = \rho Y + \frac{\partial \tau_{xy}}{\partial x} + \frac{\partial \tau_{yy}}{\partial y} + \frac{\partial \tau_{zy}}{\partial z} \quad (18)$$

$$\rho \frac{\mathfrak{D}w}{\mathfrak{D}t} = \rho Z + \frac{\partial \tau_{xz}}{\partial x} + \frac{\partial \tau_{yz}}{\partial y} + \frac{\partial \tau_{zz}}{\partial z}$$

The above equations may be expressed in terms of the velocity derivatives by using Eqs. 11 and 12. We have, finally,

$$\rho \frac{\mathfrak{D}u}{\mathfrak{D}t} = \rho X - \frac{\partial p}{\partial x} + \frac{\partial}{\partial x} (\lambda \text{ div } \mathbf{V}) + \text{div} \left(\mu \frac{\partial \mathbf{V}}{\partial x} \right) + \text{div } (\mu \text{ grad } u)$$

$$\rho \frac{\mathfrak{D}v}{\mathfrak{D}t} = \rho Y - \frac{\partial p}{\partial y} + \frac{\partial}{\partial y} (\lambda \text{ div } \mathbf{V}) + \text{div} \left(\mu \frac{\partial \mathbf{V}}{\partial y} \right) + \text{div } (\mu \text{ grad } v) \quad (19)$$

$$\rho \frac{\mathfrak{D}w}{\mathfrak{D}t} = \rho Z - \frac{\partial p}{\partial z} + \frac{\partial}{\partial z} (\lambda \text{ div } \mathbf{V}) + \text{div} \left(\mu \frac{\partial \mathbf{V}}{\partial z} \right) + \text{div } (\mu \text{ grad } w)$$

For an incompressible fluid div $\mathbf{V} = 0$ everywhere and λ and μ are constant. Then Eqs. 19 reduce to

$$\rho \frac{\mathfrak{D}u}{\mathfrak{D}t} = \rho X - \frac{\partial p}{\partial x} + \mu \nabla^2 u$$

$$\rho \frac{\mathfrak{D}v}{\mathfrak{D}t} = \rho Y - \frac{\partial p}{\partial y} + \mu \nabla^2 v \tag{20}$$

$$\rho \frac{\mathfrak{D}w}{\mathfrak{D}t} = \rho Z - \frac{\partial p}{\partial z} + \mu \nabla^2 w$$

6. CONSERVATION OF ENERGY

The mathematical formulation of the conservation-of-energy principle follows the procedure of Section 8.3. Consider a local region $\hat{R}$ bounded by a surface $\hat{S}$. The time rate of increase of the energy per unit mass e within the region is equal to the time rate at which energy crosses the boundary $\hat{S}$ of the region, plus the rate at which heat is conducted into the region through $\hat{S}$, plus the time rate at which work is done on the fluid within $\hat{R}$ by the surface stresses $\boldsymbol{\tau}$. This may be written

$$\frac{\partial}{\partial t} \iiint_{\hat{R}} \rho e \, d\hat{R} = - \iint_{\hat{S}} (\rho \mathbf{V} \cdot \mathbf{n}) e \, d\hat{S} + \iint_{\hat{S}} k\mathbf{n} \cdot \nabla T \, d\hat{S} + \iint_{\hat{S}} \boldsymbol{\tau} \cdot \mathbf{V} \, d\hat{S} \tag{21}$$

$\mathbf{n} \cdot \nabla T$ in the integrand of the second integral on the right is the derivative of the temperature in a direction normal to $d\hat{S}$. k is the thermal conductivity. The second integral is an application of the heat conduction law given by Eq. 8 of Appendix A. The integrand of the third integral is the scalar product of a force per unit area and the velocity. This is the rate at which the surface stresses do work on the fluid within $\hat{R}$, and by means of Eqs. 1 it may be written

$$\boldsymbol{\tau} \cdot \mathbf{V} = \{u\mathbf{f}_1 + v\mathbf{f}_2 + w\mathbf{f}_3\} \cdot \mathbf{n} \tag{22}$$

With the help of Eq. 22, the three surface integrals of Eq. 21 may be converted to volume integrals by using the divergence theorem. After this transformation and rearrangement of terms, Eq. 21 becomes

$$\iiint_{\hat{R}} \left\{ \frac{\partial \rho e}{\partial t} + \operatorname{div} \rho e \mathbf{V} - \operatorname{div} k \nabla T - \operatorname{div} (u\mathbf{f}_1 + v\mathbf{f}_2 + w\mathbf{f}_3) \right\} d\hat{R} = 0 \tag{23}$$

Because Eq. 23 is true for all regions no matter how small, the integrand must vanish.   After expansion and rearrangement of terms, the integrand becomes

$$e\left(\frac{\mathfrak{D}\rho}{\mathfrak{D}t} + \rho \operatorname{div} \mathbf{V}\right) + \rho\frac{\mathfrak{D}e}{\mathfrak{D}t} - \operatorname{div} k\,\nabla T - \{u\,\nabla\!\cdot\!\mathbf{f}_1 + v\,\nabla\!\cdot\!\mathbf{f}_2 + w\,\nabla\!\cdot\!\mathbf{f}_3\}$$
$$- \{\mathbf{f}_1\!\cdot\!\nabla u + \mathbf{f}_2\!\cdot\!\nabla v + \mathbf{f}_3\!\cdot\!\nabla w\} = 0 \quad (24)$$

The first expression vanishes because of continuity of the flow.   The derivative of the second term is a substantial time rate of the total internal energy e which, according to the discussion of Section 8.4, is made up of three parts.*

$$e = \tilde{u} + \frac{V^2}{2} - \mathbf{g}\!\cdot\!\mathbf{r} \quad (25)$$

$\mathbf{r}$ is the displacement vector and $\mathbf{g}\!\cdot\!\mathbf{r}$ is the gravitational potential energy. $\tilde{u}$ and $\dfrac{V^2}{2}$ are the intrinsic energy and kinetic energy † respectively.   The term $u\,\nabla\!\cdot\!\mathbf{f}_1$ in the first bracket of Eq. 24 may be expanded in the form

$$u\left\{\frac{\partial \tau_{xx}}{\partial x} + \frac{\partial \tau_{yx}}{\partial y} + \frac{\partial \tau_{zx}}{\partial z}\right\}$$

From the first of Eqs. 18 this is equivalent to

$$\rho\frac{\mathfrak{D}}{\mathfrak{D}t}\left(\frac{u^2}{2}\right) - \rho u X$$

The terms $v\,\nabla\!\cdot\!\mathbf{f}_2$ and $w\,\nabla\!\cdot\!\mathbf{f}_3$ may be expanded in a similar manner. The sum becomes

$$u\,\nabla\!\cdot\!\mathbf{f}_1 + v\,\nabla\!\cdot\!\mathbf{f}_2 + w\,\nabla\!\cdot\!\mathbf{f}_3 = \rho\frac{\mathfrak{D}}{\mathfrak{D}t}\left(\frac{V^2}{2}\right) - \rho\mathbf{V}\!\cdot\!\mathbf{g} \quad (26)$$

If Eqs. 25 and 26 are substituted into Eq. 24, there results

$$\rho\frac{\mathfrak{D}\tilde{u}}{\mathfrak{D}t} - \operatorname{div} k\,\nabla T - \{\mathbf{f}_1\!\cdot\!\nabla u + \mathbf{f}_2\!\cdot\!\nabla v + \mathbf{f}_3\!\cdot\!\nabla w\} = 0 \quad (27)$$

The last bracket is expanded using Eqs. 1 and then the stresses are

---

* The x-component of the velocity and the intrinsic energy both have been given the symbol u in the preceding chapters.   To distinguish one from the other in this appendix, the symbol $\tilde{u}$ is adopted for intrinsic energy.

† $\mathbf{V}$ is the instantaneous velocity, and so the mean value of e would include the mean energy of turbulent fluctuations.

written in terms of strains with the help of Eqs. 11 and 12. If $\lambda = -\frac{2}{3}\mu$, Eq. 27 finally becomes

$$\rho\frac{\mathfrak{D}\tilde{u}}{\mathfrak{D}t} = \operatorname{div} k\,\nabla T - p\operatorname{div}\mathbf{V} + \Phi \tag{28}$$

where

$$\Phi = -\frac{2}{3}\mu(\operatorname{div}\mathbf{V})^2 + 2\mu\left\{\left(\frac{\partial u}{\partial x}\right)^2 + \left(\frac{\partial v}{\partial y}\right)^2 + \left(\frac{\partial w}{\partial z}\right)^2\right\}$$
$$+ \mu\{\gamma_x^2 + \gamma_y^2 + \gamma_z^2\} \tag{29}$$

Φ is the dissipation function and represents the time rate at which energy is being dissipated per unit volume through the action of viscosity.

If the specific heat c_v may be considered constant, then, following the discussion of Chapter 8, we may write

$$\frac{\mathfrak{D}\tilde{u}}{\mathfrak{D}t} = c_v\frac{\mathfrak{D}T}{\mathfrak{D}t}$$

Assuming the thermal conductivity k to be constant also, Eq. 28 specializes to

$$\rho c_v\frac{\mathfrak{D}T}{\mathfrak{D}t} = k\,\nabla^2 T - p\operatorname{div}\mathbf{V} + \Phi \tag{30}$$

For incompressible viscous flows, Eq. 30 may be further specialized to

$$\rho c_v\frac{\mathfrak{D}T}{\mathfrak{D}t} = k\,\nabla^2 T + \Phi \tag{31}$$

where the dissipation function Φ is given by Eq. 29 with the omission of the term containing div $\mathbf{V}$.

A more useful form of the equation than Eq. 28 may be derived as follows. From Section 8.3

$$\tilde{u} = c_p T - \frac{p}{\rho} = h - \frac{p}{\rho}$$

where h is the enthalpy. Differentiating,

$$\frac{\mathfrak{D}\tilde{u}}{\mathfrak{D}t} = \frac{\mathfrak{D}h}{\mathfrak{D}t} - \frac{1}{\rho}\frac{\mathfrak{D}p}{\mathfrak{D}t} + \frac{p}{\rho^2}\frac{\mathfrak{D}\rho}{\mathfrak{D}t}$$

and, using continuity,

$$\rho\frac{\mathfrak{D}\tilde{u}}{\mathfrak{D}t} = \rho\frac{\mathfrak{D}h}{\mathfrak{D}t} - \frac{\mathfrak{D}p}{\mathfrak{D}t} - p\operatorname{div}\mathbf{V} \tag{32}$$

After equating Eqs. 28 and 32, we get

$$\rho \frac{\mathfrak{D}h}{\mathfrak{D}t} - \frac{\mathfrak{D}p}{\mathfrak{D}t} = \text{div} \ (k \ \text{grad} \ T) + \Phi \tag{33}$$

7. BOUNDARY LAYER EQUATIONS

The application of a perfect-fluid analysis to problems in aerodynamics was justified when Prandtl in 1904 simplified the Navier-Stokes equations to the boundary layer equations by postulating that, for a fluid of small viscosity, such as air (or water), the viscosity will alter the flow around a streamline body only in the immediate vicinity of the surface. Outside of this layer, viscosity can be neglected and the flow is predicted to a high degree of accuracy by perfect-fluid analysis.

We consider a two-dimensional flow over a cylindrical surface with the coordinate system shown in Fig. 4. The curvature of the surface

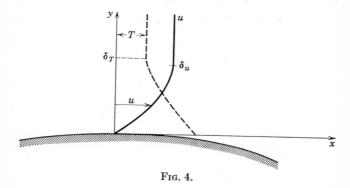

Fig. 4.

must not be too great, otherwise the centripetal terms must be included. The flow will be described by the first two momentum equations of Eqs. 19, the continuity equation, Eq. 10, and the energy equation, Eq. 33.

Simplification of these equations to obtain the boundary layer equations depends on an *order-of-magnitude* analysis based on Prandtl's hypothesis that the effects of viscosity are confined to a *thin* boundary layer.

There will, in general, be velocity and temperature boundary layers, whose respective thicknesses are designated δ_u and δ_T. To examine the relative magnitudes of δ_u and δ_T we recall that in Section 14.5 we showed that $\delta_u = \delta_T$ for a fluid with a Prandtl number of unity. Since for air the Prandtl number varies from about 0.68 to 0.75, the actual

δ_u and δ_T are not far from equal and for purposes of the order-of-magnitude analysis, we designate both thicknesses by δ.

We consider the dimensionless boundary layer thickness $\delta' = \delta/L$ where L is a characteristic length. The sequence of orders of magnitude from small to large will be δ'^2, δ', 1, $1/\delta'$, $1/\delta'^2$. If L is taken as the distance from the leading edge, δ' will in many practical cases be less than 10^{-2}.

In determining the orders of magnitude of the various terms in the equations we shall neglect those effects which will not change the orders of magnitude of the various terms. For instance, if we neglect variations in density, we are in effect postulating that $(1/\rho)\mathfrak{D}\rho/\mathfrak{D}t$ in Eq. 10 will be of order *not greater* than that of either of the other two terms in the equation, $\partial u/\partial x$ and $\partial v/\partial y$. We would then be justified in the hypothesis that $\partial u/\partial x$ and $\partial v/\partial y$ will be of the same order of magnitude in the boundary layer.* Also, since $\mu \frown T$, approximately, very large temperature gradients can be accommodated without changing the order of magnitude of the terms involving viscosity. With these simplifications, the first two of Eqs. 19, Eq. 10, and Eq. 33 become

$$\rho \frac{\mathfrak{D}u}{\mathfrak{D}t} = -\frac{\partial p}{\partial x} + \mu \nabla^2 u \tag{34}$$

$$\rho \frac{\mathfrak{D}v}{\mathfrak{D}t} = -\frac{\partial p}{\partial y} + \mu \nabla^2 v$$

$$\text{div } \mathbf{V} = 0$$

$$\rho c_p \frac{\mathfrak{D}T}{\mathfrak{D}t} - \frac{\mathfrak{D}p}{\mathfrak{D}t} = k \nabla^2 T + \Phi$$

where Φ is given by Eq. 29.

We now nondimensionalize these equations by introducing

$$u' = \frac{u}{V}, \quad v' = \frac{v}{V}, \quad x' = \frac{x}{L}, \quad y' = \frac{y}{L}$$

$$t' = \frac{tV}{L}, \quad p' = \frac{p}{\rho_1 V^2}, \quad \frac{VL}{\nu_1} = Re, \quad T' = \frac{T}{T_1}, \quad M_1 = \frac{V}{a_1} \tag{35}$$

* For flow through a normal shock, this hypothesis would be in error because there $\partial u/\partial x$ has very high values and $\partial v/\partial y = 0$.

where V and the subscript 1 refer to free-stream values. Equations 34 then become

$$\frac{\mathfrak{D}u'}{\mathfrak{D}t'} = -\frac{\partial p'}{\partial x'} + \frac{1}{Re} \nabla'^2 u'$$

$$\frac{\mathfrak{D}v'}{\mathfrak{D}t'} = -\frac{\partial p'}{\partial y'} + \frac{1}{Re} \nabla'^2 v' \qquad (36)$$

$$\text{div}' \ \mathbf{V} = 0$$

$$\frac{\mathfrak{D}T'}{\mathfrak{D}t'} - (\gamma - 1)M_1{}^2 \frac{\mathfrak{D}p'}{\mathfrak{D}t'} = \frac{1}{PrRe} \nabla'^2 T' + \frac{(\gamma - 1)M_1{}^2}{Re} \frac{\Phi'}{\mu_1}$$

We postulate that u', $\partial^n u'/\partial x'^n$, $\partial u'/\partial t'$, $\partial T'/\partial t'$ and $\partial^n T'/\partial x'^n$ are at most of order unity, that is,

$$u' = O(1), \quad \frac{\partial^n u'}{\partial x'^n} = O(1), \quad \frac{\partial u'}{\partial t'} = O(1)$$

$$\frac{\partial T'}{\partial t'} = O(1), \quad \frac{\partial^n T'}{\partial x'^n} = O(1) \qquad (37)$$

These relations should be interpreted in the sense that the equations we shall derive from them become inapplicable to problems in which the u' or T' derivatives approach a larger order of magnitude than that postulated. We shall see later that the restrictions are not serious.

Now, from the continuity equation and Eqs. 37

$$\frac{\partial u'}{\partial x'} = -\frac{\partial v'}{\partial y'} = O(1)$$

and then

$$v' = \int_0^{\delta'} \frac{\partial v'}{\partial y'} dy' \simeq \int_0^{\delta'} O(1) \, dy = O(\delta') \qquad (38)$$

In carrying out the integration we have in effect substituted a mean value for $\partial v'/\partial y'$. This is permissible since we are interested only in finding which terms in the equations of motion are small enough to neglect. Equations 37 imply that differentiation with respect to x' or t' does not change the order of magnitude of a quantity, whereas Eq. 38 implies that differentiation with respect to y' increases the order of magnitude by one; that is, $v' = O(\delta')$ and $\partial v'/\partial y' = O(1)$. Then,

$$\frac{\partial u'}{\partial y'} = O\left(\frac{1}{\delta'}\right), \quad \frac{\partial^2 u'}{\partial y'^2} = O\left(\frac{1}{\delta'^2}\right)$$

$$\frac{\partial v'}{\partial x'} = O(\delta'), \quad \frac{\partial^2 v'}{\partial x'^2} = O(\delta')$$

$$\frac{\partial v'}{\partial t'} = O(\delta'), \quad \frac{\partial^2 v'}{\partial y'^2} = O\left(\frac{1}{\delta'}\right) \tag{39}$$

$$\frac{\partial T'}{\partial y'} = O\left(\frac{1}{\delta'}\right), \quad \frac{\partial^2 T'}{\partial y'^2} = O\left(\frac{1}{\delta'^2}\right)$$

The above differentiation rule was derived by means of the equation of continuity and therefore does not apply to the pressure. However, since $v' \ll u'$, Euler's equation applied at the edge of the boundary layer and Eqs. 37 gives

$$\frac{\partial p'_1}{\partial x'} \simeq -U'_1 \frac{dU'_1}{dx'} = O(1)$$

Then, by the same reasoning that led to Eqs. 37 we may write

$$\frac{\partial p'}{\partial x'} = O(1) \tag{40}$$

Equation 40 should be interpreted as were Eqs. 37 above; it simply places an upper limit on the order of magnitude of $\partial p'/\partial x'$. Equations 36 are rewritten in expanded form and the orders of magnitude of the terms (Eqs. 37–40) inserted:

$$\overset{(1)}{\frac{\partial u'}{\partial t'}} + \overset{(1)\cdot(1)}{u'\frac{\partial u'}{\partial x'}} + \overset{(\delta')\cdot(1/\delta')}{v'\frac{\partial u'}{\partial y'}} = -\overset{(1)}{\frac{\partial p'}{\partial x'}} + \frac{1}{Re}\left(\overset{(?)}{\frac{\partial^2 u'}{\partial x'^2}} + \overset{(1/\delta'^2)}{\frac{\partial^2 u'}{\partial y'^2}}\right)$$

$$\overset{(\delta')}{\frac{\partial v'}{\partial t'}} + \overset{(1)\cdot(\delta')}{u'\frac{\partial v'}{\partial x'}} + \overset{(\delta')\cdot(1)}{v'\frac{\partial v'}{\partial y'}} = -\overset{(?)}{\frac{\partial p'}{\partial y'}} + \frac{1}{Re}\left(\overset{(?)}{\frac{\partial^2 v'}{\partial x'^2}} + \overset{(1/\delta')}{\frac{\partial^2 v'}{\partial y'^2}}\right) \tag{41}$$

$$\overset{(1)}{\frac{\partial T'}{\partial t'}} + \overset{(1)\cdot(1)}{u'\frac{\partial T'}{\partial x'}} + \overset{(\delta')\cdot(1/\delta')}{v'\frac{\partial T'}{\partial y'}} - (\gamma-1)M_1{}^2\left(\overset{(1)}{\frac{\partial p'}{\partial t'}} + \overset{(1)\cdot(1)}{u'\frac{\partial p'}{\partial x'}} + \overset{(\delta')\cdot(?)}{v'\frac{\partial p'}{\partial y'}}\right)$$

$$= \frac{1}{PrRe}\left(\overset{(?)}{\frac{\partial^2 T'}{\partial x'^2}} + \overset{(1/\delta'^2)}{\frac{\partial^2 T'}{\partial y'^2}}\right) + \frac{(\gamma-1)M_1{}^2}{Re}\overset{(1/\delta'^2)}{\frac{\Phi'}{\mu}}$$

Evaluating the first of these equations, we see (1) that $\partial^2 u'/\partial x'^2$ is negligible compared with $\partial^2 u'/\partial y'^2$; and (2) that, since all other terms are of order unity, the one involving the Reynolds number cannot be of larger order. Then, to make this term of order unity,

$$Re = O\left(\frac{1}{\delta'^2}\right) \tag{42}$$

This equation is substituted into the second of Eqs. 41, from which we see that all terms except $\partial p'/\partial y'$ are of order δ'. Therefore, this term cannot be of an order larger than δ', and we write

$$\frac{\partial p'}{\partial y'} = O(\delta') \tag{43}$$

In other words, *the pressure is approximately constant through the boundary layer.*

The following simplifications may be made in the third of Eqs. 41: by Eq. 43 we may neglect $v' \, \partial p'/\partial y'$; by reference to Eq. 29, all terms in Φ'/μ are of order unity except $(\partial u'/\partial y')^2$, which is of order $1/\delta'^2$.

It was pointed out earlier that whereas the above simplifications apply strictly to incompressible flow only, the orders of magnitudes of the terms are not changed by compressibility effects except perhaps at very high Mach numbers and temperature ratios.

Then, on the basis of the simplifications in Eqs. 41, Eqs. 19 reduce to the following for the compressible two-dimensional boundary layer.

$$\rho\left(\frac{\partial u}{\partial t} + u\frac{\partial u}{\partial x} + v\frac{\partial u}{\partial y}\right) = -\frac{\partial p}{\partial x} + \frac{\partial}{\partial y}\left(\mu\frac{\partial u}{\partial y}\right)$$

$$\rho c_p\left(\frac{\partial T}{\partial t} + u\frac{\partial T}{\partial x} + v\frac{\partial T}{\partial y}\right) - \frac{\partial p}{\partial t} - u\frac{\partial p}{\partial x} = \frac{\partial}{\partial y}\left(k\frac{\partial T}{\partial y}\right) + \mu\left(\frac{\partial u}{\partial y}\right)^2 \tag{44}$$

The boundary layer equations derived in an approximate way in Sections 12.5 and 14.2, respectively are identical to Eqs. 44. They were solved for various conditions in Chapters 13 and 14.

The above order-of-magnitude analysis is a more reliable way of obtaining the equations than that used in the text, because here we can assess the approximate magnitude of the terms neglected as well as the circumstances under which they might be large enough to affect the solution.

We can gain from the solution of Section 13.3 some appreciation of the amount by which a term must change in order to change its order of magnitude.   For instance, Eq. 15 of Chapter 13 gives

$$\frac{\delta}{x} = 5.2 \sqrt{\frac{\nu}{U_1 x}}$$

With $x = 1$ ft, $U_1 = 100$ ft/sec and $\nu = 0.0001567$ for air, $\delta = 6.2 \times 10^{-3}$ ft.   Then, for the conditions assumed, the ratio between successive orders of magnitude is $1/6.2 \times 10^{-3} = 160$.   With such a large ratio between successive orders of magnitude, we see that the approximations involved in using Eqs. 44 are not serious for a wide range of practical problems.

Aerodynamic Characteristics
of Wings

1. INTRODUCTION

The theory of wings has been discussed in many places throughout the text. For example, Chapters 5, 6, and 11 were concerned with the behavior of wings in a nonviscous fluid, whereas parts of Chapters 12 through 16 give the explanation for those characteristics of wings that depend upon viscosity. Though it has been convenient to separate viscous and nonviscous theory, the wing in flight exhibits characteristics that depend on both. Therefore, theoretical considerations from other chapters have been grouped together in this appendix and the behavior of wings as predicted by theory is compared with experiment.

The objective of theoretical and experimental investigations of airfoils is to design a shape that will have low drag over the high-speed range of the aircraft, a low moment coefficient about the aerodynamic center throughout all flight attitudes and speeds, a high maximum lift coefficient, and, if the high speed of the aircraft is in the high subsonic range, the airfoil should have a high Mach number of divergence.

Some of these objectives are reconcilable, and some tend to conflict with each other. As a result the optimum airfoil has different shapes in different speed ranges. The following paragraphs describe briefly the characteristics of a number of airfoil shapes in subsonic, transonic, and supersonic flow. Because the material in this chapter is illustrated mainly by NACA experimental data, the following short summary of the NACA airfoil numbering system is given.*

---

* A complete explanation of the NACA numbering system and the geometry and aerodynamic characteristics of NACA airfoil sections may be found in Ira H. Abbott and Albert E. von Doenhoff, *Theory of Wing Sections Including a Summary of Airfoil Data*, McGraw-Hill, New York, 1949.

Most of the NACA airfoils are classified among the three types, the four-digit, the five-digit, and the series 6 sections. The meanings of these designations are illustrated by the examples below.

NACA 4415
- 4—The maximum camber of the mean line is $0.04c$.
- 4—The position of the maximum camber is at $0.4c$.
- 15—The maximum thickness is $0.15c$.

NACA 23012
- 2—The maximum camber of the mean line is approximately $0.02c$. The design lift coefficient is 0.15 times the first digit for this series.
- 30—The position of the maximum camber is at $0.30/2 = 0.15c$.
- 12—The maximum thickness is $0.12c$.

NACA 65₃-421
- 6—Series designation.
- 5—The minimum pressure is at $0.5c$.
- 3—The drag coefficient is near its minimum value over a range of lift coefficients of 0.3 above and below the design lift coefficient.
- 4—The design lift coefficient is 0.4.
- 21—The maximum thickness is $0.21c$.

2. CHARACTERISTICS OF WING SECTIONS AT LOW SPEEDS

The NACA 4415 and 23012 are conventional airfoils and the NACA 65_3-421 is a low-drag or laminar flow airfoil section. The main difference between their aerodynamic characteristics stems from the fact that near the design lift coefficient the low-drag section has a laminar boundary layer over a considerable portion of its area. The late transition is accomplished by so designing the section that the pressure gradient is favorable over a large area; the discussion of Section 15.5 shows that a favorable pressure gradient tends to delay transition. The main geometrical difference that accounts for the change in the pressure distribution is seen from Figs. 1 and 3 to be a movement rearward of the point of maximum thickness.

Some of the characteristics of conventional sections are shown in Figs. 1 and 2. Figure 1 shows the distribution * of $(U/U_\infty)^2$, where U is the velocity at the edge of the boundary layer, over the NACA 4412

---

* By Bernoulli's equation this quantity is related to the pressure coefficient by the formula

$$\frac{p - p_\infty}{\frac{1}{2}\rho U_\infty{}^2} = 1 - \left(\frac{U}{U_\infty}\right)^2$$

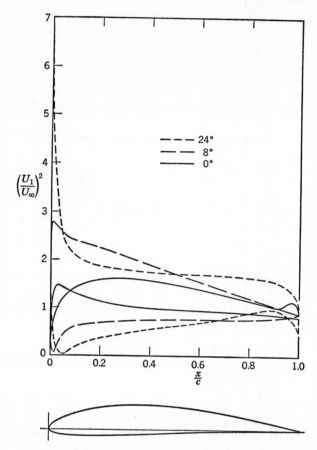

Fig. 1.   NACA measurements of the pressure distribution over the NACA 4415 airfoil at three angles of attack.

section at three angles of attack at a Reynolds number of 3×10^6.[*] At an angle of attack of 0° the pressure gradient is seen to be favorable approximately to the quarter chord point on the upper surface; at 8° the gradient is unfavorable over practically the entire surface.   At 24° the section is stalled and the strong change in the pressure distribution brings about a high form drag.   The minimum drag coefficient for this section is 0.0082 at a Reynolds number of 8×10^6 and an angle of attack near 0°; at 24° the drag coefficient is greater than 0.15.

* R. M. Pinkerton, *Calculated and Measured Pressure Distributions over the Midspan Section of the NACA 4412 Airfoil*, NACA TR 563, 1936.

Figure 2 shows the effect of Reynolds number on the minimum drag coefficient.* The broken lines correspond to the skin-friction coefficient for both sides of a flat plate for laminar, for turbulent, and for part laminar and part turbulent; a similar set of curves is shown in Fig. 4 of Chapter 16. The measured points indicate that at low Reynolds numbers an appreciable part of the boundary layer is laminar, whereas at high Reynolds numbers it is almost completely turbulent.

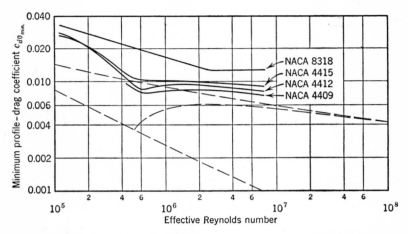

FIG. 2. NACA measured drag coefficients for various wing sections compared with theoretical skin friction for flat plate.

A rough indication of the form drag coefficient at high Reynolds numbers may be obtained by subtracting the values for the measured points from that given by the curve for a turbulent boundary layer on a flat plate. We see that the form drag increases with thickness and with camber.

Corresponding characteristics for low-drag sections are shown in Figs. 3 and 4. The pressure distribution for the NACA 65_3-018 section is shown in Fig. 3 for lift coefficients of 0 and 0.32.† In this range the

* Eastman N. Jacobs and Albert Sherman, *Airfoil Section Characteristics as Affected by Variations of the Reynolds Number*, NACA TR 586, 1936. The *effective Reynolds number* used in Figs. 2 and 14 was obtained by multiplying the actual Reynolds number by the ratio of the critical Reynolds number for a sphere in free air to that in the wind tunnel in which the airfoil tests were made. It was found that, for most of the conventional airfoil sections at high Reynolds numbers, fair agreement between tests in air streams of different turbulence levels could be obtained if the results were plotted against effective Reynolds number.

† I. H. Abbott, Albert E. von Doenhoff, and Louis S. Stivers, Jr., *Summary of Airfoil Data*, NACA Report 824, 1945.

pressure gradients over the upper and lower surfaces are favorable as far as $0.46c$. The subscript on the designation indicates that the drag coefficient is a minimum over a range of lift coefficients of 0.3 on either

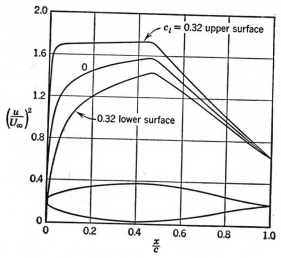

FIG. 3.   NACA 65_3-018 profile and calculated pressure distribution.

side of the design lift coefficient, which for this section is zero. Figure 4 from the same reference shows that this is actually the case. These curves show then that the drag coefficient is a minimum over the range of lift coefficients for which the pressure gradient is favorable up to

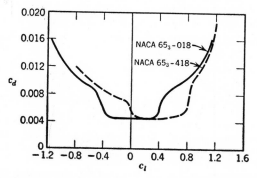

FIG. 4.   NACA measurements of drag coefficients for two low-drag sections.

$0.46c$. Tests show that when the drag coefficient curve for these airfoils has the characteristic dip shown in Fig. 4, the boundary layer is laminar until shortly behind the minimum pressure point. Under these circumstances, transition occurs as a result of local laminar separation (Section 15.5). The tests show that at the same Reynolds number the low-drag sections of Fig. 4 have a minimum drag coefficient of about 0.004, as compared with the value of 0.0082 given above for the 4412 section. The broken curve of Fig. 4 for the 65_3-418 section shows the dip in the drag coefficient curve centered about the new design lift coefficient of 0.4.

Figures 5 and 6 show further comparisons of characteristics of conventional and low-drag sections.* The minimum drag coefficient

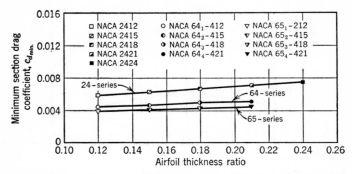

Fig. 5. NACA measurements of minimum drag coefficients for low-drag and conventional sections.

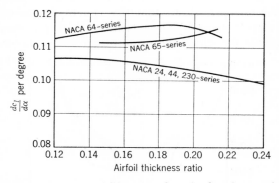

Fig. 6. NACA measurements of lift curve slope for low-drag and conventional sections.

versus thickness ratio for the 24, 64, and 65 series shows the expected decrease associated with increased area of laminar boundary layer for the low-drag sections. In Fig. 6 the slope of the lift coefficient per degree is plotted against the thickness ratio. We see that the curves

* *Ibid.*

for conventional sections lie below and that those for low-drag sections lie above the theoretical value of 0.11 (2π per radian). The theoretical value was derived for thin airfoils in Chapter 5; the more exact theory shows that the effect of thickness is to increase slightly the slope of the curve. At any rate, it appears that the Kutta condition, in which the flow at the trailing edge is parallel to the surface, is more nearly realized with the low-drag than with the conventional sections. Goldstein * reported on the design and tests of thick wing sections with a suction slot near the trailing edge. The theoretical and experimental values of the lift curve slope for a section with a maximum thickness of $0.3c$ were 0.138 and 0.128 respectively.

The measured characteristics of the low-drag sections given in Figs. 3 through 6 were obtained with extremely smooth models in a low-turbulence wind tunnel. The realization of the low drag of these sections in flight depends also on maintaining close tolerances and a smooth surface. Goldstein † described British experiences in attempting to obtain low drag for these sections on a production airplane in flight. It was found that the surface as received needed considerable reworking and that, even after reworking, the disturbance to the flow due to insects on the surface was sufficient to cause transition to occur well ahead of the minimum pressure point. Therefore, the general use of the series 6 sections on aircraft depends on the development of techniques for maintaining close tolerances and smooth surfaces on production airplanes. Another important factor affecting pressure distribution and therefore transition is the load on the wing and the resulting change in the section shape and waviness of the skin.

A comparison between tests and theory of the dependence of the moment coefficient about the aerodynamic center (c_{mac}) on the maximum mean camber and position of maximum mean camber for the five-digit sections is shown in Fig. 7.‡ The theoretical curve is worked out by the thin-airfoil theory of Chapter 5. The sections with the reflexed mean lines were calculated to give zero values of c_{mac}; the agreement with experiment for these sections as well as for those with simple camber is quite good.

Representative experimental values of those section characteristics that are mainly dependent on the potential flow have been tabulated in Fig. 8.§ It will be observed that the lift curve slope and position of

* Sydney Goldstein, "Low-Drag and Suction Airfoil," *J. Aero. Sci.*, Vol. 15, pp. 189–220, 1948.
† *Ibid.*
‡ Ira H. Abbott and A. E. von Doenhoff, *Theory of Wing Sections.*
§ Data taken from curves of NACA Report 824.

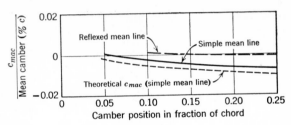

FIG. 7. NACA measurements of pitching moment coefficient compared with thin-airfoil theory.

the aerodynamic center are closely predicted by the thin-airfoil theory of Chapter 5; the variation of the angle of zero lift and the moment coefficient about the aerodynamic center with section shape also follow the predictions of thin-airfoil theory.

The above discussion summarizes the behavior of wing sections in low-speed flow when the wing is in an unstalled position, that is, when

REPRESENTATIVE EXPERIMENTAL VALUES OF THE SECTION
CHARACTERISTICS

Section Designation	$\dfrac{m_0}{2\pi}$	α_{L_0} (degrees)	a.c. $\dfrac{x}{c}$ aft of L.E.	c_{mac}
0009	0.995	0	0.25	0
2412	0.985	-1.9	0.243	-0.05
2415	0.97	-1.9	0.246	-0.05
2418	0.935	-1.85	0.242	-0.05
2421	0.925	-1.85	0.239	-0.045
2424	0.895	-1.8	0.228	-0.04
4412	0.985	-3.9	0.246	-0.095
23012	0.985	-1.2	0.241	-0.015
64_3-418	1.06	-2.9	0.271	-0.07
65_3-418	1.03	-2.5	0.266	-0.06
66_3-418	1.00	-2.5	0.264	-0.065

FIG. 8

the angle of attack is sufficiently low so that the boundary layer remains attached to the body. A discussion of the maximum lift coefficient and the character of the stall is reserved for later sections.

3. HIGH SUBSONIC AND TRANSONIC EFFECTS

It was pointed out in Chapter 11 that the critical Mach number, defined as the free-stream Mach number for which sonic velocity is reached locally at some point on the airfoil, is an important aerodynamic characteristic. The critical Mach numbers for a number of conventional and low-drag sections are shown in Fig. 9 plotted against the lift coefficient. They show in general that the critical Mach number

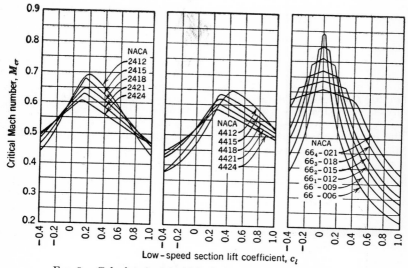

Fig. 9.   Calculated critical Mach numbers for NACA airfoils.

of a low-drag section is greater than that for a conventional section at the same lift coefficient; this behavior is associated with the fact that for the same lift coefficient the peak velocity tends to be higher on the conventional section.*

According to the Prandtl-Glauert rule given in Chapter 11, the slope of the lift-coefficient curve as a function of Mach number is given by the formula

$$\frac{dc_l}{d\alpha} = \frac{\left(\dfrac{dc_l}{d\alpha}\right)_0}{\sqrt{1 - M_\infty^2}}$$

where the subscript 0 refers to the Mach zero wing. As explained in Chapter 11, for the two-dimensional case, the Mach zero wing is simply

---

* As explained in Section 11.7, the lift decreases sharply when the *Mach number of divergence* is reached. The low-drag sections do not necessarily have higher *divergence* Mach numbers than the conventional sections.

the subsonic wing operating at zero Mach number.   The comparison
with NACA experiments on a 6-series wing section is shown in Fig. 10.

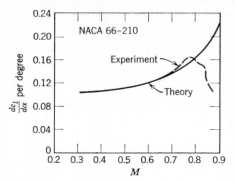

FIG. 10.   Comparison of theoretical and experimental values of the slope of the lift
curve for an NACA series 6 wing section of 10 per cent thickness ratio.

The experimental curve reaches a peak, then drops off rapidly as a
Mach number of unity is approached.

The drop in the lift curve slope is associated with the flow phenomena
in the transonic region, as shown schematically in Fig. 11.*   The

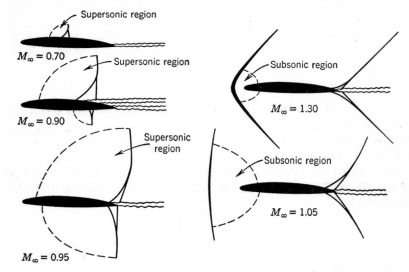

FIG. 11.   Flow patterns around an airfoil in transonic flow.   (Figure reproduced by
courtesy of NACA.)

* John V. Becker, *Characteristics of Wing Sections at Transonic Speeds*, NACA—
University Conference on Aerodynamics, pp. 127–150, Durand Reprinting Committee, Pasadena, Calif., 1948.

critical Mach number of the section is slightly less than 0.70, and the diagrams at the left show the increase in the area of the supersonic region and the growth and motion of the shock wave as the Mach number increases to 0.95. At $M_\infty = 0.90$, flow separation is caused by the propagation upstream, within the subsonic portion of the boundary layer, of the adverse pressure gradient associated with the main shock. As soon as the main flow becomes supersonic ($M_\infty = 1.05$), a detached shock is formed and the region downstream near the vertex of the shock is subsonic. Experimental data for a typical wing are shown in Fig. 12.*

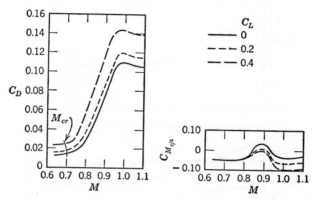

FIG. 12. NACA measurements of forces and moments on typical low-drag airfoil in transonic flow. Aspect ratio 6.4.

They show the increase in drag coefficient and moment coefficient associated with passage through the transonic range.

4. WINGS AT SUPERSONIC SPEEDS

From the linearized supersonic wing theory of Chapter 11, the aerodynamic characteristics of wings may be predicted. For the two-dimensional wing, Fig. 13 shows a comparison between the theoretical and experimental pressure distributions at a Mach number of 2.13 on a shape consisting of a flat lower surface and a circular arc upper surface with leading and trailing edge angles of 20°.† The agreement between the theoretical and experimental pressure distributions is not particularly good; it is shown in the reference that the second-order airfoil theory gives much better agreement, except near the trailing edge.

* John H. Weaver, "A Method of Wind Tunnel Testing through the Transonic Range," *J. Aero. Sci.*, Vol. 15, pp. 28–34, 1948.

† Antonio Ferri, *Experimental Results with Airfoils Tested in the High-Speed Tunnel at Guidonia*, NACA TM 946, 1940.

The flattening of the experimental curve in Fig. 13 on the upper surface near the trailing edge is shown by schlieren pictures to be associated with a shock wave at the point where the slight adverse pressure gradient begins. Flow separation occurs near this point. The separation occurs because the high pressure at the trailing edge on the lower surface propagates upstream on the upper surface through the

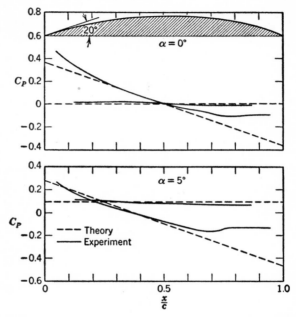

Fig. 13. Comparison between experimental and linearized theoretical pressure distribution on a supersonic airfoil. Experimental data by Ferri.

subsonic portion of the boundary layer. The separation point moves forward as the angle of attack increases, that is, as the difference in pressure across the trailing edge increases.

The theoretical and measured coefficients of lift, drag, and pitching moment are shown in Fig. 14. Since, according to the linearized theory, the angle of zero lift is zero, there is a displacement between the theoretical and experimental curves of lift coefficient; however, their slopes are in good agreement. The moment coefficient curves also agree closely as far as their slopes are concerned. The theoretical drag coefficient curve shown was obtained by adding 0.0080 to the calculated wave drag. This number was added to account approximately for the skin friction. The shapes of the two curves are in fair agreement, but they are displaced from each other along the abscissa by about the same amount as are the lift- and moment-coefficient curves.

For finite wings, the agreement between experiment and linearized theory is excellent in some cases and poor in others. The way in which the wing characteristics vary with aspect ratio and sweep is indicated in Figs. 15 to 19,[*] which show theoretical predictions as well as experimental results. Figures 15 and 16 show the influence of aspect ratio and sweep, respectively, on the lift curve slope. The agreement is, in

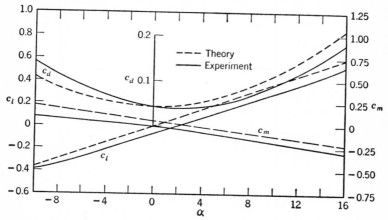

FIG. 14. Comparison between experimental and linearized theoretical values of the lift, drag, and moment coefficients versus angle of attack for a supersonic airfoil. Experimental data by Ferri.

general, very good. In the reference, it is stated that the exact agreement for aspect ratios between 2 and 6 in Fig. 15 is probably due to errors introduced by support interference and viscosity effects canceling each other.

Though the overall lifting characteristics show good agreement with experiment, the pressure distribution does not, as indicated by the moment curves of Figs. 17 and 18. The moments in these figures have been taken about the centroid of the wing area and the reference length is the mean aerodynamic chord. Therefore, the ordinate represents the position of the center of pressure ahead of the area centroid in fractions of the mean aerodynamic chord. Linear theory and shock-expansion calculations are indicated in Fig. 17 for an infinite aspect ratio wing. The extrapolation of the measured curve to infinite aspect

[*] Walter G. Vincenti, *Comparison Between Theory and Experiment for Wings at Supersonic Speeds*, NACA Report 1033, 1951.

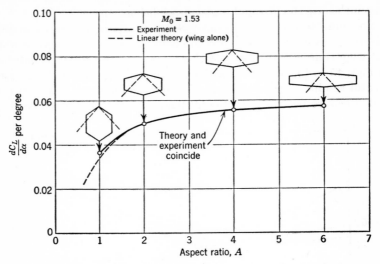

Fig. 15.   Effect of aspect ratio on lift curve slope.   (NACA.)

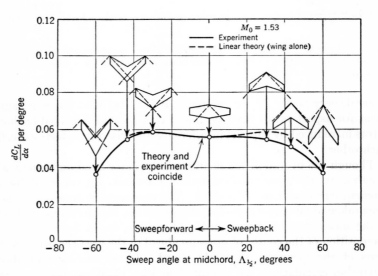

Fig. 16.   Effect of sweep on lift curve slope.   (NACA.)

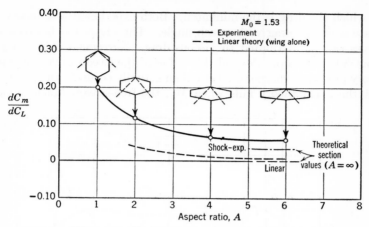

FIG. 17.   Effect of aspect ratio on moment curve slope.   (NACA.)

ratio and comparison with the infinite aspect ratio theoretical curves indicate that the discrepancy is due both to viscosity effects and to errors introduced by linearization. Figure 18 indicates that there is no agreement between experiment and the linear theory as far as the influence of sweep on center of pressure predictions is concerned.

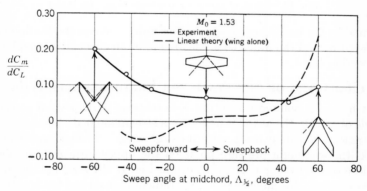

FIG. 18.   Effect of sweep on moment curve slope.   (NACA.)

The drag of a supersonic wing depends on both the pressure distribution of the potential flow and the skin friction and separation effects associated with the viscosity of the fluid. Measurements, of course, reflect the total drag. In Fig. 19 * is shown the drag coefficient versus sweep angle for the optimum lift coefficient, that is, the lift coefficient

* *Ibid.*

for which the drag is the minimum. Both experiment and theory indicate a rise in drag with sweep angle. The dispersion between the curves can be attributed to viscous drag. Agreement is good up to about 30° of sweep. Beyond this value of the sweep angle, the linear theory predicts a sharper drag rise than actually occurs. This indicates that the linear theory fails when M_n, the free-stream Mach number

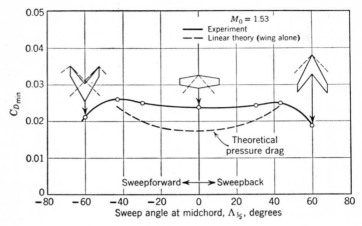

Fig. 19. Effect of sweep on minimum drag. (NACA.)

normal to the leading edge, approaches unity. When the leading edge is swept behind the Mach cone the drag falls, an effect that is explained in Section 11.14.

5. CHARACTER OF THE STALL FOR INCOMPRESSIBLE FLOW

It has been pointed out in previous sections that, beyond a certain angle of attack, the airfoil is no longer a streamline body but rather has the nature of a bluff body, with its large wake. At high angles of attack, the minimum pressure point on the upper surface of an airfoil is close to the leading edge, as shown in Fig. 1. Beyond the minimum pressure point, the adverse pressure gradient is steep and tends to cause flow separation. The nature of the stall—whether it is abrupt or gentle—depends on the nature of the boundary layer and its behavior in the presence of an adverse pressure gradient.

Ahead of the minimum pressure point, the large favorable pressure gradient tends to maintain a laminar boundary layer. Beyond the minimum pressure point, the steep adverse gradient has two effects: it tends to cause transition from laminar to turbulent flow in the boundary layer, and it tends to cause separation of the boundary layer from the airfoil. Whether transition or separation occurs first is largely dependent on the Reynolds number of the flow and on the magnitude of the pressure gradient. At low Reynolds number, laminar separation occurs, and the airfoil is stalled. As a result, the maximum lift coefficient has a low value, as shown in Fig. 20.* It will be observed that below a Reynolds number of 600,000, the 9 and 12 per cent thick airfoils have maximum lift coefficients of less than 0.9.

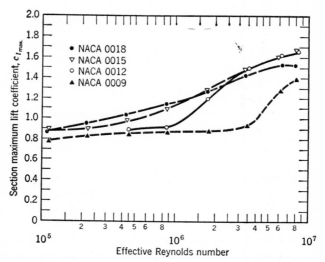

FIG. 20. Variation of maximum lift coefficient with Reynolds number. (NACA.)

At low Reynolds numbers, the separation is permanent, but, as the Reynolds number increases, there is an increasing tendency for the flow to rejoin the surface as a turbulent boundary layer, which is better able to resist separation than is the laminar layer (Section 16.10). As a result, the maximum lift coefficient increases with Reynolds number, as is shown in Fig. 20.

After the turbulent layer rejoins the surface the separation point moves rearward almost to the trailing edge. As the angle of attack is increased, the separation point moves forward and, as a result, the slope of the lift curve decreases as shown in Fig. 21. The stall may occur simply as a continuation of the bending of the lift curve, as shown in Fig. 21a. If so, the separated region at the trailing edge advances smoothly along the upper surface until the flow is entirely separated.

* Eastman N. Jacobs and Albert Sherman, *Airfoil Section Characteristics as Affected by Variations of the Reynolds Number*, NACA TR 586, 1936.

This type of stall, in which there is no sudden loss of lift, is considered to be the most desirable. In contrast, the abrupt stall, shown in Fig. 21b, occurs when the flow separates at the nose. Whether the stall is smooth or abrupt depends on whether it occurs by turbulent separation at the trailing edge or laminar separation at the nose. Still another type of stall is indicated by Fig. 21c. Here, there is an oscillation between nose stall and readherence of the turbulent layer that may result in a shuddering of the airfoil at the stall attitude.

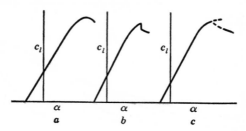

FIG. 21.   Lift coefficient versus angle of attack showing various types of stall.

At high Reynolds numbers, there is some evidence that transition to turbulence may occur before the laminar separation point. Under these conditions it is likely that nose stall does not occur, in which event the stall tends to occur as shown in Fig. 21a.

It must be remembered that the description in this section is based on the general trend of experimental evidence from tests on existing airfoils. Not all airfoils behave as described above. Furthermore, it is likely that further experimentation on other shapes will modify the description of the stall as presented here.

6. MAXIMUM LIFT COEFFICIENT

As was explained in the preceding section, the maximum lift coefficient is a function of the Reynolds number and, in general, for Reynolds numbers less than 10^7, $c_{l_{max}}$ increases with Re as shown in Fig. 20. The scale effect on $c_{l_{max}}$ is a complicated function of the thickness, camber, and leading-edge radius.* Figure 20 shows a tendency toward increasing $c_{l_{max}}$ with thickness. The larger nose radii associated with the thick airfoils generally produce a more gentle adverse pressure gradient with an attending increase in $c_{l_{max}}$. There is, of course, a limit to the increase with thickness. Maximum values appear to occur for values

---

* The values of $c_{l_{max}}$ for various airfoils and the corrections for scale effect may be found in the NACA literature. For example, see Eastman N. Jacobs and Albert Sherman, *op. cit.*

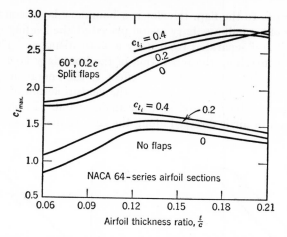

FIG. 22.   Maximum lift coefficient versus airfoil thickness for airfoils with and
without flaps.   (NACA.)

of the thickness ratio between 12 and 15 per cent for airfoils without
flaps and between 18 and 21 per cent for
airfoils with flaps. This is shown in
Fig. 22.[*]

The actual values of the maximum lift
coefficient for a series 6 airfoil with various combinations of flaps and slots are
shown in Fig. 23.[*]   It is seen to vary
between 1.5 for the plain airfoil to 3.7 for
the airfoil with a leading-edge slot and a
double-slotted flap.

As explained in Chapter 5, the flap
effectively increases the airfoil camber
without appreciably changing the stall
angle. Therefore, at the stall, an airfoil
with flap deflected will have an increment
of Δc_l due to camber over and above that
of the airfoil without flap deflected. In
effect, when a flap is deflected down, the
angle of zero lift is increased negatively,
as shown in Fig. 24.

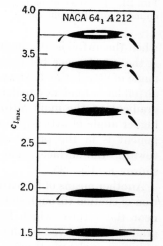

FIG. 23.   Maximum lift coefficient for an airfoil with
various high lift devices.
(NACA.)

[*] James C. Sivells, *Maximum-lift and Stalling Characteristics of Wings*, NACA—
University Conference on Aerodynamics, pp. 167–183, Durand Reprinting Committee, Pasadena, Calif., 1948.

In contrasts to the flap, the slot is a boundary layer control device. It consists of a small auxiliary airfoil placed at the leading edge of the main airfoil and separated from it by a short distance. The effect of the slot in controlling the separation of the boundary layer cannot be described simply. One prominent effect is the energizing of the retarded flow in the boundary layer by the venturi action of the channel between the auxiliary airfoil and the main airfoil. In effect, a high-speed stream of air is directed along the surface near the leading edge

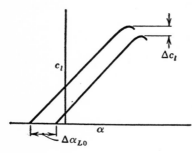

FIG. 24. Influence of flap deflection on maximum lift coefficient.

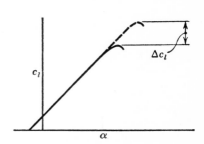

FIG. 25. Influence of slot on maximum lift coefficient.

when the airfoil is at a high angle of attack. Another important effect is the interference between the auxiliary and main airfoils. At high angle of attack the downward velocity component behind the auxiliary airfoil has a tendency to decrease the magnitude of the adverse pressure gradient on the main airfoil and thus tends to delay separation to a higher angle of attack. If separation does occur, the downward component is in the proper direction to deflect the main stream back towards the surface. The net effect on maximum lift coefficient is shown in Fig. 25.

Another means of increasing the maximum lift is through the application of suction through slots on the upper surface of the wing.* The air near the surface which has been retarded by the adverse pressure gradient is removed by the suction, and separation is therefore delayed to higher angles of attack. Indications are that the stall can be delayed to such a high angle of attack that the maximum lift coefficient has no practical significance.†

* The effect of suction in delaying transition is described in Section 15.5.

† Sydney Goldstein, "Low-Drag and Suction Airfoils," *J. Aero. Sci.*, Vol. **15**, pp. 189–220, 1948.

7. STALL OF FINITE WINGS

The stalling of any section of an unswept finite wing follows closely the description of the preceding paragraphs for two-dimensional wings. A finite wing is stalled when any section stalls. This definition is based on the practical upper limit of the usefulness of a wing in normal flight, for the stall tends to spread and a wing loses its reliability as a lifting surface when any section has stalled.

The maximum values of the sectional lift coefficients will vary along the span unless all sections are alike. For example, if the thickness,

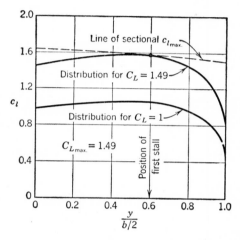

Fig. 26.   Maximum lift coefficient and position of first stall for a finite wing.

camber, or leading-edge radius of the sections changes along the span, so will the sectional values of $c_{l_{\max}}$. Further, if the wing is tapered, the various spanwise stations will be operating at different Reynolds numbers and the scale effect will cause a variation in $c_{l_{\max}}$. A method of predicting the maximum lift coefficient of the wing as a whole is shown in Fig. 26. The value of $c_{l_{\max}}$ for each section is taken from experimental data or is interpolated from experimental data. Then, for a given flight speed and altitude, the scale effect is determined and the corrected values of $c_{l_{\max}}$ are plotted versus span as shown by the dotted line on Fig. 26. The spanwise distribution of lift coefficient is then plotted for various values of the wing lift coefficient C_L.* The value

* Methods for finding the spanwise distribution of the sectional lift coefficient are given in Chapter 6.

of C_L for which the sectional lift coefficient curve is tangent to the $c_{l_{max}}$ curve is the maximum lift coefficient of the wing, $C_{L_{max}}$. The solid curve on Fig. 26 represents the sectional lift coefficient distribution when the wing is operating at $C_{L_{max}} = 1.49$. The position of the first stall is at about 60 per cent of the wing semispan outboard from the plane of symmetry.

The position of first stall is an important factor in wing design. For the sake of lateral control, it is desirable to have the stall occur first on the inboard portion of the wing rather than near the tips. In actual flight, interference and other effects that cannot be assessed theoretically play an important part in determining the position of first stall. Therefore, the method of predicting the position of first stall described above has value mostly in showing the influence of wing design on $C_{L_{max}}$ and on the position of first stall. From Fig. 26, it can be seen that the position of first stall can be greatly influenced by changing the shape of the line of sectional $c_{l_{max}}$. For example, increasing the wing taper will reduce $C_{L_{max}}$ in the tip region. If the wing thickness or camber is reduced at the tip, $c_{l_{max}}$ will generally be reduced in the tip region also. On the other hand, a leading-edge slot on the outboard position of the wing will greatly increase the sectional $c_{l_{max}}$ at the tip. The position of first stall can be influenced also by changing the shape of the lift distribution line. For example, if the wing is washed out at the tips, then, at a given angle of attack of the wing as a whole, the tips will be at a lower sectional angle of attack than the root. This fact will, of course, lower the sectional c_l curve in the tip region.

8. EFFECTS OF SWEEP

The discussion of Section 11.14 showed that for an infinite cylindrical body the Mach number normal to the cylinder $M_n = M_\infty \cos \sigma$, where σ is the angle of sweep measured from the coordinate normal to the flow, determines the characteristics for every section normal to the axis of the cylinder. Consequently, it should be possible, with a highly sweptback wing, to delay to high-flight Mach numbers the troublesome aerodynamic characteristics associated with transonic flow, as shown in Fig. 11. For instance, for a flight Mach number of 0.9 and a sweepback angle of 35°, the chordwise section characteristics would correspond to $M_n = 0.9 \cos 35° = 0.736$.

Some pressure distributions on a 9 per cent thick airfoil at angles of yaw of 0°, 20°, and 40° are shown in Fig. 27.* The normal Mach

---

* A. Lippisch and W. Beushausen, *Pressure Distribution Measurement at High Speed and Oblique Incidence of Flow*, Translation No. F-TS-634-EW, Air Matériel Command, 1946.

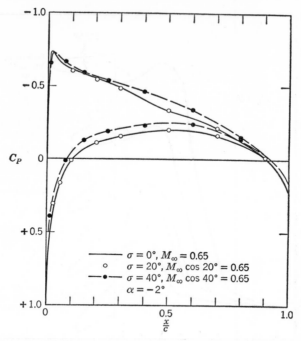

C_P

$\sigma = 0°, M_\infty = 0.65$
○ $\sigma = 20°, M_\infty \cos 20° = 0.65$
● $\sigma = 40°, M_\infty \cos 40° = 0.65$
$\alpha = -2°$

$\frac{x}{c}$

FIG. 27. Pressure distribution measurements, by Lippisch and Beushausen, over an airfoil at various angles of yaw.

number for the results shown in the figure was 0.65; the pressure coefficient C_p is given by

$$C_p = \frac{p - p_\infty}{\frac{1}{2}\rho_\infty U_\infty^2 \cos^2 \sigma}$$

It is seen that good agreement is obtained between the results at the different angles of yaw when the data are plotted according to the "cosine rule" of Section 11.14.

For wings of finite aspect ratio, the tip and root effects counteract to a certain extent the beneficial effects of sweep, but the gain is still appreciable. Figure 28 shows some wind-tunnel results obtained on wings with various angles of sweepback.* The series of wings tested is not quite consistent, since the airfoil section normal to the sweepback line should be kept constant; the results show, nevertheless, that the drag coefficient decreases markedly with sweepback in the transonic range.

* John H. Weaver, "A Method of Wind-Tunnel Testing through the Transonic Range."

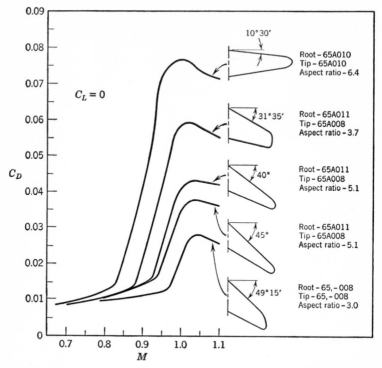

FIG. 28. Measurements by Weaver of the effect of sweepback angle on C_D versus M

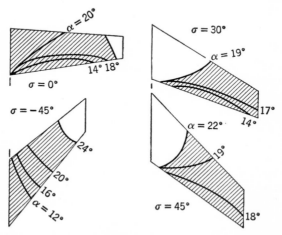

FIG. 29. Progression of the stall on wings with and without sweepback. The boundaries of the stalled regions at different angles of attack are designated. (NACA.)

The effect of sweepback in a viscous fluid and the resulting development of a three-dimensional laminar boundary layer is described in Section 13.8. The method of analysis depends on the fact that for an infinite swept cylinder in an incompressible fluid all derivatives with respect to the spanwise coordinate vanish and we can solve separately for the chordwise and spanwise components of velocity in the boundary layer. In a turbulent layer, on the other hand, the velocity fluctuations are three-dimensional (Chapter 16), and therefore the spanwise derivatives cannot be neglected. Nevertheless, experiments indicate that for wings of reasonable aspect ratio with sweepback angles up to 25° to 30°, the chordwise turbulent velocity profiles resemble strongly those on a two-dimensional surface.

Near the tips of a finite wing, especially at high angles of attack, we would expect strong departures from the above superposition principle. These departures are illustrated by the stalling characteristics shown in Fig. 29.*

* James C. Sivells, *Maximum-lift and Stalling Characteristics of Wings.*

Real Fluid Effects
in High-Speed Flight

1. INTRODUCTION—MODEL OF A GAS

In the body of this book the "real fluid effects" taken into account are compressibility, viscosity, and heat conduction, for gases at ordinary pressures and temperatures. At the high altitudes and high velocities reached by long-range ballistic missiles, additional effects associated with the high temperatures and low densities can appreciably alter the heat transfer and viscous drag. This appendix gives a brief account of these effects.*

The prospects for escape from, as well as for re-entry through, the atmosphere by various types of vehicles may be described in terms of the "flight corridor" † shown in Fig. 1. An aircraft or missile in continuous flight is confined to a corridor (Fig. 1), the width of which depends on the allowable skin temperature (lower boundary) and on the dynamic lift generated (upper boundary). The upper boundary of the corridor shown in Fig. 1 was calculated for a dynamic pressure $(\frac{1}{2}\rho V^2)$ of 80 lb/sq ft (except at low altitudes) on the assumption that for lower values the sum of the lift and centrifugal force will be less

---

* More complete accounts of the various topics may be found in the following books: Princeton Series, High Speed Aerodynamics and Jet Propulsion, Vol. I, *Thermodynamics and Physics of Matter*, edited by F. D. Rossini, 1955; and Vol. III, *Fundamentals of Gas Dynamics*, edited by H. W. Emmons, 1958. H. W. Liepmann and A. Roshko, *Elements of Gasdynamics*, John Wiley and Sons, New York, 1957; G. N. Patterson, *Molecular Flow of Gases*, John Wiley and Sons, New York, 1956; and A. B. Cambel and B. H. Jennings, *Gas Dynamics*, McGraw-Hill Book Co., New York, 1958. Wallace D. Hayes and Ronald F. Probstein, *Hypersonic Flow Theory*, Academic Press, New York, 1959.

† D. J. Masson and Carl Gazley, Jr., "Surface Protection and Cooling Systems for High-Speed Flight," *Aero. Eng. Review*, Vol. 15, No. 11, pp. 46–55, 1956.

than the weight of the aircraft. Although the placing of this upper boundary depends on the configuration of the aircraft, it is clear that there will be such a boundary associated with any given configuration. Typical flight paths are shown for a satellite, a glide missile, and for two ballistic missiles re-entering the atmosphere.

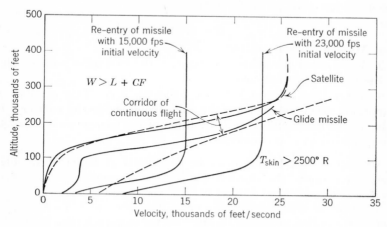

Fig. 1. Flight corridor for continuous flight. (Reproduced by courtesy of the Institute Aeronautical Sciences.)

The temperature of the air near the stagnation point is high enough to cause the properties of the air to depart appreciably from their values at ordinary temperatures. The succeeding sections are devoted to brief descriptions of the flow phenomena and air properties at high altitudes and high-stagnation temperatures.

2. FLOW REGIMES FOR REAL GASES AT ORDINARY TEMPERATURES

It will be shown in this section that under conditions of low density, high Mach number, and low Reynolds number, a flow field exhibits some deviations from that predicted by continuum considerations. These deviations are functions of the molecular properties and the scale factors which they define. These are:

1. Distance between molecules, d. If n is the number of molecules per unit volume

$$d \backsim n^{-\frac{1}{3}} \tag{1}$$

The numbers of molecules, or atoms, is governed by *Avogadro's law*, which states that equal volumes of different gases at the same pressure and temperature contain equal numbers of molecules, or atoms. Under standard conditions the number is 6.0247×10^{23} per mole.

2. Mean free path between collisions, λ.

3. Collision cross section of a molecule, S. The collision cross section of a molecule is related to the number of molecules per unit volume and the mean free path by the formula

$$S = 1/n\lambda \tag{2}$$

4. Mass of molecule, m.

5. Mean speed of random motion, c, is the root mean square value of the speed of the molecules.

6. Mean time interval between collisions, λ/c. This quantity is important when we calculate the time required for the collisions to bring about the equilibrium distribution of the energy among the degrees of freedom of the molecule.

Additional scale factors must be considered at temperatures high enough for appreciable dissociation, ionization, chemical reactions, or excitation of additional degrees of freedom (Section 4).

At ordinary temperatures the most important scale factors are λ and c. According to kinetic theory * the following relations hold

$$\lambda = 2\frac{\nu}{c} \tag{3}\dagger$$

$$c = \sqrt{\frac{8}{\pi}}\sqrt{\frac{p}{\rho}} \tag{4}$$

With the speed of sound $a = \sqrt{\gamma p/\rho}$, Eq. 4 becomes

$$c = \frac{1.59}{\sqrt{\gamma}}a \tag{5}$$

and Eq. 3 becomes

$$\lambda = 1.26\sqrt{\gamma}\frac{\nu}{a} \tag{6}$$

For purposes of determining the important similarity parameters, the factors 2, $1.59/\sqrt{\gamma}$, and $1.26\sqrt{\gamma}$ occurring in Eqs. 3, 5, and 6 may be taken as unity.

The physical properties governing the flow of an isothermal gas at ordinary temperatures are ρ, V, l, μ, a (or c), and λ, where l is a charac-

---

* S. Chapman, and T. G. Cowling, *The Mathematical Theory of Non-Uniform Gases.* Cambridge University Press, Cambridge, 1939.

† Equation 3 was derived in a rough way in Section 1.6.

teristic length and a or c are used interchangeably since they are, according to Eq. 5, nearly equal to each other. According to the II theorem of Appendix A, the six properties determine three independent dimensionless parameters. These are

$$\text{Knudsen number, } K = \frac{\lambda}{l}$$

$$\text{Mach number, } M = \frac{V}{a} = \frac{V}{c} \tag{7}$$

$$\text{Reynolds number, } Re = \frac{\rho V l}{\mu} = \frac{V l}{c\lambda}$$

If $K \ll 1$ the gas flows as a continuum, and if $M \ll 1$ compressibility effects are unimportant. Under these circumstances, the Reynolds number, which may be written as the ratio M/K, becomes the only similarity parameter governing the flow.

Tsien * defined the limits of the various regimes in fluid mechanics by a dimensional analysis as follows. Consider the ratio of mean free path to boundary layer thickness,

$$\frac{\lambda}{\delta} = \frac{\lambda}{l} \cdot \frac{l}{\delta} = \frac{l}{\delta} K = \frac{l}{\delta} \frac{M}{Re} \tag{8}$$

Because the boundary layer thickness varies inversely with Reynolds number, there will be a range of low Reynolds numbers for which δ is of the same order as l. Then

$$\frac{\lambda}{\delta} \simeq \frac{M}{Re} = K \text{ for low } Re \tag{9a}$$

For high Reynolds numbers we consider the flat plate flow, where $\delta \simeq x/\sqrt{Re}$ (see Section 13.3). With $l = x$, Eq. 8 becomes

$$\frac{\lambda}{\delta} \simeq \frac{M}{\sqrt{Re}} \text{ for high } Re \tag{9b}$$

Schaaf and Chambré † suggest on the basis of experimental results that $\lambda/\delta > 3$ is the criterion for free-molecule flow. Under these conditions,

* H. S. Tsien, "Superaerodynamics, Mechanics of Rarefied Gases," *J. Aero. Sci.*, Vol. 13, pp. 653–664, 1946.

† S. A. Schaaf and P. L. Chambré, "Flow of Rarefied Gases," Section H of Vol. III, *Fundamentals of Gas Dynamics*, edited by H. W. Emmons, Princeton Series, High Speed Aerodynamics and Jet Propulsion, Princeton University Press, Princeton, 1958.

few collisions occur between the molecules approaching and those leaving the body. Hence the concept of the gas as a fluid must be abandoned in the vicinity of $K = 3$. We may express this criterion in terms of altitude by writing

$$K = \frac{M}{Re} = \frac{\nu}{al}$$

With $l = 1$, the right side becomes a function of altitude. Tsien estimates that for $\lambda/\delta < 0.01$ the gas behaves as a fluid, thus defining the "gas dynamics" flow regime.

Schaaf and Chambré's representation of the flow regimes is reproduced in Fig. 2. Curves of constant altitude (for $l = 1$ ft) are drawn as well as those corresponding to different values of λ/δ, calculated from Eqs. 9. λ as a function of altitude is shown in Fig. 3.

As $M/\sqrt{Re}$ increases, we encounter first, "slip flow" effects, that is, a progressive relaxation of the no-slip condition at the surface over the estimated interval $0.01 < M/\sqrt{Re} < 0.1$. For still higher values of the parameter the flow field approaches "free-molecule" conditions in which the gas no longer has the properties of a fluid.

FREE-MOLECULE FLOW

Under conditions of very low density, the mean free path is so great that molecules which strike the surface and are reflected do not on the average collide with another molecule until they are *relatively* far from the surface.* Under these conditions the Navier-Stokes equations (Appendix B) are not valid; in fact, the flow properties even a short distance from the body are not appreciably affected by the presence of the body. It follows that the gradients existing in boundary layers and shock waves are so small as to make them practically indistinguishable.

The energy and momentum transferred by the molecules to the surface depend markedly on the character of the surface and on the material. The aerodynamic properties of various body shapes have been calculated.†

In Section 3 the application of the "free-molecule concept" to hypersonic flow past a blunt body is described.

SLIP FLOW

In this regime, comparisons between theory and experiment indicate that the Navier-Stokes equations (Appendix B) are approximately valid

---

* It should be emphasized that the fact that the mean free path is large does not imply that the molecules are "few and far between." In fact, at an altitude of 80 miles the mean free path is about one ft, while the molecular density is still 10^{13} molecules per cubic centimeter.

† Schaaf and Chambré, *loc. cit.*

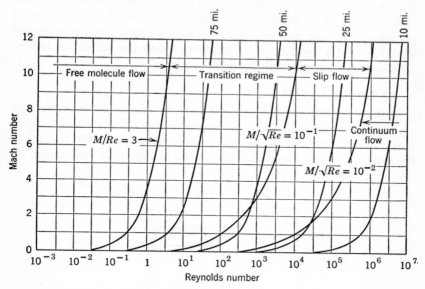

FIG. 2.   The regimes of gas dynamics.   (Courtesy of Princeton University Press.)

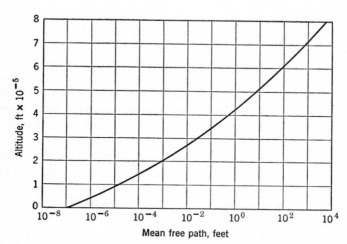

FIG. 3.   Mean molecular free path.   (Courtesy of Princeton University Press.)

382 APPENDIX D

if a slip at the surface is postulated. In other words, as $M/\sqrt{Re} \to 0.1$ there is a gradual relaxation of the "no-slip condition" at a solid boundary. In fact, these comparisons indicate that the Navier-Stokes equations are a good approximation well into the transition regime between free-molecule and slip flow.

3. NEWTONIAN FLOW

In the simple theory first brought forth by Isaac Newton, molecules are assumed to move in a straight line until they strike the body, where they immediately lose the component of their momentum normal to the surface; that is, the molecules, shown in Fig. 4, are unaffected by

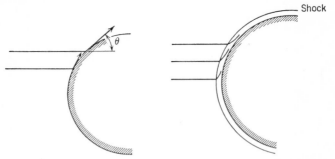

FIG. 4. Newtonian flow in free-molecule flow.   FIG. 5. Newtonian flow in high Mach number flow.

the body until they strike the surface. After striking the surface they flow along parallel to it. Such a process, called *Newtonian flow*, will be approached in free-molecule flow. Newtonian flow is also realized approximately near the nose of a body in high Mach number flow because the shock is so near the surface (Fig. 5) that the reaction to the change in flow direction is taken by the surface very near the point where the change occurs. This reaction determines the pressure at the point on the surface.

The pressure coefficient in Newtonian flow can be determined as follows. The molecules passing per second through unit area normal to the stream have a momentum component normal to the surface of $\rho_\infty V_\infty{}^2 \sin\theta$. They strike an area of the surface of $\csc\theta$. Then the change in momentum per second per unit surface area is $\rho_\infty V_\infty{}^2 \sin^2\theta$, and this expression represents the pressure on the surface. At high Mach numbers we may neglect p_∞ so that the pressure coefficient

$$C_p = \frac{p - p_\infty}{\frac{1}{2}\rho_\infty V_\infty{}^2} = 2\sin^2\theta$$

The value thus given is obviously wrong at the stagnation point, where

$C_{p_0} = (p_0 - p_\infty)/\frac{1}{2}\rho_\infty V_\infty^2$, will be a function of the Mach number. However, Lees * has shown that if the coefficient of $\sin^2 \theta$ is adjusted to give the correct value of C_p at the stagnation point, that is,

$$C_p = C_{p_0} \sin^2 \theta \qquad (10)$$

the agreement with experiment, as shown in Fig. 6, is good. We see

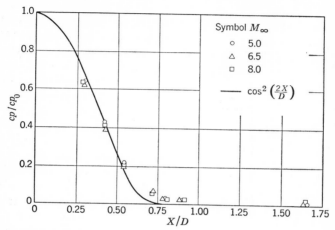

Fig. 6.   Distribution of pressure coefficient over hemisphere-cylinder at various Mach numbers. X is the distance from the stagnation point, D is the diameter of the body. $2X/D = \dfrac{\pi}{2} - \theta$. Winkler and Danberg, Inst. Aero. Sci., Preprint No. 622, 1956. (Reproduced by courtesy of Institute of Aeronautical Sciences.)

that, even at moderate Mach numbers, Eq. 10 holds over a considerable range in θ. Numerical solutions of the equations of motion † also show the accuracy and limitations of the method.

4. SOME ASPECTS OF HIGH TEMPERATURE FLOWS

The effects of changes in temperature will be discussed briefly in terms of an approximate model of a molecule. The composition of air at sea level, except for trace amounts, is (by volume)

Nitrogen N_2	78.09%
Oxygen O_2	20.95%
Argon A	0.93%
Carbon Dioxide CO_2	0.03%

* Lees, Lester, "Hypersonic Flow," *Proc. 5th Inter. Conference, R. A. S. -I. A. S.,* pp. 241–276, June 1955.

† Van Dyke, Milton D., "The Supersonic Blunt-Body Problems—Review and Extension," *J. Aero Space Sci.,* Vol. 25, No. 8, pp. 485–497, August 1958.

We see that over 99 per cent of air is made up of nitrogen N_2 and oxygen O_2. These are diatomic molecules of nearly the same molecular weight. Hence the model of an air molecule is taken as diatomic, as shown in Fig. 7.

An important molecule property is the number of "degrees of freedom." These are: three in translation, two in rotation (the moment of inertia for rotation about the axis connecting the atoms is zero), and two in vibration of the bond between the atoms. At ordinary temperatures, however, the bond is so stiff that the vibrational degrees of freedom are not excited. As the temperature increases, the excitation of the vibrational mode will absorb some energy, and at higher temperatures additional energy will be absorbed by oxygen dissociation, nitrogen dissociation, and finally by ionization of the atoms. These reactions will affect the composition of the air and its temperature at the stagnation point of a body to a greater and greater degree as the flight velocity increases. Figure

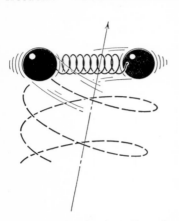

FIG. 7.   Model of a diatomic molecule.

8 * shows the approximate ranges of flight speeds over which the various reactions predominate as functions of the altitude.

According to kinetic theory the intrinsic energy of a gas is distributed equally among the "excited" degrees of freedom. Each degree possesses specific intrinsic energy $\frac{1}{2}RT$ so that at ordinary temperatures the intrinsic energy of air is $\tilde{u} = 5RT/2$. At temperatures at which the vibrational degrees are excited the intrinsic energy rises by RT to $7RT/2$.

When dissociation and ionization occur we would expect large increases in the specific heat because of the large amount of heat absorbed in the reactions. Figure 9 shows accordingly three peaks occurring respectively at the temperatures where (1) dissociation of oxygen, (2)

* C. Frederick Hansen and Steve P. Heims, *A Review of the Thermodynamic, Transport and Chemical Reaction Rate Properties of High-Temperature Air*, NACA TN 4359, 1958.   General references are: Gerhard Herzberg, *Molecular Spectra and Molecular Structure*, second edition, D. Van Nostrand Co., New York, 1950; Joseph O. Hirschfelder, Charles F. Curtiss, and R. Byron Bird, *Molecular Theory of Gases and Liquids*, John Wiley and Sons, New York, 1954; R. D. Present, *Kinetic Theory of Gases*, McGraw-Hill, New York, 1958.

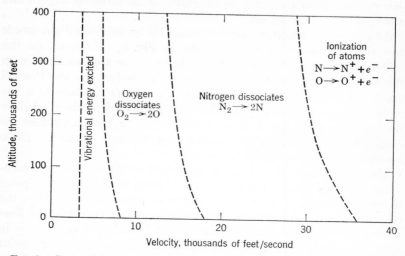

FIG. 8.   State of the air at the stagnation point of a body.   NACA TN 4359.

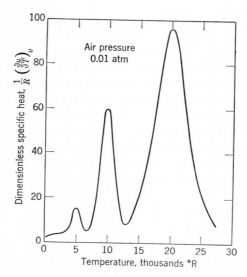

FIG. 9.   Specific heat of air as a function of temperature.   NACA TN 4359.

dissociation of nitrogen, and (3) ionization of the atoms of oxygen and nitrogen become important.

All of the gas properties vary between wide limits as the flight speeds and altitudes cover the ranges shown in Fig. 8. However, for the calculations of skin friction and heat transfer, we are concerned with three combinations of these properties: the product $\rho\mu$, the Prandtl number $c_p\mu/k$, and the Lewis number, $Le = c_p\rho D/k$, where D is the *atomic diffusion coefficient*.* The heat transfer also depends on whether the boundary layer flow is *frozen* or in *equilibrium*, and on whether the surface is *catalytic* to the dissociation-recombination reaction. These factors will be discussed briefly below.

The flow in the boundary layer is *frozen* if no dissociation or recombination takes place within the layer. From a physical standpoint the flow is frozen if the time taken for an atom to diffuse from the edge of the layer to the wall is small compared to a characteristic time of the reaction. On the other hand, the boundary layer flow is in *equilibrium* if the rate of reaction is high enough so that at every point the concentration of molecules and atoms is a function only of the temperature at that point.

The flow outside the boundary layer is presumed to be in equilibrium. If, for instance, the boundary layer is frozen, no dissociation or recombination will occur within the layer, but if the wall is cooler than the main flow, recombination will occur at the surface. The rate of recombination will be determined by the temperature and by whether the surface is catalytic, that is, whether the material of which the surface is composed tends to increase the rate of reaction.

The importance of the factor $\rho\mu$ is based on the observation that we can describe the theoretical and experimental results over a wide range of Mach and Reynolds numbers by simply using the relations for incompressible flow with values of ρ and μ at some reference temperature, or enthalpy.† For instance, consider the Blasius result for incompressible laminar flow over a flat plate (Eq. 19 of Chapter 13)

$$C_f\sqrt{Re} = \frac{\int_0^l \tau_w\, dx}{\frac{1}{2}\rho U_1^2 l} \sqrt{\frac{U_1 l\rho}{\mu}} = 1.328$$

---

* ρD has the same dimensions as μ, so Le is dimensionless and is interpreted as the ratio of the rate of transport of energy by atomic diffusion to that by conduction.

† M. W. Rubesin and J. A. Johnson, "A Critical Review of Skin Friction and Heat Transfer Solutions of the Laminar Boundary Layer on a Flat Plate," *Transactions*, A.S.M.E., Vol. 71, pp. 385–388, 1949; also E. R. G. Eckert, "Engineering Relations for Friction and Heat Transfer to Surfaces," *J. Aero. Sci.*, Vol. 22, No. 8, pp. 585–587, August 1955.

Now, for the compressible layer it is found that, to a good approximation,

$$\frac{\int_0^l \tau_w \, dx}{\frac{1}{2}\rho_* U_1^2 l} \sqrt{\frac{U_1 l \rho_*}{\mu_*}} = 1.328 \tag{11}$$

where ρ_* and $\bar{\mu}_*$ are the values corresponding to a reference temperature T_* given by

$$T^* = T_1 + 0.5(T_w - T_1) + 0.22(T_r - T_1) \tag{12}$$

where T_1, T_w, T_r refer, respectively, to the static temperature in the main stream, the temperature of the wall, and the recovery temperature (Section 14.6). Then, if we refer C_f and Re to free stream conditions, Eq. 11 may be written

$$C_f \sqrt{Re} = 1.328 \sqrt{\frac{\rho_* \mu_*}{\rho_1 \mu_1}} \tag{13}$$

The factor on the right side varies only slowly with temperature, so, as was seen in Fig. 6 of Chapter 14, $C_f \sqrt{Re}$ varies little over a wide range of Mach numbers.

Variation of the Prandtl number is small according to Table 5, page 435, over the temperature range 200° to 1800° R. Approximate calculations † indicate that the Prandtl number lies between 0.5 and 1.0 for temperatures up to at least 12,000° R.

For Lewis number, according to calculations by S. Penner, is also approximately constant up to around 12,000° R. Its value is estimated at 1.4.

The most serious aerodynamic heating problem occurs at the stagnation point of a body during re-entry to the atmosphere. One of the most accurate of the many investigations of the heat transfer rate to the body in the vicinity of the stagnation point of a body of revolution ‡ gives, for the equilibrium boundary layer,

$$\frac{Nu}{\sqrt{Re}} = 0.76 Pr^{0.4} \left(\frac{\rho_w \mu_w}{\mu_1 \rho_1}\right)^{0.1} \left[1 + (Le^{0.58} - 1) \frac{h_D}{h_s}\right] \tag{14}$$

In this result, the Prandtl number dependence is introduced from other investigations, Nu and Re use values of ρ, μ, and k for stagnation con-

† C. Frederick Hansen, "Note on the Prandtl number for Dissociated Air," *J. Aero. Sci.*, Vol. 20, No. 11, pp. 789–790, November 1953.

‡ J. A. Fay, and F. R. Riddell, "Theory of Stagnation Point Heat Transfer in Dissociated Air," *J. Aero. Sci*, Vol. 25, No. 2, pp. 73–85, February 1958.

ditions in the flow outside the boundary layer, h_s is the stagnation point enthalpy outside the boundary layer, and h_D is the product of the average atomic dissociation energy and the atom mass fraction in the flow outside the boundary layer.

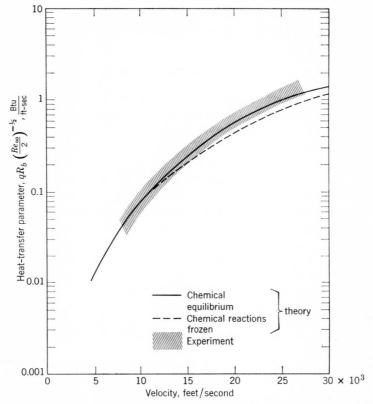

FIG. 10.   Heat transfer at the stagnation point of a blunt body.   Comparison between theory and experiment.   NACA TN 4229.

Equation 14, which applies to a blunt body of revolution, may be applied to a flat plate by dividing by $\sqrt{2}$. *   Thus we may compare this equation with Eq. 49 of Chapter 14.

Considering the fact that Eq. 49 of Chapter 14 is derived with constant ρ, μ, and k, and that Eq. 14 above incorporates the extreme variations of these quantities applicable to high rates of heat transfer

* See H. Schlichting, *Boundary Layer Theory*, translated by H. Kestin, p. 167, McGraw-Hill, New York, 1955.

in dissociated air, the agreement between them is remarkable. Since the Lewis number is near unity, Eq. 14 shows that its effect on heat transfer is quite small unless a large part of the air is dissociated.

Figure 10 is a comparison between some theoretical and experimental values of the heat transfer rate * at the stagnation point. Though the difference between the results for frozen and equilibrium boundary layer flow is small, the experimental results seem to indicate that the actual flow is near equilibrium.

The heat transfer over the entire nose of a blunt body also shows excellent agreement between theory and experiment.†

A new phenomenon enters as soon as appreciable ionization occurs. An electromagnetic body force, analogous to the gravity force treated briefly in Chapter 3, acts on the fluid particles and must be taken into account when a flow is analyzed. The flow field can be further influenced by the introduction of an external magnetic field. The study of flows of a conducting gas under the action of a magnetic field is termed *magneto-aerodynamics*.‡ Some theoretical investigations indicate possibilities of reducing skin friction and heat transfer to a surface and of delaying boundary layer transition by imposing a magnetic field on an ionized flow.

* A. J. Eggers, Jr., C. Frederick Hansen, and Bernard E. Cunningham, *Stagnation Point Heat Transfer to Blunt Shapes in Hypersonic Flight, Including Effects of Yaw*, NACA TN 4229, 1958.

† Lester Lees, "Laminar Heat Transfer over Blunt Nosed Bodies at Hypersonic Flight Speeds," *Jet Propulsion*, Vol. 26, No. 4, pp. 259–269, April 1956.

‡ T. G. Cowling, *Magnetohydrodynamics*, Interscience Publishers, New York, 1957; see also *Conference on Extremely High Temperatures*, edited by Heinz Fischer and Lawrence C. Mansur, John Wiley and Sons, New York, 1958. E. L. Ressler, Jr., and W. R. Sears, "The Prospects of Magneto-Aerodynamics," *J. Aero. Sci.*, Vol. 25, No. 4, pp. 235–246, 1958; Vernon J. Rossow, *Boundary Layer Stability Diagrams for Electrically Conducting Fluids in the Presence of a Magnetic Field*, NACA TN 4284, 1958; Rudolph C. Meyer, "On Reducing Aerodynamic Heat Transfer Rates by Magnetohydrodynamic Techniques," *J. Aero Space Sci.*, Vol. 25, No. 9, p. 561, 1958.

Problems

Section 2.2

1. A two-dimensional pressure field is defined by the expression

$$P = x^2 y + y^2$$

Find the derivative of P in the direction of a line that makes an angle of $45°$ with the positive x-axis. What is the value of this derivative at the point $(3, 2)$?

2. For the pressure field described in Problem 1, what is the derivative at the point $(3, 2)$ in the direction of the curve

$$3y^2 - 4x = 0$$

What is the derivative in the direction for which the derivative is the maximum? What is direction for which the derivative is the maximum?

3. A temperature field is described by the equation

$$T = x^3 y$$

What is the magnitude and direction of the gradient of the temperature at the point $(1, 2)$? Write the equations of the gradient line and isotherm passing through the point $(1, 2)$.

Section 2.3

1. A two-dimensional velocity field is described in terms of its cartesian components

$$u = 2xy^2$$

$$v = 2x^2 y$$

Write the equation of the streamline passing through the point $(1, 7)$.

2. The absolute value of the velocity is constant along circles that are concentric with the origin. The streamlines are straight lines passing through the origin. In functional form, write the cartesian components of the velocity u and v and write the polar components u_r and u_θ.

3. Expand the function $y \cos x$ in a Taylor series about the point $(0, 0)$. Show that for small values of x and y

$$y \cos x \simeq y - \tfrac{1}{2} x^2 y$$

391

4. The absolute value of the velocity and the equation of the streamlines in a velocity field are given by

$$|\mathbf{V}| = \sqrt{2y^2 + x^2 + 2xy}$$

$$y^2 + 2xy = \text{constant}$$

Find u and v.

5. In the flow field of Problem 4, in what direction is the rate of change of u the maximum? Does it make sense to speak of the *gradient* of u? If so, what is its value?

Section 2.4

1. In two-dimensional polar coordinates, show that the divergence of the velocity vector $\mathbf{V}$ is

$$\text{div } \mathbf{V} = \frac{\partial u_r}{\partial r} + \frac{1}{r}\left\{u_r + \frac{\partial u_\theta}{\partial \theta}\right\}$$

Hint: Apply Eq. 5 to a region formed by two circular arcs and two radius vectors as shown.

PROB. 2.4.1

2. The streamlines of a two-dimensional velocity field are straight lines through the origin described by the equation

$$y = mx$$

The absolute value of the velocity varies according to the law

$$|\mathbf{V}| = \frac{m_1}{2\pi}\frac{1}{r}$$

Find the value of div $\mathbf{V}$ at the point $(1, 2)$ using both cartesian and polar coordinates. In general, what can be said about the div $\mathbf{V}$ at all points in the field? What can be said about div $\mathbf{V}$ at the point $(0, 0)$?

Section 2.5

1. Which of the following flows satisfy *conservation of mass* for the flow of an incompressible fluid?

(a) $u = -x^3 \sin y$ (b) $u = x^3 \sin y$

     $v = -3x^2 \cos y$ $v = -3x^2 \cos y$

(c) $u_r = 2r \sin \theta \cos \theta$ (d) $|\mathbf{V}| = \dfrac{k}{r^2}$

     $u_\theta = -2r \sin^2 \theta$ $x^2 + y^2 = c$ (streamlines)

2. For a certain flow field, the absolute value of the velocity and the equation of the streamlines are given by

$$|\mathbf{V}| = f(r)$$

$$y = mx$$

Show that $f(r)$ must have the form for source flow (and no other) if the pattern is to satisfy *conservation of mass* for the flow of an incompressible fluid.

Hint: Apply the condition div $\mathbf{V} = 0$ and solve the resulting differential equation for $f(r)$.

3. A flow field is described by

$$|\mathbf{V}| = f(r)$$

$$x^2 + y^2 = c$$

What form must $f(r)$ have if *continuity* is to be satisfied? Explain your result.

4. A flow field is described by

$$|\mathbf{V}| = f(r, \theta)$$

$$x^2 + y^2 = c$$

Can this field ever satisfy *continuity*? Explain your answer.

Section 2.6

1. The stream function of a two-dimensional incompressible flow is given by the equation

$$\psi = x^2 + 2y$$

(a) What is the magnitude and direction of the velocity at the point (2, 3)?

(b) What is the magnitude of the velocity component at the point (2, 3) that makes a direction of 30° with the positive x-axis?

2. The existence of a stream function depends upon the flow satisfying *continuity*. Therefore, any velocity field derived from a stream function automatically satisfies *continuity*. Prove the latter statement.

3. An incompressible two-dimensional flow is described by the stream function

$$\psi = x^2 + y^3$$

Write the equation of the streamline that passes through the point (2, 1). Show that the magnitude of $\mathbf{V}$ at (2, 1) is equal to the absolute value of grad ψ at (2, 1). Show that the direction of the velocity is perpendicular to the direction of grad ψ.

4. A two-dimensional incompressible flow is described by the velocity components

$$u = 2x$$

$$v = -6x - 2y$$

Does a stream function exist? If so, find it.

Section 2.7

1. The streamlines of a certain flow pattern are concentric circles about the origin, and the absolute value of the velocity varies according to the law

$$|\mathbf{V}| = kr^n$$

Find the mean rotation ω at any point r as a function of the exponent n. For what value of n does ω vanish?

2. In Problem 1, what is the value of the strain γ for the value of n which makes the rotation vanish? What is the value of γ for $n = 1$?

Section 2.8

1. In two-dimensional polar coordinates, show that the curl of the velocity vector $\mathbf{V}$ is

$$\text{curl } \mathbf{V} = \frac{\partial u_\theta}{\partial r} + \frac{1}{r} \left\{ u_\theta - \frac{\partial u_r}{\partial \theta} \right\}$$

Hint: Apply Eq. 19 to a region formed by two circular arcs and two radius vectors.

2. For the flow of Problem 2.7.1, find the circulation about the origin when $n = 1$. For the path of integration, use a circle of radius 3 with center at the origin. What is the circulation when the path has a radius of 4?

3. The stream function of a two-dimensional incompressible flow is given by

$$\psi = \frac{\Gamma}{2\pi} \log r$$

Find the circulation about a path enclosing the origin. For the path of integration use a circle of radius 3 with center at the origin. How does the circulation depend upon the radius?

Section 2.9

1. Using two-dimensional polar coordinates, find the absolute value of the velocity as a function of r for an irrotational field that has streamlines that are concentric circles about the origin. Is this the only possible irrotational field with concentric circular streamlines?

2. Does the irrotational field of Problem 1 satisfy *continuity?*

Section 2.10

1. Find the integral along the path $\mathbf{s}$ between the points $(0, 0)$ and $(1, 2)$ of the component of $\mathbf{V}$ in the direction of $\mathbf{s}$ for the following three cases:

(a) $\mathbf{s}$ a straight line.
(b) $\mathbf{s}$ a parabola with vertex at the origin and opening to the right.
(c) $\mathbf{s}$ a portion of the x-axis and a straight line perpendicular to it.

The components of $\mathbf{V}$ are given by the expressions

$$u = x^2 + y^2$$

$$v = 2xy^2$$

2. The absolute value of the velocity and the equation of the streamlines in a two-dimensional velocity field are given by the expressions

$$|\mathbf{V}| = \sqrt{5y^2 + x^2 + 4xy}$$

$$xy + y^2 = c$$

Find the integral over the surface shown of the normal component of curl **V** by two methods.

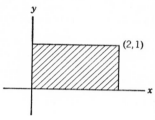

PROB. 2.10.2

Section 2.11

1. Find the velocity potential of the velocity field whose components are given by

$$u = 2xy$$

$$v = x^2 + 1$$

2. Does a potential exist for the field described by

$$u = 3xy$$

$$v = x^2 + 1$$

Show that every field which is derived from a potential is necessarily irrotational.

3. A two-dimensional velocity field is described in the following manner:

$$u = x^2 - y^2 + x$$

$$v = -(2xy + y)$$

Show that this field satisfies *continuity* and is also irrotational. Find the potential. Find the line integral of **V**·*d*s along a straight line connecting (0, 0) and (2, 3) by reducing the line integral to a definite integral. Check your answer by computing the value of the line integral directly from the potential.

4. A two-dimensional potential field is described in the following manner:

$$\varphi = \frac{x^3}{3} - x^2 - xy^2 + y^2$$

Find the velocity component in the direction of the path $x^2y = -4$ at the point (2, −1).

5. Prove that the work involved in moving a mass between any two points in the earth's gravitational field is independent of the path.

6. If a velocity field has a potential, are we guaranteed that the conservation of mass principle is satisfied?

7. Show that the two fields described below are identical.

$$\psi = 2xy + y$$

$$\varphi = x^2 + x - y^2$$

Section 2.12

1. Find the velocity induced at the center of a circular vortex filament of strength Γ and radius A.

2. A rectangular vortex filament of strength 12.6×10^4 ft^2/sec is shown in the figure below. What is the velocity in magnitude and direction induced at point A

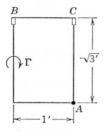

PROB. 2.12.2

by 0.01 ft of filament at point B? What is the velocity induced at point A by 0.01 ft of filament at C?

Section 3.1

1. Find the resultant acceleration of a fluid particle as it moves through the point $(1, 2)$ in the steady two-dimensional field described by

$$|\mathbf{V}| = \sqrt{5y^2 + x^2 + 4xy}$$

$$xy + y^2 = k \text{ (streamlines)}$$

2. Find the acceleration of a fluid particle whose motion is described by

$$|\mathbf{V}| = \omega r$$

$$x^2 + y^2 = k$$

Compare your answer to the centripetal acceleration of a rigid particle moving along a curved path.

3. Find the acceleration in the x-direction of a fluid particle in a velocity field described in the following manner:

$$u = xy + 20t$$

$$v = x - \tfrac{1}{2}y^2 + t^2$$

4. Find the acceleration at a point 2 ft from the center of a source flow that has a strength of 62.3 ft^3/sec.

5. The velocity potential of a steady flow field is given by the expression

$$\varphi = 2xy + y$$

The temperature is the following function of the field coordinates:

$$T = x^2 + 3xy + 2$$

Find the time rate of change of temperature of a fluid element as it passes through the point $(2, 3)$.

Section 3.2

1. Find the pressure gradient (magnitude and direction) for vortex flow as a function of the distance from the center of the vortex. Neglect gravity.

2. A two-dimensional incompressible flow is described by the stream function

$$\psi = x^2 - y^2$$

Find the pressure gradient in magnitude and direction at the point $(1, 2)$. Assume sea level air.

Section 3.3

1. Derive the momentum theorem (Eqs. 14 of Section 3.3) for the case of a non-viscous fluid by integrating Euler's equation throughout a fixed region $\hat{R}$. Note that the equation of continuity must be satisfied at all times.

Hint: Apply the divergence theorem to convert volume integrals to surface integrals where necessary.

2. Air at a pressure of 2200 lb/ft^2 and a velocity of 100 ft/sec enters the tank shown in the figure below at A and B. The entrance areas are each 1 in.^{2} The air

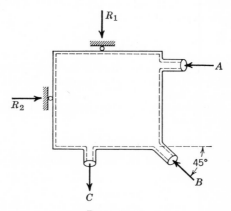

PROB. 3.3.2.

discharges at atmospheric pressure at C through an area of 2 in.^{2} Assuming steady conditions at the entrances and exit, find the reactions at 1 and 2. The density of the air may be considered to have the sea level value everywhere.

Section 3.5

1. An airfoil is traveling through sea level air at a speed of 100 mph. What is the pressure at a stagnation point? (A stagnation point is a position on the airfoil where the velocity is zero.) What is the static pressure at a point on the airfoil where the velocity of the air relative to the airfoil is 200 fps?

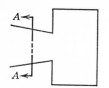

2. A fluid is rotating as a solid body according to the law

$$|\mathbf{V}| = \omega r$$

Find the difference in total head along streamlines whose radii are 5 ft and 5.1 ft, respectively. The density of the fluid is ρ.

PROB. 3.5.3

3. Sea level air is being drawn into a vacuum tank through a duct as shown in the accompanying diagram. The static pressure at station AA in the duct measures 13.5 lb/in.² What is the velocity at station AA? Assume an incompressible nonviscous flow.

4. In Fig. a below, sea level air is being drawn into a vacuum tank through a duct. In Fig. b, the airfoil is moving through sea level air at a speed of 100 ft/sec.

(a)   (b)

PROB. 3.5.4

In both cases, the relative velocity between airfoil and air at point A is 200 ft/sec. Find the *static* pressure at point A in each case.

Section 4.1

1. Let $G(x, y)$ be a solution of the two-dimensional Laplace equation. Show that $G(x, y)$ may represent the velocity potential or stream function of a two-dimensional, nonviscous, incompressible flow.

2. State clearly what boundary conditions are required to isolate a particular solution of Laplace's equation.

Section 4.3

1. Derive the velocity potential for the three-dimensional source (Eq. 6a of Section 4.3).

Section 4.4

1. A source and sink of equal strength are located symmetrically about the origin on a line that makes an angle of 45° with the positive x-axis. Write the stream function of the doublet formed from this source-sink pair and draw the streamlines.

2. Show that a source-sink pair (source and sink of equal strength) when viewed from infinity looks like a doublet.

Section 4.5

1. Let a uniform stream in the direction of the positive x-axis be added to a doublet that has been formed from a source on the *positive* x-axis and a sink on the *negative* x-axis. Draw the streamlines.

2. The stream functions for two flows are given by the equations

$$\psi = 2\theta$$

$$\psi = -5y$$

Superimpose these flows and plot the streamlines outside the streamline $\psi = 0$.

3. For the flow of Problem 2 write the equations of the streamlines that contain a point of zero velocity. One of these streamlines forms the shape of a body that extends to infinity in one direction. Find the point on this streamline where the velocity is the maximum. What is the value of the velocity at this point?

Section 4.7

1. A circular cylinder of radius unity is moving in the direction of the negative x-axis with a velocity of 100 ft/sec. The circulation around the cylinder is $2\pi \times 10^2$ ft^2/sec. Using Bernoulli's equation, plot the polar pressure coefficient distribution about the cylinder. The pressure coefficient is defined as the pressure at the surface, minus the static pressure of the stream at a great distance from the body, divided by the dynamic pressure of the stream at a great distance from the body (axes attached to body).

2. A source located on the x-axis at $x = -a$ and a sink located at $x = +a$ are in the presence of a uniform stream in the direction of the positive x-axis. Plot the streamlines and write the equations of the streamlines that contain the stagnation points.

3. The velocity pattern for the flow about a circular cylinder is described by the stream function

$$\psi = 100y \left\{ 1 - \frac{25}{r^2} \right\} + \frac{628}{2\pi} \log \frac{r}{5}$$

Sketch the streamlines. Write the equation of the streamline passing through the point $(0, 6)$.

4. Assuming sea level conditions in the fluid at a great distance from the cylinder of Problem 3, find the pressure in the fluid at the point $(6, -1)$.

Section 4.10

1. A uniform stream is flowing past a vortex at the origin. Using the momentum theorem, show that the force on the vortex is

$$|\mathbf{F}| = \rho |\mathbf{V}| \Gamma$$

where $\mathbf{F}$ is perpendicular to $\mathbf{V}$. Hint: In this problem the inner boundary may be taken as a point at the origin.

Section 5.2

1. Prove that the velocity induced in the region surrounding a doubly infinite vortex sheet satisfies the equation of continuity everywhere.

Section 5.4

1. Show that the distribution

$$\gamma = 2\alpha V_\infty \frac{1 + \cos\theta}{\sin\theta}$$

satisfies both the Kutta condition and the condition of parallel flow at the boundary.

2. Plot the γ/V_∞ distribution versus chord for lift coefficients of 0.1, 0.5, 1.0. Explain your results at the leading edge. How is the parameter related to the pressure coefficient

$$c_p = \frac{p}{\frac{1}{2}\rho V_\infty{}^2}$$

3. At what angle of attack must a symmetrical airfoil fly in order to develop a sectional-lift coefficient of 0.5? What is the direction of the lift? Through what point on the airfoil does the line of action of the lift act?

4. Using the method of Section 5.4, derive an expression for the moment about a point $\frac{3}{4}$ chord behind the leading edge of the wing section. Check your work by using the known result that the center of pressure for a symmetrical wing is at the $\frac{1}{4}$ chord point for all angles of attack.

Section 5.5

1. An airfoil has a mean camber line that has the shape of a circular arc (constant radius of curvature). The maximum mean camber is equal to k/c, where k is a constant and c is the chord. The free-stream velocity is V_∞, and the angle of attack is α. Write an expression for the γ distribution. Simplify your mathematics by neglecting terms that are small when k/c is small.

Section 5.6

1. For the circular-arc airfoil described in Problem 1 of Section 5.4, find the angle of zero lift and the moment coefficient about the aerodynamic center as functions of k/c.

Section 5.7

1. A mean camber line with a reflexed trailing edge must have a point of inflection, and, therefore, the simplest equation that can describe it is a cubic. Four boundary conditions are required to determine a cubic. Two of them are the condition of zero camber at the leading and trailing edges. Therefore, if a reflexed mean camber line is represented by a cubic, the equation will contain two arbitrary constants and may be written in the form

$$y = a\{(b - 1)x^3 - bx^2 + x\}$$

Find the values of the constants if the α_{L0} of the airfoil is zero. What is the c_{mac} when α_{L0} is zero? Find the values of the constants that make c_{mac} vanish. Plot the mean camber line in each case.

Section 5.8

1. The mean camber line of an airfoil consists of two parabolas joined at their vertices as shown. The maximum mean camber is 4 per cent of the chord, and the

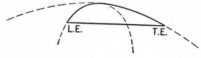

PROB. 5.8.1

position of the maximum mean camber behind the leading edge is 20 per cent of the chord.

Find the c_{mac} and α_{L0} of this section. What is the lift coefficient, and the direction and line of action of the lift when the geometric angle of attack is 3°? Without changing the angle of attack, a flap that is 15 per cent of the entire chord of the airfoil is deflected 2°. With flap deflected, what is the magnitude, direction, and line of action of the lift?

Section 6.2

1. The bound vortex AB shown in the accompanying figure is in the presence of a sea level stream of velocity equal to 100 ft/sec. The force on the vortex is

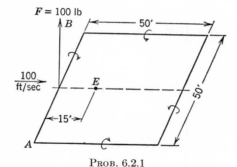

PROB. 6.2.1

100 lb. At the end of $\frac{1}{2}$ sec, the vorticity formation in the fluid is as shown in the figure. Using the law of Biot and Savart, find the induced velocity at the point E, which is 15 ft downstream of the bound vortex filament on a line that lies in the plane rectangle and bisects the filament.

Section 6.5

1. Derive an expression for the drag created by the starting vortex filament in the form

$$D = f(\rho, \Gamma, l, b)$$

where l is the distance between the starting vortex and the lifting line and b is the span of the lifting line. Assume that the lift is constant along the span. In finite-wing calculations, this drag is neglected. Why?

2. The downwash on the tail resulting from the wing wake is almost twice as great as the downwash on the wing resulting from the wing wake. Why?

3. Find the velocity in both magnitude and direction induced at the wing tip (point A) by unit area of the vortex sheet that forms the wake. The unit area is downstream of the lifting line by a distance b and off the centerline of the wing by a

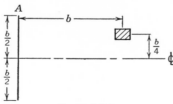

PROB. 6.5.3

distance $b/4$. Assume that the vorticity is constant over the unit area and equal to the value at the center of the area. The lift distribution varies linearly from root to tip according to the equation

$$L' = L'_s \left[1 - \frac{1}{2}\left(\frac{y}{b/2}\right) \right]$$

Section 6.6

1. A wing with an elliptical plan form is flying through sea level air at a speed of 100 mph. The wing loading $W/S = 14$. The wing is untwisted and has the same section from root to tip. The lift curve slope of the section m_0 is 5.7. The span of the wing is 30 ft, and the aspect ratio is 6. Find the sectional-lift and induced-drag coefficients and the effective, induced, and absolute angles of attack as a function of span. What horsepower is required to propel this wing at the given speed if all the drag is induced drag?

2. Two similar wings having the same weight and flying at the same speed are arranged in tandem. Which wing requires the greater horsepower? Hint: Consider the velocities induced by one wing on the other.

Section 6.7

1. Show that the even values of A_n (see Eq. 22) for a symmetrically loaded wing vanish.

Section 6.9

1. The Eq. 24 for a twisted wing is solved twice. At a point midway between the root and tip, the local-lift coefficient is found to be 0.8 when the wing-lift coefficient is 0.85. For the second solution, the local-lift coefficient is found to be 0.5 when the wing-lift coefficient is 0.52. What is the local lift coefficient at this station when the wing is flying level at a speed of 100 ft/sec through sea level air ($\rho = .002378$)? The wing loading $W/S = 15$.

2. Show that the induced-drag coefficient has a constant term, a term proportional to C_L, and a term proportional to $C_L{}^2$.

3. A wing having the properties described below is flying through sea level air at a speed of 180 mph. The wing loading $W/S = 15$ (lift = weight). Plot $c_{l_{a1}}$ and c_{l_b} versus span. Plot c_l and c_{d_i} versus span. Solve for at least four values of A_n. Notice that the even values of A_n for a symmetrically loaded wing vanish.

Wing Properties

Taper ratio = Tip chord/Root chord = 0.6.

Aspect ratio = 7.

Twist = 3° geometric washout (linear twist from root to tip).

Root section   NACA 23012⎱ Assume a linear variation in properties from root to
Tip section   NACA 2412 ⎰ tip.

Section 6.11

1. For the wing described in Problem 3 of Section 6.9, assume that the trailing edge is perpendicular to the plane of symmetry. Find the position of the aerodynamic center, the moment coefficient about the aerodynamic center, and the angle of zero lift of the wing. Reference the angle of zero lift to the chord line of the root section.

If the wing weighs 6000 lb, what is the induced drag when it is flying through sea level air at 180 mph?

2. For a wing that has a constant value of the sectional c_{mac}, find the influence of taper ratio λ on C_{M_S}.

Section 9.3

1. A surface temperature of $1000°$ R is recorded for a missile that is flying at an altitude of 50,000 ft. Assume that the conditions at the surface are the same as those at a stagnation point. At what speed is the missile flying?

Note: The no-slip condition at the surface of a body requires that the flow velocity be zero at the surface. The full stagnation temperature is not reached, however, because the fluid is not brought to rest adiabatically.

2. An intermittent wind tunnel is designed for a Mach number of 4 at the test section. The tunnel operates by sucking air from the atmosphere through a duct and into a vacuum tank. The tunnel is located in Denver (altitude 5000 ft). What density can be expected at the test section? Assume isentropic flow.

3. Sea level air is drawn from the atmosphere through a duct and into a vacuum tank. If the air remains a perfect gas at all temperatures, and if it can be expanded reversibly, what is the maximum velocity that the air can attain?

4. An airplane is flying through sea level air at $M = 0.6$. What is the pressure that will be recorded at the head of a pitot tube that is directed into the stream?

Section 9.6

1. Near a Mach number of unity, small variations in the free cross-sectional area of a tunnel (tunnel cross-sectional area minus model cross-sectional area) cause large variations in the flow parameters. Find the percentage of change in Mach number corresponding to a 1 per cent change in free area at test Mach numbers of 1.1, 1.2, 1.5, and 2.0.

2. Sea level air is being drawn through a duct into a vacuum tank. The cross-sectional areas of the duct at the mouth, at the throat, and at the entrance to the vacuum tank are 2 ft², 1 ft², and 4 ft², respectively. What is the maximum number

of slugs of air that can be drawn into the vacuum tank each second? Assume isentropic flow.

3. For the duct-tank configuration of Problem 2, what must be the pressure in the vacuum tank if the maximum flow is to be attained?

4. The geometry of a Laval nozzle is shown on the figure below. The cross-

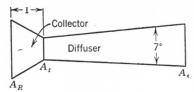

PROB. 9.6.4

sectional diameters vary linearly from the reservoir to the throat and from the throat to the exit. The throat area $A_t = 1$ ft^2. The ratio of the reservoir area to the throat area $(A_R/A_t) = 20$. The ratio of the exit area to the throat area $(A_e/A_t) = 4$. The length of the collector $L_c = 1$ ft. The diffusion angle is $7°$.

(a) For a Mach number of unity at the throat, plot the distribution of M and p/p_0 along the tube.

(b) For a Mach number of 0.5 at the throat, plot the distribution of M and p/p_0 along the tube.

Section 9.8

1. Sea level air enters a constant area duct in which heat is added at the rate of 0.1×10^6 ft-lb/slug. Find the temperature, pressure, density, and velocity of the air after heat addition.

2. In Problem 1, find the heat rate that will produce thermal choking.

3. In the tube shown, sea level air enters at $M = 0.68$ and reaches a value of $M = 0.25$ at the exit of the diffuser (station B). The entrance area is 1 ft^2.

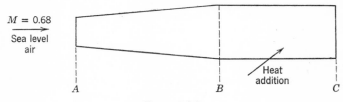

PROB. 9.8.3

(a) What is the area of station B assuming no dissipative losses in the diffuser? Will the area be larger or smaller if losses are present?

(b) What is the static pressure at station B assuming no losses? If losses are present, will the stagnation pressure rise or fall from station A to station B? Will the stagnation density rise or fall?

(c) Heat is added at $M = 0.25$ between station B and station C until thermal choking occurs. How much heat per slug of air is added? What is the stagnation temperature at station C?

Section 10.2

1. Sea level air moving at a Mach number of 1.5 is turned in an expansion direction through an angle of 5°. What is the approximate Mach number of the flow after turning? How can you improve your answer?

2. In Problem 1, the air is turned in an expansion direction through an angle of 15°. Find the approximate Mach number after turning by dividing the turn into three 5° increments.

Section 10.3

1. Sea level air moving at a Mach number of 1.5 is turned in a compressive direction through an angle of 5°. What is the approximate Mach number of the flow after turning? Why is your answer approximate?

Section 10.4

1. Sea level air moving at a Mach number of 1.5 is turned in an expansive direction through an angle of 15°. Find the exact Mach number at the end of 5° turning and at the end of 15° turning. Compare your answers with those obtained in Problems 10.2.1 and 10.2.2.

2. For the flow of Problem 1, find the static and stagnation values of the pressure, density, and temperature after 15° of turning.

Section 10.5

1. Using the procedure of Section 10.5, derive the following relation among u_1, u_2, and v_2 (see Fig. 9).

$$v_2^2 = (u_1 - u_2)^2 \frac{u_1 u_2 - a^{*2}}{[2/(\gamma + 1)]u_1^2 - u_1 u_2 + a^{*2}}$$

A plot of the above equation using the dimensionless variables $u_1^* = u_1/a^*$, $u_2^* = u_2/a^*$, and $v_2^* = v_2/a^*$ is the shock polar diagram illustrated below. The polar has been drawn for a particular value of u_1^*.

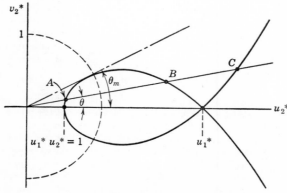

PROB. 10.5.1

Interpret the points A, B, and C corresponding to the turning angle θ. Interpret the two points on the polar corresponding to $\theta = 0$ in terms of the waves produced. How does the maximum turning angle θ_m vary with $u_1{}^*$?

Section 10.6

1. Using a value of γ of 1.4, show that the ratios of the flow parameters across a shock wave in terms of the normal Mach number may be written

$$\frac{p_2}{p_1} = \frac{7M_{1n}{}^2 - 1}{6}$$

$$\frac{\rho_2}{\rho_1} = \frac{6M_{1n}{}^2}{M_{1n}{}^2 + 5}$$

$$\frac{T_2}{T_1} = \frac{(7M_{1n}{}^2 - 1)(M_{1n}{}^2 + 5)}{36M_{1n}{}^2}$$

$$\frac{p_2{}^0}{p_1{}^0} = \left\{\frac{6}{7M_{1n}{}^2 - 1}\right\}^{2.5} \left\{\frac{6M_{1n}{}^2}{M_{1n}{}^2 + 5}\right\}^{3.5}$$

2. A body with a conical nose is traveling through sea level air at a Mach number of 2. The shock wave at the nose is observed to make an angle of 50° with the flow direction. Find the pressure, density, temperature, and total head immediately downstream of the shock.

3. Other conditions remaining unchanged, what is the influence of altitude on the quantities computed in Problem 2?

Section 10.7

1. Show that if $(V_1/a^*) > 1$, then V_1/a_1 is also greater than unity; that is, show that $(V_1/a^*) > 1$ means that the flow is supersonic.

2. Sea level air at a Mach number of 3 passes through a normal shock wave. How much does the static pressure of the air rise in passing through the shock wave? What is the stream speed upstream and downstream of the wave? What do you think of the normal shock wave as a pressure-recovery device? Reserve your judgment until you have worked Problem 3.

3. Let the stream of Problem 2 be expanded between the initial and final speeds isentropically. What is the pressure rise? This is the maximum pressure recovery that can be obtained.

Section 10.8

1. Sea level air moving at a Mach number of 1.5 is turned in a compressive direction through an angle of 5°. What is the Mach number of the flow after turning? Compare your answer with that of Problem 10.3.1. What is your conclusion?

2. A wedge having a total vertex angle of 60° is traveling at a Mach number of 3 at an altitude of 50,000 ft. Find the static and stagnation values of the pressure, density, and temperature downstream of the shock. What percentage of the stagnation pressure is lost across the shock wave?

3. Find the percentage loss in stagnation pressure across the shock of Problem 2 if the total vertex angle of the wedge is 30° instead of 60°.

4. How slowly may the wedge of Problem 2 travel and maintain an oblique shock attached to the nose?

5. Just above the critical speed (speed at which the shock detaches from the nose), what is the static pressure immediately behind the shock of Problem 4? What is the static pressure at the surface of the wedge? What is the wave angle? What is the stagnation pressure loss in crossing the shock?

Section 10.9

1. What is the vertex angle of the cone that will have the same critical speed as the wedge of Problem 10.8.5? At this critical speed, what is the pressure at the surface of the cone?

2. What is the pressure immediately downstream of the shock of Problem 1? What is the direction of the flow immediately downstream of the shock?

Section 10.10

1. Sea level air is being drawn into a vacuum tank through a duct as shown in the accompanying figure. The cross-sectional areas at the mouth, at the throat, and at

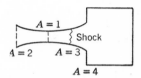

PROB. 10.10.1

the entrance to the vacuum tank are 2 ft², 1 ft², and 4 ft², respectively. By schlieren photography a normal shock is detected at a position in the duct where the cross-sectional area is 3 ft². What is the pressure in the vacuum tank?

Section 11.2

1. Combine the basic equations of steady incompressible flow theory into the form

$$\mathbf{V} \cdot \frac{d\mathbf{V}}{dt} = a^2 \operatorname{div} \mathbf{V}$$

Using the relation Curl $\mathbf{V} = 0$, show that the Cartesian form of the above is Eq. 6 of Section 11.2.

Section 11.3

1. Prove that the linearized potential equation for three-dimensional steady compressible flow

$$(1 - M_\infty^2) \frac{\partial^2 \varphi}{\partial x^2} + \frac{\partial^2 \varphi}{\partial y^2} + \frac{\partial^2 \varphi}{\partial z^2} = 0$$

is a valid approximation, provided:

$$M_\infty^2 \frac{u'}{V_\infty} \ll 1 \qquad M_\infty^2 \frac{v'}{V_\infty} \ll 1 \qquad M_\infty^2 \frac{w'}{V_\infty} \ll 1 \qquad \frac{M_\infty^2}{M_\infty^2 - 1} \frac{u'}{V_\infty} \ll 1$$

Section 11.4

1. From the development of Section 11.4, the perturbation density ρ' appears only in combination with perturbation velocities, and therefore in the linear problem it can make no contribution to the pressure coefficient. With this in mind, show that the pressure coefficient could have been derived from Bernoulli's equation for incompressible flow:

$$p_\infty + \tfrac{1}{2}\rho_\infty V_\infty{}^2 = p + \tfrac{1}{2}\rho_\infty V^2$$

Section 11.5

1. The geometric boundary condition for the lifting and nonlifting problems determines the sign relationships of $\partial\varphi/\partial z$ at $z = 0+$ and $z = 0-$. Show that the pressure coefficient for the lifting and nonlifting problems plays a similar rôle for the derivative $\partial\varphi/\partial x$ at $z = 0+$ and $z = 0-$. Can anything be said about the signs of $\partial\varphi/\partial y$ at $z = 0+$ and $z = 0-$ for the lifting and nonlifting problems?

Section 11.6

1. A rectangular wing of aspect ratio 10 is flying at a Mach number of 0.6. Find the approximate value of $m = dC_L/d\alpha$.

Section 11.7

1. A two-dimensional airfoil is so oriented that its point of minimum pressure occurs on the lower surface. At a free stream Mach number of 0.3 the pressure coefficient at this point is -0.782. Using the Prandtl-Glauert rule, estimate the critical Mach number of the airfoil.

Section 11.8

1. An infinite wing with a symmetrical diamond-shaped section is traveling to the left through sea level air at a Mach number of 2. The angle of attack is 2° and the maximum thickness to chord ratio is 0.15. Using shock-expansion theory, find the pressure at point B on the airfoil indicated in the figure to the left.

2. An infinite wing whose symmetrical cross section is composed of two circular arcs is flying at a Mach number of 3. The angle of attack is zero degrees and the maximum thickness

PROB. 11.8.1

to chord ratio is 0.2. Compute the drag coefficient by the shock-expansion method. Neglect viscous drag.

Section 11.9

1. Verify that

$$\varphi = \frac{-C}{h}$$

$$h = \sqrt{(x - \xi)^2 - B^2\{(y - \eta)^2 + (z - \zeta)^2\}}$$

is a solution of

$$-B^2\varphi_{xx} + \varphi_{yy} + \varphi_{zz} = 0$$

2. Show that the hyperbolic radius h goes from zero on the Mach cone to a maximum of $h = x - \xi$ on the axis. Show that h is imaginary on all cones whose vertex angle is greater than the Mach angle.

3. Show that the perturbation velocities φ_x and φ_y at $(x, y, 0)$ arising from a source sheet in the $z = 0$ plane are integrated properties of the source distribution rather than point properties.

Section 11.10

1. Assume the wing of Problem 11.8.1 is at a zero angle of attack. Compare the answers obtained for the pressure at point B using linearized theory and shock expansion theory.

Section 11.11

1. In what Mach number range does the wing shown have a supersonic leading edge? In what Mach number range is the trailing edge subsonic?

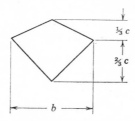

PROB. 11.11.1

2. A two-dimensional flat plate is flying at an altitude of 20,000 ft and a Mach number of 2. If the angle of attack is 10°, find the pressure on the upper and lower surfaces by the shock-expansion method and by linearized theory.

Section 11.13

1. The airfoil shown in the accompanying diagram is traveling at a Mach number of 3 and at an angle of attack of 2°. The thickness to chord ratio is 0.1, and the

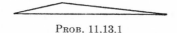

PROB. 11.13.1

maximum thickness occurs 30 per cent of the chord downstream from the leading edge. Using the linearized theory, compute the angle of zero lift, the moment coefficient about the aerodynamic center, and the position of the center of pressure.

2. For the wing of Problem 11.8.2, compute the drag coefficient by linearized theory.

Section 11.14

1. A wing at a given altitude has a critical Mach number of 0.7. It is desired to fly this wing at $M = 0.9$. How much sweep must be incorporated in the wing to reduce the compressibility drag? Is the compressibility drag entirely eliminated by this method? Explain.

Section 12.4

1. From kinetic considerations similar to those in Section 1.5 for the derivation of the coefficient of viscosity, show that the thermal conductivity k is related to the specific heat of a gas c by the equation $k = \mu c$.

Section 12.5

1. Consider a boundary layer of 0.1-in. thickness on a surface with a radius of curvature of 3 in. The fluid is air, and the velocity distribution in the boundary layer is given by

$$\frac{u}{U_1} = 2\left(\frac{y}{\delta}\right) - \left(\frac{y}{\delta}\right)^2$$

Assume that the streamlines in the boundary layer have the same curvature as the surface. Set up the equilibrium condition for the pressure and centrifugal forces and integrate to find the change in pressure through the boundary layer as a function of ρU_1^2. Assume standard conditions at the edge of the boundary layer and find the change of pressure through the boundary layer for $U_1 = 200$ ft/sec.

2. Show that for flow through a normal shock the momentum equation is $\rho u \partial u/\partial x = -\partial p/\partial x + \partial/\partial x(\sigma\, \partial u/\partial x)$, where σ is a viscosity coefficient.

Section 12.6

1. Consider a two-dimensional flow in the xy-plane. By differentiating and subtracting the two equations of motion (Eqs. 6), eliminate the pressure and get

$$\frac{\mathfrak{D}\zeta}{\mathfrak{D}t} = \nu\, \nabla^2 \zeta$$

where ζ is the z-component of the vorticity derived in Section 2.8. Assume a perfect fluid and interpret the above equation in terms of the Helmholtz vortex laws given in Section 2.14.

The equation for the diffusion of heat in a two-dimensional incompressible flow field is (see Eq. 31, Appendix B)

$$c_v\rho\, \frac{\mathfrak{D}T}{\mathfrak{D}t} = k\, \nabla^2 T$$

where T is the temperature, c_v is the specific heat at constant volume, and k is the thermal conductivity. In this equation the density and thermal conductivity are assumed constant. The analogy between the diffusion of heat and of vorticity in a two-dimensional flow field is evident from a comparison of the two equations.

Section 13.2

1. Show that the fundamental equation for Poiseuille flow in a tube may also be derived by means of the complete Navier-Stokes equations for incompressible flow given in Section 12.6.

2. Find the velocity distribution for fully developed axial flow between two concentric cylinders of radii a and b. The cylinders are stationary and the flow is caused by a pressure gradient along the length. Derive the result both by means of the equations of this section and by means of the method employed in Problem 1.

3. Find the velocity distribution between the two cylinders of Problem 2 if the entire flow is caused by moving the inner cylinder parallel to itself with velocity U relative to the outer.

4. Are the solutions of Problems 2 and 3 additive? Why?

5. From the Navier-Stokes equations given in Section 12.6, show that fully developed flow in a pipe of any cross section is

$$\frac{\partial^2 u}{\partial y^2} + \frac{\partial^2 u}{\partial z^2} = \frac{1}{\mu}\frac{\partial p}{\partial x}$$

Show that this equation is identical with that for the deflection of a diaphragm stretched over the pipe cross section with a pressure difference across it.

Section 13.3

1. Substitute $\xi = y/x^n$, $\psi = (U_1 v x)^{1/2} f(\xi)$ into Eqs. 7 and show that $n = \frac{1}{2}$ is the condition that neither x nor y appear explicitly in the resulting differential equation.

Section 13.4

1. Compare qualitatively a boundary layer that has just traversed an unfavorable pressure gradient and is now traversing a favorable gradient with one for which the gradient has been favorable from the leading edge. How many inflection points are there in the velocity distributions in each case?

Section 13.6

1. Consider the steady flow of air along a flat plate parallel to the flow. At a particular station the velocity distribution is given by

$$u = 4 \times 10^4 y - 2 \times 10^6 y^2$$

What is the rate of change of the momentum thickness of the boundary layer with x?

2. Imagine the flat plate to be warped in such a way that we still have at some point the velocity distribution given above. Find the value of $\partial U_1/\partial x$ necessary to make $\partial\theta/\partial x = 0$ at that point.

Section 13.7

1. Assume that the velocity distribution for steady flow in the boundary layer is given by

$$\frac{u}{U_1} = \frac{y}{\delta}$$

Substitute this expression in Eq. 33, and obtain the differential equation

$$\frac{d}{dx}(\delta^2) + \frac{10 dU_1/dx}{U_1}\delta^2 = 12\frac{\nu}{U_1}$$

the solution of which is

$$\delta^2 = \frac{12\nu}{U_1^{10}}\int_0^x U_1^9\, dx$$

Assume U_1 constant ($\partial p/\partial x = 0$), check the following relations, and compare with the Blasius solution.

$$\delta = \sqrt{\frac{12\nu x}{U_1}}$$

$$c_f = 0.577 \sqrt{\frac{\nu}{U_1 x}}$$

$$C_f = 1.154 \sqrt{\frac{\nu}{U_1 l}}$$

Section 14.6

1. Show that for Couette flow (flow between two infinite parallel plates, one of which is sliding parallel to itself with velocity U_1) the temperature recovery factor at the stationary plate is equal to the Prandtl number. Find the temperature distribution between the plates (a) when one plate is insulated and (b) when both plates are maintained at temperature T_1.

2. Plot the distribution of stagnation temperature through the boundary layer as predicted by the Pohlhausen analysis of the flow past an insulated flat plate (Section 14.6). Take $M_1 = 2$ and $T_1 = 500°$ R. Use the values for θ and u/U_1 given in Fig. 2 of Chapter 14 and in Fig. 5 of Chapter 13, respectively.

Section 14.7

1. Show that for fully developed incompressible flow between parallel plates (see Section 13.2 for definition ($\partial p/\partial x \neq 0$) of fully developed)

$$u = u_m \left(1 - \frac{y^2}{h^2} \right)$$

where u_m is the velocity at $y = 0$. Assume small temperature differences so that incompressibility is not seriously violated and show that the temperature at the center, T_m, in terms of that at the walls, T_w, is $T_m = T_w - 5\mu U_m^2/6k$. Find the Nusselt number.

Section 15.4

1. In Tollmien-type laminar instability (Section 15.4) the "disturbance stream function" is given by (see Fig. 8)

$$\psi' = \varphi(y) \exp i\alpha(x - ct)$$

Where α is real and positive, $c = c_r + ic_i$. The velocity components in the boundary layer are given respectively by $U(y) + \partial \psi'/\partial y$ and $-\partial \psi'/\partial x$. Give the physical meanings of α, c_r, and c_i.

Section 15.5

1. In Taylor-Goertler type of boundary layer instability the disturbance is described by (see Fig. 17)

$$u' = u_1(y)e^{\beta t}\cos \alpha z$$

$$v' = v_1(y)e^{\beta t}\cos \alpha z$$

$$w' = w_1(y)e^{\beta t}\sin \alpha z$$

When the total velocity components are, respectively, $U(y) + u', v', w'$. The boundary layer profile without the instability is $U(y)$. Give the physical meanings of α and β.

Section 16.3

1. Calculate the shearing stresses $-\rho\overline{u'v'}$ for the disturbance described in Problem 1, Section 15.4.

2. Show that $-\rho\overline{u'^2v'}$ represents a rate of energy transfer.

Tables

TABLE 1

Properties of the Standard Atmosphere

h (ft)	T (°F)	a (ft/sec)	p (lb/ft²)	ρ (slugs/ft³)	$\mu \times 10^7$ (slugs/ft sec)
0	59.00	1117	2116.2	0.002378	3.719
1,000	57.44	1113	2040.9	.002310	3.699
2,000	51.87	1109	1967.7	.002242	3.679
3,000	48.31	1105	1896.7	.002177	3.659
4,000	44.74	1102	1827.7	.002112	3.639
5,000	41.18	1098	1760.8	.002049	3.618
6,000	37.62	1094	1696.0	.001988	3.598
7,000	34.05	1090	1633.0	.001928	3.577
8,000	30.49	1086	1571.9	.001869	3.557
9,000	26.92	1082	1512.8	.001812	3.536
10,000	23.36	1078	1455.4	.001756	3.515
11,000	19.80	1074	1399.8	.001702	3.495
12,000	16.23	1070	1345.9	.001649	3.474
13,000	12.67	1066	1293.7	.001597	3.453
14,000	9.10	1062	1243.2	.001546	3.432
15,000	5.54	1058	1194.3	.001497	3.411
16,000	1.98	1054	1147.0	.001448	3.390
17,000	-1.59	1050	1101.1	.001401	3.369
18,000	-5.15	1046	1056.9	.001355	3.347
19,000	-8.72	1041	1014.0	.001311	3.326
20,000	-12.28	1037	972.6	.001267	3.305
21,000	-15.84	1033	932.5	.001225	3.283
22,000	-19.41	1029	893.8	.001183	3.262
23,000	-22.97	1025	856.4	.001143	3.240
24,000	-26.54	1021	820.3	.001104	3.218
25,000	-30.10	1017	785.3	.001066	3.196
26,000	-33.66	1012	751.7	.001029	3.174
27,000	-37.23	1008	719.2	.000993	3.153
28,000	-40.79	1004	687.9	.000957	3.130
29,000	-44.36	999	657.6	.000923	3.108
30,000	-47.92	995	628.5	.000890	3.086
31,000	-51.48	991	600.4	.000858	3.064
32,000	-55.05	987	573.3	.000826	3.041
33,000	-58.61	982	547.3	.000796	3.019
34,000	-62.18	978	522.2	.000766	2.997
35,000	-65.74	973	498.0	.000737	2.974
40,000	-67.6	971	391.8	.0005857	2.961
45,000	-67.6	971	308.0	.0004605	2.961
50,000	-67.6	971	242.2	.0003622	2.961
60,000	-67.6	971	150.9	.0002240	2.961
70,000	-67.6	971	93.5	.0001389	2.961
80,000	-67.6	971	58.0	.0000861	2.961
90,000	-67.6	971	36.0	.0000535	2.961
100,000	-67.6	971	22.4	.0000331	2.961
150,000	113.5	1174	3.003	.00000305	4.032
200,000	159.4	1220	.6645	.00000062	4.277
250,000	-8.2	1042	.1139	.00000015	3.333

Data taken from NACA TN 1428. Courtesy of the National Advisory Committee for Aeronautics.

TABLE 2

FLOW PARAMETERS VERSUS M FOR SUBSONIC FLOW

M	p/p_0	ρ/ρ_0	T/T_0	a/a_0	A^*/A
.00	1.0000	1.0000	1.0000	1.0000	.00000
.01	.9999	1.0000	1.0000	1.0000	.01728
.02	.9997	.9998	.9999	1.0000	.03455
.03	.9994	.9996	.9998	.9999	.05181
.04	.9989	.9992	.9997	.9998	.06905
.05	.9983	.9988	.9995	.9998	.08627
.06	.9975	.9982	.9993	.9996	.1035
.07	.9966	.9976	.9990	.9995	.1206
.08	.9955	.9968	.9987	.9994	.1377
.09	.9944	.9960	.9984	.9992	.1548
.10	.9930	.9950	.9980	.9990	.1718
.11	.9916	.9940	.9976	.9988	.1887
.12	.9900	.9928	.9971	.9986	.2056
.13	.9883	.9916	.9966	.9983	.2224
.14	.9864	.9903	.9961	.9980	.2391
.15	.9844	.9888	.9955	.9978	.2557
.16	.9823	.9873	.9949	.9974	.2723
.17	.9800	.9857	.9943	.9971	.2887
.18	.9776	.9840	.9936	.9968	.3051
.19	.9751	.9822	.9928	.9964	.3213
.20	.9725	.9803	.9921	.9960	.3374
.21	.9697	.9783	.9913	.9956	.3534
.22	.9668	.9762	.9904	.9952	.3693
.23	.9638	.9740	.9895	.9948	.3851
.24	.9607	.9718	.9886	.9943	.4007
.25	.9575	.9694	.9877	.9938	.4162
.26	.9541	.9670	.9867	.9933	.4315
.27	.9506	.9645	.9856	.9928	.4467
.28	.9470	.9619	.9846	.9923	.4618
.29	.9433	.9592	.9835	.9917	.4767
.30	.9395	.9564	.9823	.9911	.4914
.31	.9355	.9535	.9811	.9905	.5059
.32	.9315	.9506	.9799	.9899	.5203
.33	.9274	.9476	.9787	.9893	.5345
.34	.9231	.9445	.9774	.9886	.5486

TABLE 2 (*Continued*)

Flow Parameters versus M for Subsonic Flow

M	p/p_0	ρ/ρ_0	T/T_0	a/a_0	A^*/A
.35	.9188	.9413	.9761	.9880	.5624
.36	.9143	.9380	.9747	.9873	.5761
.37	.9098	.9347	.9733	.9866	.5896
.38	.9052	.9313	.9719	.9859	.6029
.39	.9004	.9278	.9705	.9851	.6160
.40	.8956	.9243	.9690	.9844	.6289
.41	.8907	.9207	.9675	.9836	.6416
.42	.8857	.9170	.9659	.9828	.6541
.43	.8807	.9132	.9643	.9820	.6663
.44	.8755	.9094	.9627	.9812	.6784
.45	.8703	.9055	.9611	.9803	.6903
.46	.8650	.9016	.9594	.9795	.7019
.47	.8596	.8976	.9577	.9786	.7134
.48	.8541	.8935	.9560	.9777	.7246
.49	.8486	.8894	.9542	.9768	.7356
.50	.8430	.8852	.9524	.9759	.7464
.51	.8374	.8809	.9506	.9750	.7569
.52	.8317	.8766	.9487	.9740	.7672
.53	.8259	.8723	.9468	.9730	.7773
.54	.8201	.8679	.9449	.9721	.7872
.55	.8142	.8634	.9430	.9711	.7968
.56	.8082	.8589	.9410	.9701	.8063
.57	.8022	.8544	.9390	.9690	.8155
.58	.7962	.8498	.9370	.9680	.8244
.59	.7901	.8451	.9349	.9669	.8331
.60	.7840	.8405	.9328	.9658	.8416
.61	.7778	.8357	.9307	.9647	.8499
.62	.7716	.8310	.9286	.9636	.8579
.63	.7654	.8262	.9265	.9625	.8657
.64	.7591	.8213	.9243	.9614	.8732
.65	.7528	.8164	.9221	.9603	.8806
.66	.7465	.8115	.9199	.9591	.8877
.67	.7401	.8066	.9176	.9579	.8945
.68	.7338	.8016	.9153	.9567	.9012
.69	.7274	.7966	.9131	.9555	.9076

TABLE 2 (*Continued*)

FLOW PARAMETERS VERSUS *M* FOR SUBSONIC FLOW

M	p/p_0	ρ/ρ_0	T/T_0	a/a_0	A^*/A
.70	.7209	.7916	.9107	.9543	.9138
.71	.7145	.7865	.9084	.9531	.9197
.72	.7080	.7814	.9061	.9519	.9254
.73	.7016	.7763	.9037	.9506	.9309
.74	.6951	.7712	.9013	.9494	.9362
.75	.6886	.7660	.8989	.9481	.9412
.76	.6821	.7609	.8964	.9468	.9461
.77	.6756	.7557	.8940	.9455	.9507
.78	.6690	.7505	.8915	.9442	.9551
.79	.6625	.7452	.8890	.9429	.9592
.80	.6560	.7400	.8865	.9416	.9632
.81	.6495	.7347	.8840	.9402	.9669
.82	.6430	.7295	.8815	.9389	.9704
.83	.6365	.7242	.8789	.9375	.9737
.84	.6300	.7189	.8763	.9361	.9769
.85	.6235	.7136	.8737	.9347	.9797
.86	.6170	.7083	.8711	.9333	.9824
.87	.6106	.7030	.8685	.9319	.9849
.88	.6041	.6977	.8659	.9305	.9872
.89	.5977	.6924	.8632	.9291	.9893
.90	.5913	.6870	.8606	.9277	.9912
.91	.5849	.6817	.8579	.9262	.9929
.92	.5785	.6764	.8552	.9248	.9944
.93	.5721	.6711	.8525	.9233	.9958
.94	.5658	.6658	.8498	.9218	.9969
.95	.5595	.6604	.8471	.9204	.9979
.96	.5532	.6551	.8444	.9189	.9986
.97	.5469	.6498	.8416	.9174	.9992
.98	.5407	.6445	.8389	.9159	.9997
.99	.5345	.6392	.8361	.9144	.9999
1.00	.5283	.6339	.8333	.9129	1.0000

Numerical values taken from NACA TN 1428, courtesy of the National Advisory Committee for Aeronautics.

TABLE 3

FLOW PARAMETERS VERSUS M FOR SUPERSONIC FLOW

M	$\dfrac{p}{p_0}$	$\dfrac{\rho}{\rho_0}$	$\dfrac{T}{T_0}$	$\dfrac{a}{a_0}$	$\dfrac{A^*}{A}$	$\dfrac{\frac{\rho}{2}V^2}{p_0}$	θ
1.00	.5283	.6339	.8333	.9129	1.0000	.3698	0
1.01	.5221	.6287	.8306	.9113	.9999	.3728	.04473
1.02	.5160	.6234	.8278	.9098	.9997	.3758	.1257
1.03	.5099	.6181	.8250	.9083	.9993	.3787	.2294
1.04	.5039	.6129	.8222	.9067	.9987	.3815	.3510
1.05	.4979	.6077	.8193	.9052	.9980	.3842	.4874
1.06	.4919	.6024	.8165	.9036	.9971	.3869	.6367
1.07	.4860	.5972	.8137	.9020	.9961	.3895	.7973
1.08	.4800	.5920	.8108	.9005	.9949	.3919	.9680
1.09	.4742	.5869	.8080	.8989	.9936	.3944	1.148
1.10	.4684	.5817	.8052	.8973	.9921	.3967	1.336
1.11	.4626	.5766	.8023	.8957	.9905	.3990	1.532
1.12	.4568	.5714	.7994	.8941	.9888	.4011	1.735
1.13	.4511	.5663	.7966	.8925	.9870	.4032	1.944
1.14	.4455	.5612	.7937	.8909	.9850	.4052	2.160
1.15	.4398	.5562	.7908	.8893	.9828	.4072	2.381
1.16	.4343	.5511	.7879	.8877	.9806	.4090	2.607
1.17	.4287	.5461	.7851	.8860	.9782	.4108	2.839
1.18	.4232	.5411	.7822	.8844	.9758	.4125	3.074
1.19	.4178	.5361	.7793	.8828	.9732	.4141	3.314
1.20	.4124	.5311	.7764	.8811	.9705	.4157	3.558
1.21	.4070	.5262	.7735	.8795	.9676	.4171	3.806
1.22	.4017	.5213	.7706	.8778	.9647	.4185	4.057
1.23	.3964	.5164	.7677	.8762	.9617	.4198	4.312
1.24	.3912	.5115	.7648	.8745	.9586	.4211	4.569
1.25	.3861	.5067	.7619	.8729	.9553	.4223	4.830
1.26	.3809	.5019	.7590	.8712	.9520	.4233	5.093
1.27	.3759	.4971	.7561	.8695	.9486	.4244	5.359
1.28	.3708	.4923	.7532	.8679	.9451	.4253	5.627
1.29	.3658	.4876	.7503	.8662	.9415	.4262	5.898
1.30	.3609	.4829	.7474	.8645	.9378	.4270	6.170
1.31	.3560	.4782	.7445	.8628	.9341	.4277	6.445
1.32	.3512	.4736	.7416	.8611	.9302	.4283	6.721
1.33	.3464	.4690	.7387	.8595	.9263	.4289	7.000
1.34	.3417	.4644	.7358	.8578	.9223	.4294	7.279

TABLE 3 (*Continued*)

FLOW PARAMETERS VERSUS *M* FOR SUPERSONIC FLOW

M	$\dfrac{p}{p_0}$	$\dfrac{\rho}{\rho_0}$	$\dfrac{T}{T_0}$	$\dfrac{a}{a_0}$	$\dfrac{A^*}{A}$	$\dfrac{\frac{\rho}{2}V^2}{p_0}$	θ
1.35	.3370	.4598	.7329	.8561	.9182	.4299	7.561
1.36	.3323	.4553	.7300	.8544	.9141	.4303	7.844
1.37	.3277	.4508	.7271	.8527	.9099	.4306	8.128
1.38	.3232	.4463	.7242	.8510	.9056	.4308	8.413
1.39	.3187	.4418	.7213	.8493	.9013	.4310	8.699
1.40	.3142	.4374	.7184	.8476	.8969	.4311	8.987
1.41	.3098	.4330	.7155	.8459	.8925	.4312	9.276
1.42	.3055	.4287	.7126	.8442	.8880	.4312	9.565
1.43	.3012	.4244	.7097	.8425	.8834	.4311	9.855
1.44	.2969	.4201	.7069	.8407	.8788	.4310	10.15
1.45	.2927	.4158	.7040	.8390	.8742	.4308	10.44
1.46	.2886	.4116	.7011	.8373	.8695	.4306	10.73
1.47	.2845	.4074	.6982	.8356	.8647	.4303	11.02
1.48	.2804	.4032	.6954	.8339	.8599	.4299	11.32
1.49	.2764	.3991	.6925	.8322	.8551	.4295	11.61
1.50	.2724	.3950	.6897	.8305	.8502	.4290	11.91
1.51	.2685	.3909	.6868	.8287	.8453	.4285	12.20
1.52	.2646	.3869	.6840	.8270	.8404	.4279	12.49
1.53	.2608	.3829	.6811	.8253	.8354	.4273	12.79
1.54	.2570	.3789	.6783	.8236	.8304	.4266	13.09
1.55	.2533	.3750	.6754	.8219	.8254	.4259	13.38
1.56	.2496	.3710	.6726	.8201	.8203	.4252	13.68
1.57	.2459	.3672	.6698	.8184	.8152	.4243	13.97
1.58	.2423	.3633	.6670	.8167	.8101	.4235	14.27
1.59	.2388	.3595	.6642	.8150	.8050	.4226	14.56
1.60	.2353	.3557	.6614	.8133	.7998	.4216	14.86
1.61	.2318	.3520	.6586	.8115	.7947	.4206	15.16
1.62	.2284	.3483	.6558	.8098	.7895	.4196	15.45
1.63	.2250	.3446	.6530	.8081	.7843	.4185	15.75
1.64	.2217	.3409	.6502	.8064	.7791	.4174	16.04
1.65	.2184	.3373	.6475	.8046	.7739	.4162	16.34
1.66	.2151	.3337	.6447	.8029	.7686	.4150	16.63
1.67	.2119	.3302	.6419	.8012	.7634	.4138	16.93
1.68	.2088	.3266	.6392	.7995	.7581	.4125	17.22
1.69	.2057	.3232	.6364	.7978	.7529	.4112	17.52

TABLE 3 (*Continued*)

FLOW PARAMETERS VERSUS *M* FOR SUPERSONIC FLOW

M	$\dfrac{p}{p_0}$	$\dfrac{\rho}{\rho_0}$	$\dfrac{T}{T_0}$	$\dfrac{a}{a_0}$	$\dfrac{A^*}{A}$	$\dfrac{\dfrac{\rho}{2}V^2}{p_0}$	θ
1.70	.2026	.3197	.6337	.7961	.7476	.4098	17.81
1.71	.1996	.3163	.6310	.7943	.7423	.4086	18.10
1.72	.1966	.3129	.6283	.7926	.7371	.4071	18.40
1.73	.1936	.3095	.6256	.7909	.7318	.4056	18.69
1.74	.1907	.3062	.6229	.7892	.7265	.4041	18.98
1.75	.1878	.3029	.6202	.7875	.7212	.4026	19.27
1.76	.1850	.2996	.6175	.7858	.7160	.4011	19.56
1.77	.1822	.2964	.6148	.7841	.7107	.3996	19.86
1.78	.1794	.2932	.6121	.7824	.7054	.3980	20.15
1.79	.1767	.2900	.6095	.7807	.7002	.3964	20.44
1.80	.1740	.2868	.6068	.7790	.6949	.3947	20.73
1.81	.1714	.2837	.6041	.7773	.6897	.3931	21.01
1.82	.1688	.2806	.6015	.7756	.6845	.3914	21.30
1.83	.1662	.2776	.5989	.7739	.6792	.3897	21.59
1.84	.1637	.2745	.5963	.7722	.6740	.3879	21.88
1.85	.1612	.2715	.5936	.7705	.6688	.3862	22.16
1.86	.1587	.2686	.5910	.7688	.6636	.3844	22.45
1.87	.1563	.2656	.5884	.7671	.6584	.3826	22.73
1.88	.1539	.2627	.5859	.7654	.6533	.3808	23.02
1.89	.1516	.2598	.5833	.7637	.6481	.3790	23.30
1.90	.1492	.2570	.5807	.7620	.6430	.3771	23.59
1.91	.1470	.2542	.5782	.7604	.6379	.3753	23.87
1.92	.1447	.2514	.5756	.7587	.6328	.3734	24.15
1.93	.1425	.2486	.5731	.7570	.6277	.3715	24.43
1.94	.1403	.2459	.5705	.7553	.6226	.3696	24.71
1.95	.1381	.2432	.5680	.7537	.6175	.3677	24.99
1.96	.1360	.2405	.5655	.7520	.6125	.3657	25.27
1.97	.1339	.2378	.5630	.7503	.6075	.3638	25.55
1.98	.1318	.2352	.5605	.7487	.6025	.3618	25.83
1.99	.1298	.2326	.5580	.7470	.5975	.3598	26.10
2.00	.1278	.2300	.5556	.7454	.5926	.3579	26.38
2.01	.1258	.2275	.5531	.7437	.5877	.3559	26.66
2.02	.1239	.2250	.5506	.7420	.5828	.3539	26.93
2.03	.1220	.2225	.5482	.7404	.5779	.3518	27.20
2.04	.1201	.2200	.5458	.7388	.5730	.3498	27.48

TABLE 3 *(Continued)*

FLOW PARAMETERS VERSUS *M* FOR SUPERSONIC FLOW

M	$\dfrac{p}{p_0}$	$\dfrac{\rho}{\rho_0}$	$\dfrac{T}{T_0}$	$\dfrac{a}{a_0}$	$\dfrac{A^*}{A}$	$\dfrac{\frac{\rho}{2}V^2}{p_0}$	θ
2.05	.1182	.2176	.5433	.7371	.5682	.3478	27.75
2.06	.1164	.2152	.5409	.7355	.5634	.3458	28.02
2.07	.1146	.2128	.5385	.7338	.5586	.3437	28.29
2.08	.1128	.2104	.5361	.7322	.5538	.3417	28.56
2.09	.1111	.2081	.5337	.7306	.5491	.3396	28.83
2.10	.1094	.2058	.5313	.7289	.5444	.3376	29.10
2.11	.1077	.2035	.5290	.7273	.5397	.3355	29.36
2.12	.1060	.2013	.5266	.7257	.5350	.3334	29.63
2.13	.1043	.1990	.5243	.7241	.5304	.3314	29.90
2.14	.1027	.1968	.5219	.7225	.5258	.3293	30.16
2.15	.1011	.1946	.5196	.7208	.5212	.3272	30.43
2.16	.09956	.1925	.5173	.7192	.5167	.3252	30.69
2.17	.09802	.1903	.5150	.7176	.5122	.3231	30.95
2.18	.09650	.1882	.5127	.7160	.5077	.3210	31.21
2.19	.09500	.1861	.5104	.7144	.5032	.3189	31.47
2.20	.09352	.1841	.5081	.7128	.4988	.3169	31.73
2.21	.09207	.1820	.5059	.7112	.4944	.3148	31.99
2.22	.09064	.1800	.5036	.7097	.4900	.3127	32.25
2.23	.08923	.1780	.5014	.7081	.4856	.3106	32.51
2.24	.08785	.1760	.4991	.7065	.4813	.3085	32.76
2.25	.08648	.1740	.4969	.7049	.4770	.3065	33.02
2.26	.08514	.1721	.4947	.7033	.4727	.3044	33.27
2.27	.08382	.1702	.4925	.7018	.4685	.3023	33.53
2.28	.08252	.1683	.4903	.7002	.4643	.3003	33.78
2.29	.08123	.1664	.4881	.6986	.4601	.2982	34.03
2.30	.07997	.1646	.4859	.6971	.4560	.2961	34.28
2.31	.07873	.1628	.4837	.6955	.4519	.2941	34.53
2.32	.07751	.1609	.4816	.6940	.4478	.2920	34.78
2.33	.07631	.1592	.4794	.6924	.4437	.2900	35.03
2.34	.07512	.1574	.4773	.6909	.4397	.2879	35.28
2.35	.07396	.1556	.4752	.6893	.4357	.2859	35.53
2.36	.07281	.1539	.4731	.6878	.4317	.2839	35.77
2.37	.07168	.1522	.4709	.6863	.4278	.2818	36.02
2.38	.07057	.1505	.4688	.6847	.4239	.2798	36.26
2.39	.06948	.1488	.4668	.6832	.4200	.2778	36.50

TABLE 3 (*Continued*)

FLOW PARAMETERS VERSUS M FOR SUPERSONIC FLOW

M	$\dfrac{p}{p_0}$	$\dfrac{\rho}{\rho_0}$	$\dfrac{T}{T_0}$	$\dfrac{a}{a_0}$	$\dfrac{A^*}{A}$	$\dfrac{\frac{\rho}{2}V^2}{p_0}$	θ
2.40	.06840	.1472	.4647	.6817	.4161	.2758	36.75
2.41	.06734	.1456	.4626	.6802	.4123	.2738	36.99
2.42	.06630	.1439	.4606	.6786	.4085	.2718	37.23
2.43	.06527	.1424	.4585	.6771	.4048	.2698	37.47
2.44	.06426	.1408	.4565	.6756	.4010	.2678	37.71
2.45	.06327	.1392	.4544	.6741	.3973	.2658	37.95
2.46	.06229	.1377	.4524	.6726	.3937	.2639	38.18
2.47	.06133	.1362	.4504	.6711	.3900	.2619	38.42
2.48	.06038	.1347	.4484	.6696	.3864	.2599	38.66
2.49	.05945	.1332	.4464	.6681	.3828	.2580	38.89
2.50	.05853	.1317	.4444	.6667	.3793	.2561	39.12
2.51	.05762	.1302	.4425	.6652	.3757	.2541	39.36
2.52	.05674	.1288	.4405	.6637	.3722	.2522	39.59
2.53	.05586	.1274	.4386	.6622	.3688	.2503	39.82
2.54	.05500	.1260	.4366	.6608	.3653	.2484	40.05
2.55	.05415	.1246	.4347	.6593	.3619	.2465	40.28
2.56	.05332	.1232	.4328	.6579	.3585	.2446	40.51
2.57	.05250	.1218	.4309	.6564	.3552	.2427	40.75
2.58	.05169	.1205	.4289	.6549	.3519	.2409	40.96
2.59	.05090	.1192	.4271	.6535	.3486	.2390	41.19
2.60	.05012	.1179	.4252	.6521	.3453	.2371	41.41
2.61	.04935	.1166	.4233	.6506	.3421	.2353	41.64
2.62	.04859	.1153	.4214	.6492	.3389	.2335	41.86
2.63	.04784	.1140	.4196	.6477	.3357	.2317	42.09
2.64	.04711	.1128	.4177	.6463	.3325	.2298	42.31
2.65	.04639	.1115	.4159	.6449	.3294	.2280	42.53
2.66	.04568	.1103	.4141	.6435	.3263	.2262	42.75
2.67	.04498	.1091	.4122	.6421	.3232	.2245	42.97
2.68	.04429	.1079	.4104	.6406	.3202	.2227	43.19
2.69	.04362	.1067	.4086	.6392	.3172	.2209	43.40
2.70	.04295	.1056	.4068	.6378	.3142	.2192	43.62
2.71	.04229	.1044	.4051	.6364	.3112	.2174	43.84
2.72	.04165	.1033	.4033	.6350	.3083	.2157	44.05
2.73	.04102	.1022	.4015	.6337	.3054	.2140	44.27
2.74	.04039	.1010	.3998	.6323	.3025	.2123	44.48

TABLE 3 (*Continued*)

FLOW PARAMETERS VERSUS M FOR SUPERSONIC FLOW

M	$\dfrac{p}{p_0}$	$\dfrac{\rho}{\rho_0}$	$\dfrac{T}{T_0}$	$\dfrac{a}{a_0}$	$\dfrac{A^*}{A}$	$\dfrac{\frac{\rho}{2}V^2}{p_0}$	θ
2.75	.03978	.09994	.3980	.6309	.2996	.2106	44.69
2.76	.03917	.09885	.3963	.6295	.2968	.2089	44.91
2.77	.03858	.09778	.3945	.6281	.2940	.2072	45.12
2.78	.03799	.09671	.3928	.6268	.2912	.2055	45.33
2.79	.03742	.09566	.3911	.6254	.2884	.2039	45.54
2.80	.03685	.09463	.3894	.6240	.2857	.2022	45.75
2.81	.03629	.09360	.3877	.6227	.2830	.2006	45.95
2.82	.03574	.09259	.3860	.6213	.2803	.1990	46.16
2.83	.03520	.09158	.3844	.6200	.2777	.1973	46.37
2.84	.03467	.09059	.3827	.6186	.2750	.1957	46.57
2.85	.03415	.08962	.3810	.6173	.2724	.1941	46.78
2.86	.03363	.08865	.3794	.6159	.2698	.1926	46.98
2.87	.03312	.08769	.3777	.6146	.2673	.1910	47.19
2.88	.03263	.08675	.3761	.6133	.2648	.1894	47.39
2.89	.03213	.08581	.3745	.6119	.2622	.1879	47.59
2.90	.03165	.08489	.3729	.6106	.2598	.1863	47.79
2.91	.03118	.08398	.3712	.6093	.2573	.1848	47.99
2.92	.03071	.08307	.3696	.6080	.2549	.1833	48.19
2.93	.03025	.08218	.3681	.6067	.2524	.1818	48.39
2.94	.02980	.08130	.3665	.6054	.2500	.1803	48.59
2.95	.02935	.08043	.3649	.6041	.2477	.1788	48.78
2.96	.02891	.07957	.3633	.6028	.2453	.1773	48.98
2.97	.02848	.07872	.3618	.6015	.2430	.1758	49.18
2.98	.02805	.07788	.3602	.6002	.2407	.1744	49.37
2.99	.02764	.97705	.3587	.5989	.2384	.1729	49.56
3.00	.02722	.07623	.3571	.5976	.2362	.1715	49.76
3.01	.02682	.07541	.3556	.5963	.2339	.1701	49.95
3.02	.02642	.07461	.3541	.5951	.2317	.1687	50.14
3.03	.02603	.07382	.3526	.5938	.2295	.1673	50.33
3.04	.02564	.07303	.3511	.5925	.2273	.1659	50.52
3.05	.02526	.07226	.3496	.5913	.2252	.1645	50.71
3.06	.02489	.07149	.3481	.5900	.2230	.1631	50.90
3.07	.02452	.07074	.3466	.5887	.2209	.1618	51.09
3.08	.02416	.06999	.3452	.5875	.2188	.1604	51.28
3.09	.02380	.06925	.3437	.5862	.2168	.1591	51.46

TABLE 3 (*Continued*)

FLOW PARAMETERS VERSUS M FOR SUPERSONIC FLOW

M	$\dfrac{p}{p_0}$	$\dfrac{\rho}{\rho_0}$	$\dfrac{T}{T_0}$	$\dfrac{a}{a_0}$	$\dfrac{A^*}{A}$	$\dfrac{\dfrac{\rho}{2}V^2}{p_0}$	θ
3.10	.02345	.06852	.3422	.5850	.2147	.1577	51.65
3.11	.02310	.06779	.3408	.5838	.2127	.1564	51.84
3.12	.02276	.06708	.3393	.5825	.2107	.1551	52.02
3.13	.02243	.06637	.3379	.5813	.2087	.1538	52.20
3.14	.02210	.06568	.3365	.5801	.2067	.1525	52.39
3.15	.02177	.06499	.3351	.5788	.2048	.1512	52.57
3.16	.02146	.06430	.3337	.5776	.2028	.1500	52.75
3.17	.02114	.06363	.3323	.5764	.2009	.1487	52.93
3.18	.02083	.06296	.3309	.5752	.1990	.1475	53.11
3.19	.02053	.06231	.3295	.5740	.1971	.1462	53.29
3.20	.02023	.06165	.3281	.5728	.1953	.1450	53.47
3.21	.01993	.06101	.3267	.5716	.1934	.1438	53.65
3.22	.01964	.06037	.3253	.5704	.1916	.1426	53.83
3.23	.01936	.05975	.3240	.5692	.1898	.1414	54.00
3.24	.01908	.05912	.3226	.5680	.1880	.1402	54.18
3.25	.01880	.05851	.3213	.5668	.1863	.1390	54.35
3.26	.01853	.05790	.3199	.5656	.1845	.1378	54.53
3.27	.01826	.05730	.3186	.5645	.1828	.1367	54.71
3.28	.01799	.05671	.3173	.5633	.1810	.1355	54.88
3.29	.01773	.05612	.3160	.5621	.1793	.1344	55.05
3.30	.01748	.05554	.3147	.5609	.1777	.1332	55.22
3.31	.01722	.05497	.3134	.5598	.1760	.1321	55.39
3.32	.01698	.05440	.3121	.5586	.1743	.1310	55.56
3.33	.01673	.05384	.3108	.5575	.1727	.1299	55.73
3.34	.01649	.05329	.3095	.5563	.1711	.1288	55.90
3.35	.01625	.05274	.3082	.5552	.1695	.1277	56.07
3.36	.01602	.05220	.3069	.5540	.1679	.1266	56.24
3.37	.01579	.05166	.3057	.5529	.1663	.1255	56.41
3.38	.01557	.05113	.3044	.5517	.1648	.1245	56.58
3.39	.01534	.05061	.3032	.5506	.1632	.1234	56.75
3.40	.01513	.05009	.3019	.5495	.1617	.1224	56.91
3.41	.01491	.04958	.3007	.5484	.1602	.1214	57.07
3.42	.01470	.04908	.2995	.5472	.1587	.1202	57.24
3.43	.01449	.04858	.2982	.5461	.1572	.1193	57.40
3.44	.01428	.04808	.2970	.5450	.1558	.1183	57.56

TABLE 3 (*Continued*)

FLOW PARAMETERS VERSUS M FOR SUPERSONIC FLOW

M	$\dfrac{p}{p_0}$	$\dfrac{\rho}{\rho_0}$	$\dfrac{T}{T_0}$	$\dfrac{a}{a_0}$	$\dfrac{A^*}{A}$	$\dfrac{\frac{\rho}{2}V^2}{p_0}$	θ
3.45	.01408	.04759	.2958	.5439	.1543	.1173	57.73
3.46	.01388	.04711	.2946	.5428	.1529	.1163	57.89
3.47	.01368	.04663	.2934	.5417	.1515	.1153	58.05
3.48	.01349	.04616	.2922	.5406	.1501	.1144	58.21
3.49	.01330	.04569	.2910	.5395	.1487	.1134	58.37
3.50	.01311	.04523	.2899	.5384	.1473	.1124	58.53
3.60	.01138	.04089	.2784	.5276	.1342	.1033	60.09
3.70	9.903×10^{-3}	.03702	.2675	.5172	.1224	.09490	61.60
3.80	8.629×10^{-3}	.03355	.2572	.5072	.1117	.08722	63.04
3.90	7.532×10^{-3}	.03044	.2474	.4974	.1021	.08019	64.44
4.00	6.586×10^{-3}	.02766	.2381	.4880	.09329	.07376	65.78
4.10	5.769×10^{-3}	.02516	.2293	.4788	.08536	.06788	67.08
4.20	5.062×10^{-3}	.02292	.2208	.4699	.07818	.06251	68.33
4.30	4.449×10^{-3}	.02090	.2129	.4614	.07166	.05759	69.54
4.40	3.918×10^{-3}	.01909	.2053	.4531	.06575	.05309	70.71
4.50	3.455×10^{-3}	.01745	.1980	.4450	.06038	.04898	71.83
4.60	3.053×10^{-3}	.01597	.1911	.4372	.05550	.04521	72.92
4.70	2.701×10^{-3}	.01464	.1846	.4296	.05107	.04177	73.97
4.80	2.394×10^{-3}	.01343	.1783	.4223	.04703	.03861	74.99
4.90	2.126×10^{-3}	.01233	.1724	.4152	.04335	.03572	75.97
5.00	1.890×10^{-3}	.01134	.1667	.4082	.04000	.03308	76.92
6.00	6.334×10^{-4}	5.194×10^{-3}	.1220	.3492	.01880	.01596	84.96
7.00	2.416×10^{-4}	2.609×10^{-3}	.09259	.3043	9.602×10^{-3}	8.285×10^{-3}	90.97

TABLE 3 (*Continued*)

FLOW PARAMETERS VERSUS M FOR SUPERSONIC FLOW

M	$\dfrac{p}{p_0}$	$\dfrac{\rho}{\rho_0}$	$\dfrac{T}{T_0}$	$\dfrac{a}{a_0}$	$\dfrac{A^*}{A}$	$\dfrac{\frac{\rho}{2}V^2}{p_0}$	θ
8.00	1.024×10^{-4}	1.414×10^{-3}	.07246	.2692	5.260×10^{-3}	4.589×10^{-3}	95.62
9.00	4.739×10^{-5}	8.150×10^{-4}	.05814	.2411	3.056×10^{-3}	2.687×10^{-3}	99.32
10.00	2.356×10^{-5}	4.948×10^{-4}	.04762	.2182	1.866×10^{-3}	1.649×10^{-3}	102.3
100.00	2.790×10^{-12}	5.583×10^{-9}	4.998×10^{-4}	.02236	2.157×10^{-8}	1.953×10^{-8}	127.6
∞	0	0	0	0	0	0	130.5

Numerical values taken from NACA TN 1428, courtesy of the National Advisory Committee for Aeronautics.

TABLE 4

PARAMETERS FOR SHOCK FLOW

M_{1n}	p_2/p_1	ρ_2/ρ_1	T_2/T_1	a_2/a_1	p_2^0/p_1^0	M_2 for Normal Shocks Only
1.00	1.000	1.000	1.000	1.000	1.0000	1.0000
1.01	1.023	1.017	1.007	1.003	1.0000	.9901
1.02	1.047	1.033	1.013	1.007	1.0000	.9805
1.03	1.071	1.050	1.020	1.010	1.0000	.9712
1.04	1.095	1.067	1.026	1.013	.9999	.9620
1.05	1.120	1.084	1.033	1.016	.9999	.9531
1.06	1.144	1.101	1.039	1.019	.9998	.9444
1.07	1.169	1.118	1.046	1.023	.9996	.9360
1.08	1.194	1.135	1.052	1.026	.9994	.9277
1.09	1.219	1.152	1.059	1.029	.9992	.9196
1.10	1.245	1.169	1.065	1.032	.9989	.9118
1.11	1.271	1.186	1.071	1.035	.9986	.9041
1.12	1.297	1.203	1.078	1.038	.9982	.8966
1.13	1.323	1.221	1.084	1.041	.9978	.8892
1.14	1.350	1.238	1.090	1.044	.9973	.8820
1.15	1.376	1.255	1.097	1.047	.9967	.8750
1.16	1.403	1.272	1.103	1.050	.9961	.8682
1.17	1.430	1.290	1.109	1.053	.9953	.8615
1.18	1.458	1.307	1.115	1.056	.9946	.8549
1.19	1.485	1.324	1.122	1.059	.9937	.8485
1.20	1.513	1.342	1.128	1.062	.9928	.8422
1.21	1.541	1.359	1.134	1.065	.9918	.8360
1.22	1.570	1.376	1.141	1.068	.9907	.8300
1.23	1.598	1.394	1.147	1.071	.9896	.8241
1.24	1.627	1.411	1.153	1.074	.9884	.8183
1.25	1.656	1.429	1.159	1.077	.9871	.8126
1.26	1.686	1.446	1.166	1.080	.9857	.8071
1.27	1.715	1.463	1.172	1.083	.9842	.8016
1.28	1.745	1.481	1.178	1.085	.9827	.7963
1.29	1.775	1.498	1.185	1.088	.9811	.7911
1.30	1.805	1.516	1.191	1.091	.9794	.7860
1.31	1.835	1.533	1.197	1.094	.9776	.7809
1.32	1.866	1.551	1.204	1.097	.9758	.7760
1.33	1.897	1.568	1.210	1.100	.9738	.7712
1.34	1.928	1.585	1.216	1.103	.9718	.7664

TABLE 4 (*Continued*)

PARAMETERS FOR SHOCK FLOW

M_{1n}	p_2/p_1	ρ_2/ρ_1	T_2/T_1	a_2/a_1	p_2^0/p_1^0	M_2 for Normal Shocks Only
1.35	1.960	1.603	1.223	1.106	.9697	.7618
1.36	1.991	1.620	1.229	1.109	.9676	.7572
1.37	2.023	1.638	1.235	1.111	.9653	.7527
1.38	2.055	1.655	1.242	1.114	.9630	.7483
1.39	2.087	1.672	1.248	1.117	.9606	.7440
1.40	2.120	1.690	1.255	1.120	.9582	.7397
1.41	2.153	1.707	1.261	1.123	.9557	.7355
1.42	2.186	1.724	1.268	1.126	.9531	.7314
1.43	2.219	1.742	1.274	1.129	.9504	.7274
1.44	2.253	1.759	1.281	1.132	.9476	.7235
1.45	2.286	1.776	1.287	1.135	.9448	.7196
1.46	2.320	1.793	1.294	1.137	.9420	.7157
1.47	2.354	1.811	1.300	1.140	.9390	.7120
1.48	2.389	1.828	1.307	1.143	.9360	.7083
1.49	2.423	1.845	1.314	1.146	.9329	.7047
1.50	2.458	1.862	1.320	1.149	.9298	.7011
1.51	2.493	1.879	1.327	1.152	.9266	.6976
1.52	2.529	1.896	1.334	1.155	.9233	.6941
1.53	2.564	1.913	1.340	1.158	.9200	.6907
1.54	2.600	1.930	1.347	1.161	.9166	.6874
1.55	2.636	1.947	1.354	1.164	.9132	.6841
1.56	2.673	1.964	1.361	1.166	.9097	.6809
1.57	2.709	1.981	1.367	1.169	.9061	.6777
1.58	2.746	1.998	1.374	1.172	.9026	.6746
1.59	2.783	2.015	1.381	1.175	.8989	.6715
1.60	2.820	2.032	1.388	1.178	.8952	.6684
1.61	2.857	2.049	1.395	1.181	.8914	.6655
1.62	2.895	2.065	1.402	1.184	.8877	.6625
1.63	2.933	2.082	1.409	1.187	.8838	.6596
1.64	2.971	2.099	1.416	1.190	.8799	.6568
1.65	3.010	2.115	1.423	1.193	.8760	.6540
1.66	3.048	2.132	1.430	1.196	.8720	.6512
1.67	3.087	2.148	1.437	1.199	.8680	.6485
1.68	3.126	2.165	1.444	1.202	.8640	.6458
1.69	3.165	2.181	1.451	1.205	.8599	.6431

TABLE 4 (*Continued*)

PARAMETERS FOR SHOCK FLOW

M_{1n}	p_2/p_1	ρ_2/ρ_1	T_2/T_1	a_2/a_1	p_2^0/p_1^0	M_2 for Normal Shocks Only
1.70	3.205	2.198	1.458	1.208	.8557	.6405
1.71	3.245	2.214	1.466	1.211	.8516	.6380
1.72	3.285	2.230	1.473	1.214	.8474	.6355
1.73	3.325	2.247	1.480	1.217	.8431	.6330
1.74	3.366	2.263	1.487	1.220	.8389	.6305
1.75	3.406	2.279	1.495	1.223	.8346	.6281
1.76	3.447	2.295	1.502	1.226	.8302	.6257
1.77	3.488	2.311	1.509	1.229	.8259	.6234
1.78	3.530	2.327	1.517	1.232	.8215	.6210
1.79	3.571	2.343	1.524	1.235	.8171	.6188
1.80	3.613	2.359	1.532	1.238	.8127	.6165
1.81	3.655	2.375	1.539	1.241	.8082	.6143
1.82	3.698	2.391	1.547	1.244	.8038	.6121
1.83	3.740	2.407	1.554	1.247	.7993	.6099
1.84	3.783	2.422	1.562	1.250	.7948	.6078
1.85	3.826	2.438	1.569	1.253	.7902	.6057
1.86	3.870	2.454	1.577	1.256	.7857	.6036
1.87	3.913	2.469	1.585	1.259	.7811	.6016
1.88	3.957	2.485	1.592	1.262	.7765	.5996
1.89	4.001	2.500	1.600	1.265	.7720	.5976
1.90	4.045	2.516	1.608	1.268	.7674	.5956
1.91	4.089	2.531	1.616	1.271	.7628	.5937
1.92	4.134	2.546	1.624	1.274	.7581	.5918
1.93	4.179	2.562	1.631	1.277	.7535	.5899
1.94	4.224	2.577	1.639	1.280	.7488	.5889
1.95	4.270	2.592	1.647	1.283	.7442	.5862
1.96	4.315	2.607	1.655	1.287	.7395	.5844
1.97	4.361	2.622	1.663	1.290	.7349	.5826
1.98	4.407	2.637	1.671	1.293	.7302	.5808
1.99	4.453	2.652	1.679	1.296	.7255	.5791
2.00	4.500	2.667	1.688	1.299	.7209	.5773
2.01	4.547	2.681	1.696	1.302	.7162	.5757
2.02	4.594	2.696	1.704	1.305	.7115	.5740
2.03	4.641	2.711	1.712	1.308	.7069	.5723
2.04	4.689	2.725	1.720	1.312	.7022	.5707

TABLE 4 (*Continued*)

PARAMETERS FOR SHOCK FLOW

M_{1n}	p_2/p_1	ρ_2/ρ_1	T_2/T_1	a_2/a_1	$p_2{}^0/p_1{}^0$	M_2 for Normal Shocks Only
2.05	4.736	2.740	1.729	1.315	.6975	.5691
2.06	4.784	2.755	1.737	1.318	.6928	.5675
2.07	4.832	2.769	1.745	1.321	.6882	.5659
2.08	4.881	2.783	1.754	1.324	.6835	.5643
2.09	4.929	2.798	1.762	1.327	.6789	.5628
2.10	4.978	2.812	1.770	1.331	.6742	.5613
2.11	5.027	2.826	1.779	1.334	.6696	.5598
2.12	5.077	2.840	1.787	1.337	.6649	.5583
2.13	5.126	2.854	1.796	1.340	.6603	.5568
2.14	5.176	2.868	1.805	1.343	.6557	.5554
2.15	5.226	2.882	1.813	1.347	.6511	.5540
2.16	5.277	2.896	1.822	1.350	.6464	.5525
2.17	5.327	2.910	1.831	1.353	.6419	.5511
2.18	5.378	2.924	1.839	1.356	.6373	.5498
2.19	5.429	2.938	1.848	1.359	.6327	.5484
2.20	5.480	2.951	1.857	1.363	.6281	.5471
2.21	5.531	2.965	1.866	1.366	.6236	.5457
2.22	5.583	2.978	1.875	1.369	.6191	.5444
2.23	5.635	2.992	1.883	1.372	.6145	.5431
2.24	5.687	3.005	1.892	1.376	.6100	.5418
2.25	5.740	3.019	1.901	1.379	.6055	.5406
2.26	5.792	3.032	1.910	1.382	.6011	.5393
2.27	5.845	3.045	1.919	1.385	.5966	.5381
2.28	5.898	3.058	1.929	1.389	.5921	.5368
2.29	5.951	3.071	1.938	1.392	.5877	.5356
2.30	6.005	3.085	1.947	1.395	.5833	.5344
2.31	6.059	3.098	1.956	1.399	.5789	.5332
2.32	6.113	3.110	1.965	1.402	.5745	.5321
2.33	6.167	3.123	1.974	1.405	.5702	.5309
2.34	6.222	3.136	1.984	1.408	.5658	.5297
2.35	6.276	3.149	1.993	1.412	.5615	.5286
2.36	6.331	3.162	2.002	1.415	.5572	.5275
2.37	6.386	3.174	2.012	1.418	.5529	.5264
2.38	6.442	3.187	2.021	1.422	.5486	.5253
2.39	6.497	3.199	2.031	1.425	.5444	.5242

TABLE 4 (*Continued*)

PARAMETERS FOR SHOCK FLOW

M_{1n}	p_2/p_1	ρ_2/ρ_1	T_2/T_1	a_2/a_1	p_2^0/p_1^0	M_2 for Normal Shocks Only
2.40	6.553	3.212	2.040	1.428	.5401	.5231
2.41	6.609	3.224	2.050	1.432	.5359	.5221
2.42	6.666	3.237	2.059	1.435	.5317	.5210
2.43	6.722	3.249	2.069	1.438	.5276	.5200
2.44	6.779	3.261	2.079	1.442	.5234	.5189
2.45	6.836	3.273	2.088	1.445	.5193	.5179
2.46	6.894	3.285	2.098	1.449	.5152	.5169
2.47	6.951	3.298	2.108	1.452	.5111	.5159
2.48	7.009	3.310	2.118	1.455	.5071	.5149
2.49	7.067	3.321	2.128	1.459	.5030	.5140
2.50	7.125	3.333	2.138	1.462	.4990	.5130
2.51	7.183	3.345	2.147	1.465	.4950	.5120
2.52	7.242	3.357	2.157	1.469	.4911	.5111
2.53	7.301	3.369	2.167	1.472	.4871	.5102
2.54	7.360	3.380	2.177	1.476	.4832	.5092
2.55	7.420	3.392	2.187	1.479	.4793	.5083
2.56	7.479	3.403	2.198	1.482	.4754	.5074
2.57	7.539	3.415	2.208	1.486	.4715	.5065
2.58	7.599	3.426	2.218	1.489	.4677	.5056
2.59	7.659	3.438	2.228	1.493	.4639	.5047
2.60	7.720	3.449	2.238	1.496	.4601	.5039
2.61	7.781	3.460	2.249	1.500	.4564	.5030
2.62	7.842	3.471	2.259	1.503	.4526	.5022
2.63	7.903	3.483	2.269	1.506	.4489	.5013
2.64	7.965	3.494	2.280	1.510	.4452	.5005
2.65	8.026	3.505	2.290	1.513	.4416	.4996
2.66	8.088	3.516	2.301	1.517	.4379	.4988
2.67	8.150	3.527	2.311	1.520	.4343	.4980
2.68	8.213	3.537	2.322	1.524	.4307	.4972
2.69	8.275	3.548	2.332	1.527	.4271	.4964
2.70	8.338	3.559	2.343	1.531	.4236	.4956
2.71	8.401	3.570	2.354	1.534	.4201	.4949
2.72	8.465	3.580	2.364	1.538	.4166	.4941
2.73	8.528	3.591	2.375	1.541	.4131	.4933
2.74	8.592	3.601	2.386	1.545	.4097	.4926

TABLE 4 (*Continued*)

PARAMETERS FOR SHOCK FLOW

M_{1n}	p_2/p_1	ρ_2/ρ_1	T_2/T_1	a_2/a_1	p_2^0/p_1^0	M_2 for Normal Shocks Only
2.75	8.656	3.612	2.397	1.548	.4062	.4918
2.76	8.721	3.622	2.407	1.552	.4028	.4911
2.77	8.785	3.633	2.418	1.555	.3994	.4903
2.78	8.850	3.643	2.429	1.559	.3961	.4896
2.79	8.915	3.653	2.440	1.562	.3928	.4889
2.80	8.980	3.664	2.451	1.566	.3895	.4882
2.81	9.045	3.674	2.462	1.569	.3862	.4875
2.82	9.111	3.684	2.473	1.573	.3829	.4868
2.83	9.177	3.694	2.484	1.576	.3797	.4861
2.84	9.243	3.704	2.496	1.580	.3765	.4854
2.85	9.310	3.714	2.507	1.583	.3733	.4847
2.86	9.376	3.724	2.518	1.587	.3701	.4840
2.87	9.443	3.734	2.529	1.590	.3670	.4833
2.88	9.510	3.743	2.540	1.594	.3639	.4827
2.89	9.577	3.753	2.552	1.597	.3608	.4820
2.90	9.645	3.763	2.563	1.601	.3577	.4814
2.91	9.713	3.773	2.575	1.605	.3547	.4807
2.92	9.781	3.782	2.586	1.608	.3517	.4801
2.93	9.849	3.792	2.598	1.612	.3487	.4795
2.94	9.918	3.801	2.609	1.615	.3457	.4788
2.95	9.986	3.811	2.621	1.619	.3428	.4782
2.96	10.06	3.820	2.632	1.622	.3398	.4776
2.97	10.12	3.829	2.644	1.626	.3369	.4770
2.98	10.19	3.839	2.656	1.630	.3340	.4764
2.99	10.26	3.848	2.667	1.633	.3312	.4758
3.00	10.33	3.857	2.679	1.637	.3283	.4752
3.10	11.05	3.947	2.799	1.673	.3012	.4695
3.20	11.78	4.031	2.922	1.709	.2762	.4643
3.30	12.54	4.112	3.049	1.746	.2533	.4596
3.40	13.32	4.188	3.180	1.783	.2322	.4552
3.50	14.13	4.261	3.315	1.821	.2129	.4512
3.60	14.95	4.330	3.454	1.858	.1953	.4474
3.70	15.80	4.395	3.596	1.896	.1792	.4439
3.80	16.68	4.457	3.743	1.935	.1645	.4407
3.90	17.58	4.516	3.893	1.973	.1510	.4377

TABLE 4 (*Continued*)

PARAMETERS FOR SHOCK FLOW

M_{1n}	p_2/p_1	ρ_2/ρ_1	T_2/T_1	a_2/a_1	p_2^0/p_1^0	M_2 for Normal Shocks Only
4.00	18.50	4.571	4.047	2.012	.1388	.4350
5.00	29.00	5.000	5.800	2.408	.06172	.4152
6.00	41.83	5.268	7.941	2.818	.02965	.4042
7.00	57.00	5.444	10.47	3.236	.01535	.3974
8.00	74.50	5.565	13.39	3.659	8.488×10^{-3}	.3929
9.00	94.33	5.651	16.69	4.086	4.964×10^{-3}	.3898
10.00	116.5	5.714	20.39	4.515	3.045×10^{-3}	.3876
100.00	11,666.5	5.997	1945.4	44.11	3.593×10^{-8}	.3781
∞	∞	6	∞	∞	0	.3780

Data taken from NACA TN 1428, courtesy of National Advisory Committee of Aeronautics.

TABLE 5

THERMAL PROPERTIES OF GASES

($p = 1$ atmosphere)

°R	P_r	c_p/R	$z = \dfrac{\rho V}{RT}$	γ
200	.768	3.56	0.985	1.420
400	.732	3.51	0.998	1.405
600	.701	3.51	1.000	1.400
800	.684	3.55	1.000	1.393
1000	.680	3.63	1.000	1.381
1200	.682	3.73	1.000	1.368
1400	.688	3.81	1.000	1.356
1600	.698	3.90	1.000	1.346
1800	.702	3.98	1.000	1.336
2000		4.05	1.000	1.329
3000		4.41	1.000	1.294
4000		4.99	1.001	1.261
5000		7.66	1.011	1.198

Data from Tables of *Thermal Properties of Gases*, Dept. of Commerce, National Bureau of Standards Circular 564, U.S. Government Printing Office, 1955.

Shock-wave angle β, degrees

Deflection
OBLIQUE SI
From NACA Report 1135. (Continued on the

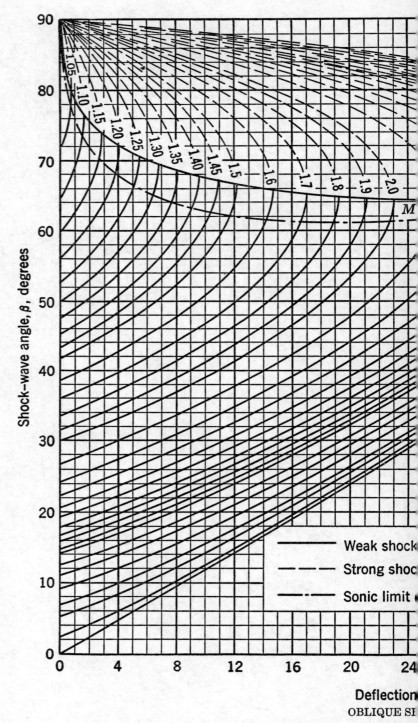

From NACA Report 1135. (Courtesy of the

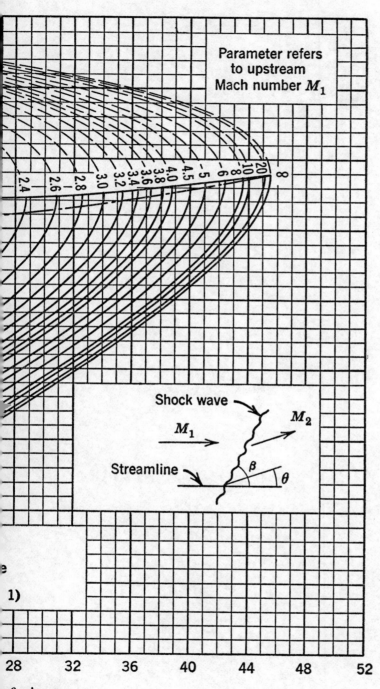

Parameter refers to upstream Mach number M_1

2.4 2.6 2.8 3.0 3.2 3.4 3.6 3.8 4.0 4.5 5 6 8 10 20 ∞

Shock wave

M_1

M_2

Streamline

β

θ

1)

28   32   36   40   44   48   52

$,\theta$, degrees

:HART

Advisory Committee for Aeronautics.)

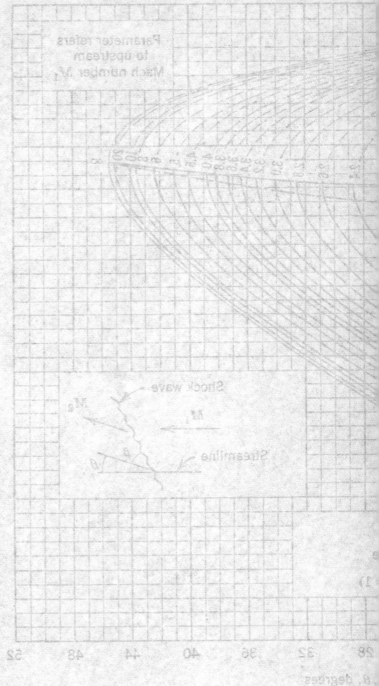

Index